The Loving God
Story of Shirdi
Sai Baba

"He, who carps and cavils at others, pierces Me in the heart and injures Me, but he that suffers and endures, pleases Me most."

-Sai Baba

"What we can do for another is the test of powers; what we can suffer for is the test of love."

-Sri Narasimha Swamiji

"Love people, but not their faults."

-Sri Radhakrishna Swamiji

The Loving God
Story of **Shirdi Sai Baba**

Dr G.R. Vijayakumar
Sri Sai Spiritual Centre

STERLING PAPERBACKS
An imprint of
Sterling Publishers (P) Ltd.
A-59, Okhla Industrial Area, Phase-II,
New Delhi-110020.
Tel: 26387070, 26386209; Fax: 91-11-26383788
E-mail: mail@sterlingpublishers.com
www.sterlingpublishers.com

The Loving God: Story of Shirdi Sai Baba
© 2014, Sri Sai Spiritual Centre, Bangalore
ISBN 978 81 207 8079 8

Printed in India

Printed and Published by Sterling Publishers Pvt. Ltd.,
New Delhi-110 020.

DEDICATION

This humble offering is placed
at the holy feet of
Sainath Maharaj
Who is our Almighty God

Our Pranams to
Sadguru Sri Narasimha Swamiji
whose inspired zeal and matchless dedication
discovered and presented to the troubled world
Sai Baba, the Saviour par excellence.

Our obeisance to Gurudev,
Sadguru Sri Radhakrishna Swamiji
who is always close behind our thoughts and
looking after our welfare.

"All things are possible to him, who believes, they are less difficult to him who hopes, they are easier to him who loves, and still more easy to him who practices and perseveres in these three virtues."

- Sri Radhakrishna Swamiji
(from a message for Guru Poornima)

FOREWORD

*S*ai Baba was confined to the remote village of Shirdi in Maharashtra prior to 1936 and it was Sri Narasimha Swamiji's untiring efforts for two decades that made Sai Baba a household name all over India. Sai Baba touched the lives of people from all walks of life, who had been all their lives searching for an anchorage. He gave them a healing and inspiring touch. He offered them the magical formula of love. The new life he gave them is a new page in 'Bhakti Marg'.

Many books have been written on Sai Baba but hardly any in a chronological order or in a novel style. A spiritual odyssey is not easy to reconstruct on paper in a story form. The usual materials, the plethora of which is often the despair of the biographer and the historian, simply do not exist. There are no archives of papers, no back volumes of newspapers and periodicals, tapes and films from which significant facts are to be gleaned. Sai Baba attracted thousands of devotees to Shirdi in those days when there was hardly any means of communication. The struggles of those devotees, their ordeals, travails and the triumphs have their dramatic moments, but the world knows little about them. Difficult as the task was, it was the good fortune of Dr.G.R.Vijayakumar that Sai Baba took him to those days so that he could write this biography of Sai Baba in a novel form and publish it in the diamond jubilee year of Sri Sai Spiritual Centre. We hope that this work reaches a wider circle of readers all over the country.

Dr.Vijayakumar, a doctor of Medicine, has been a Sai devotee since 1977 and is well versed in religion and philosophy. He has written several books in English and Kannada including a biography each on Sri Narasimha Swamiji and Sri Radhakrishna Swamiji and a few books on 'public health'. A good number of his articles have been published in several Sai magazines all over the country.

May the merciful blessings of Sai Baba, Sri Narasimha Swamiji, and Sri Radhakrishna Swamiji be upon us!

Bangalore
15th August 2013

R. Seshadri
President
Sri Sai Spiritual Centre

A NOTE FROM
SRI SAI SPIRITUAL CENTRE

We have a great pleasure in presenting this book *The Loving God* – a comprehensive biography of Sai Baba written in the form of a novel. In these pages, Sai Baba's life has been depicted in a chronological order and in the simplest style.

Difficult as the task was, it was a happy idea of Dr.G.R.Vijayakumar to write this biography of Sai Baba in a novel form and to publish it in the Diamond Jubilee year of Sri Sai Spiritual Centre and 95th 'Punya Tithi' of Sai Baba. Dr.Vijayakumar has collected and sifted information from *Life of Sai Baba* by Sri Narasimha Swamiji and *Sai Satcharita* by Hemad Pant. He has pieced together a coherent and vivid narrative.

We are grateful to our President, Sri R. Seshadri who is closely connected with the Sai movement for over five decades, for having gone through the typescript meticulously and penning a scholarly foreword. .

Let me here record our sincere gratitude to Sai Baba, Sri Narasimha Swamiji and Sri Radhakrishna Swamiji for raining down their mercy upon us in the form of this spiritual biography, full of noble ideas and sentiments. Written in a charming and lucid style, this book will certainly help to engender faith in spiritual truths and encourage Sai devotees to lead a spiritual life. No doubt, this book will prove an ornament to Sai literature.

This book is an inspiring saga of the life and mission of Sai Baba which the readers will find interesting and enlightening.

M.S. Jothi Raghavan
Bangalore   *Hon. Secretary*
15th August 2013   Sri Sai Spiritual Centre

GURU'S GRACE

"Everything needs Guru's grace. When Guru's grace descends, the heart blossoms forth like a lotus when the sun shines upon it. When thus opened, he feels that his heart encompasses the whole world of his relationships and shapes his conduct and destiny through the promptings of his heart.

A kind heart is a spring of joy to all within its reach. So let everyone allow his or her heart to speak and tread the paths of spiritual life refreshing the shade of truth and love.

I feel forlorn in Sai-Love. He has possessed me and I have surrendered my all to that 'Living Chaitanya'."

Sri Narasimha Swamiji

"I searched for a 'Sadguru' all over - in the South, in the East and, in the West. When I came to Shirdi, I found Him in my heart."

"I wandered ceaselessly. I went to many places and met many great beings. Still I wandered on. My spiritual hunger was not satisfied till I came over to Shirdi and saw Sai Baba face to face. He stopped my wandering — and with this the wandering of many. At Shirdi, I was given more than I could take. I had at last discovered my 'Sadguru'. He is Sainatha Sadguru, and I live in constant communion with Him."

-Sri Narasimha Swamiji

PREFACE

*T*he world exists just because love still exists on earth. If this one divine quality left the world, then there could be no existence on earth. Let us love the root of the tree. Then we shall see that the branches, the leaves, and the foliage of the tree also feel our love.

Love is the secret key that allows a human being to open the door to God.

Where there is love there is fulfillment. What is love? Love means giving and becoming one with everything, with humanity and divinity. Where there is Oneness, there is pure love. If we give someone something and expect something in return, this is human love. But if we love someone unconditionally, that is divine love.

Divine love makes no demand. It is unlimited in every way. Divine love at every moment illumines us and there is complete fulfillment. In divine love there is no possession – only a feeling of oneness. This oneness can enter into an animal, flower, tree or even a wall. Divine love tells us that we are greater than the greatest, larger than the largest and that our life is infinite.

My wife Seetha and I were initiated into Sai marg by Sri Radhakrishna Swamiji in 1977. Swamiji predicted that we will be blessed with two sons whereas an astrologer said no progeny for us! Through Swamiji's grace Seetha practised divine love and always desired that a book on Sai Baba should be brought out, which would inspire everyone to practise divine love.

Unfortunately this could not be done when she was physically with us. Seetha prompted me to take this up on 'Akshaya Tritiya' which was on 13th April 2013. One day I had a divine encounter with Sai Baba and traversed to the past to his time and Baba himself narrated me the details of his life and so this book *The Loving God* got completed on *naga panchami* (11th August 2013) and is now in your hands!

Each one of us is unique. And the loving God Sai Baba has a specific role for us to play in the ever unfolding cosmic drama of life. Let us discover that special purpose and fulfill it. I pray to Lord Ganesha to give me a lot of strength and power to complete this task. Sai Baba himself in the form of Lord Vinayaka will write his story making me a mere instrument or medium for it.

Bangalore
11th August 2007   **Dr. G.R. Vijayakumar**

CONTENTS

ADVENT OF THE DIVINE

*I*f you take any mode of transport in Bangalore – whether it is the local city bus, an autorickshaw, or a cab, very often you would notice a picture of an elderly man, a white cloth tied tightly round his head, sitting with his right leg over the left, barefoot and with a compassionate look in his eyes.

The left hand rests gently on the ankle of the right foot, its thumb, fore-finger, and middle finger wide open; it is the picture of a man at peace with himself. He is wearing a cloak that must have seen better days. The right sleeve is torn at the shoulder. The man has large ears, a somewhat flat nose, and thick lips. A cropped beard gives him the appearance of a holy man. He is Sai Baba of Shirdi. He is the most popular deity for all!

The world knows very little about this man who was born sometime between 1838 and 1842 – nobody knows exactly when – and attained *Nirvana* or *Mahasamadhi* - on 15th October 1918 on the auspicious day of *Vijayadashami*.

Sai Baba's life is so wondrous that legends have grown around him. He wrought miracles. He was the friend of his devotees then as he remains friend of his devotees now! Every day more and more people are becoming his devotees. All we can say is – 'Baba's help comes to a devotee who merely seeks his help sincerely. Though there cannot be any degrees of one's sincerity, Baba's response to a devotee's call for help is as eager, as ardent, and as urgent as the devotee's call itself! Once a man is Baba's devotee, he looks after him one life after another! Surrender yourself to Sai Baba and he will never let you down is a belief in devotees so deep rooted that nobody disputes over this.

Sai Baba lived in a small village called Shirdi most of his life time. People from all walks of life came to see him at his humble abode. Today Shirdi is a bustling place, but when Sai Baba lived there it was no more than a cluster of houses. Sai Baba did not have any formal education. He was a saint totally different from other saints known to mankind. He hinted that he had not come to teach, but to awaken. He integrated his teachings through love so that his devotees straightaway get down to the sheer practice of spiritual *sadhana* .

It was 1854. Sai Baba appeared as a young lad of sixteen years meditating under a *neem* tree at Shirdi. Shirdi was a sleeping hamlet in the district of Ahmednagar in the state of Maharashtra. Herein were scattered few shrines consecrated to Ganesha, Shiva, Shani, Hanuman and Khandoba, all Hindu deities. There were two mosques one of which was dilapidated. Hindus and Muslims lived in harmony and affectionate hospitality of the villagers always welcomed mendicants and *sadhus*!

This young man attracted the attention of the villagers. Ganapat Kote Patil accompanied by his wife Bayja and their young son Tatya were the earliest to reach. Some others from the village like Kashinath Tailor, Appa Kulkarni were making glances and commenting at the young boy. They were all appreciative of the deep sense of meditation the young man had developed. His face appeared lustrous and spiritual vibrations pervaded throughout. The young man in meditation was not aware of what was happening around him.

Bayja ma's motherly instinct prompted her to go home and prepare a couple of *rotis* for the boy. A villager ran and brought a *chaddar* to cover the boy to protect him from the cold. Bayja Ma woke him up and fed him with rotis. He looked at her and only when he was about to partake the food, suddenly from nowhere a pig appeared on the scene. The young lad called the pig and fed it with the rotis given to him. He partook a little. But this task made the villagers recoil in horror. They felt – "'What sort of a boy is this?' He shares his food with a dirty pig and that too eats the leftover also."

Suddenly the villagers saw Ganagir Baba of Punatambe, who was visiting Shirdi after a long time. Nobody knew from where he came but he left like a whirlwind after greeting the young Yogi. He proclaimed – "Here is a great man who sees God in everyone but he is the Loving God in human form." He announced a great truth to the crowd.

The villagers left behind were Ganapat Kote Patil, his wife Bayja and son Tatya and Mhalsapathy, the priest of Khandoba temple. They prostrated before the Yogi, but the Yogi did not permit. "What is all this? Am I not one among you?" Bayja asked him – "Dear Child. Who are you? Who are your fortunate parents?"

The young man replied, "Mother, I am your son, just like your Tatya!"

Bayja ma persisted, "True! But what is your name? Which is your native place?" He replied, "What is there in the name, mother? Name is to be left behind after our earthly sojourn. And where is my place? Is not the entire world my own residence?"

Everyone concluded that it was impossible to know his identity. Suddenly Mhalsapathy was possessed by the spirit of Lord Khandoba and he roared in his trance – "I know who he is! Bring a pick-axe and dig here." He pushed the Yogi to a side and commanded the villagers to dig at the place where he was meditating. The villagers looked forward to something auspicious.

The pick-axe struck a stone. When it was pushed aside, an entrance to a cave was exposed. The villagers entered the cave and were surprised to see what was in the cave – 'a wooden seat decorated with fresh flowers and four burning earthen oil lamps' as if someone had offered worship just then.

The villagers came out and bowed down reverentially to the Yogi and asked him – "Yogi Maharaj, we have never witnessed such a miracle in our village. Please disclose who you are?" The Yogi just smiled and changed the topic saying – "This is my Guru's Samadhi. Close the cave and cover it with mud as before." The villagers expressed that the four burning lamps seem to have been lighted just now. The Yogi told them, "They are burning from time immemorial and they represent God's grace. My Guru is interned here and do not excavate this place again. You burn incense here on Thursdays and Fridays and you will obtain his grace." The villagers promptly obeyed and covered the cave.

Next morning the Yogi had mysteriously disappeared. The villagers searched for him in the neighbouring villages. But he was not to be seen anywhere. Everyone was disappointed.

2

UNIQUE RENDEZVOUS

It was the year 1858 now!

A year had passed since the Sepoy mutiny against the British rule was suppressed. The young Yogi who had disappeared from Shirdi four years ago was now seen meditating under a tree in the forest in Maharashtra adjoining the Nizam's state.

Unlike what he appeared four years ago at Shirdi, the Yogi was in a Fakir's garb today and wore a piece of white cloth tied over his head with a big knot behind his neck. He had put on a long gown of similar cloth covering the entire body. The Fakir was motionless, quiet and in trance.

As the Fakir was meditating under the tree, a man who looked to be from a well-to-do family came along. He was restless! With a white turban tied around his head wearing a Muslim costume, he was carrying reins and a carpet used to sit on a horse. He was searching for something in the forest. The rich man's sad thoughts struck the Fakir's soul!

The Fakir opened his eyes and saw the rich man deeply engrossed in sorrow and searching for something he had lost. The Fakir felt sympathy for him and decided to shower his grace on the rich man.

The lucky rich man heard a sweet voice – "Chand! Chand Patel......"

Chand was startled! He stopped! He looked around in surprise! He saw a strange Fakir as he looked around.

Chand mused – "My own name! An unknown Fakir calling me by my own name! How did he know my name?"

With hesitation he approached the Fakir. A soft breeze which blew through the loose sleeves of his long gown showed the torn holes in it. It displayed his poverty! By his side were a wooden begging bowl, a wooden club, an old smoking pipe, a piece of old rag hanging over his shoulder! These were all his worldly possessions!

The Fakir asked him – "Chand, you are wondering who I am?"

Chand was embarrassed and hurriedly said, "Yes! I have not met you before and yet………."

"…..I called you by your name! Isn't it?" The Fakir completed Chand's sentence and continued, "Chand, I blurt like a mad chap. Ignore it. Now tell me – are you searching your lost horse?"

"Oh Allah! You know everything!" Chand spoke in amazement.

"Do not bother! It is my habit to talk at random! You love your mare Chandani very much! Am I correct?" The Fakir continued.

"Yes my Lord!" Chand uttered in amazement.

"Lord! Not me! Lord is one who created us all. I am only his slave – *Yaad-e-huque*."

"No, no – you are my God. You know everything." Chand said.

"Chand, Chandani came into your house and brought prosperity……"

"Yes my Lord, Chandani is everything to me. I love her as my daughter. It is now four months that I lost her near Aurangabad. Every day I have been going around in search of her. But Allah has not been kind to me!" Chand was sad. His voice trembled and tears rolled down his cheeks.

The Fakir consoled him – "No, no Chand. God is indeed kind. He has heard your prayers. Chandani is close by. She is grazing across the rivulet. Give her a call. She will run to you."

Chand got up and walked a few meters to go near the rivulet and shouted, "Chandani, Chandani, where are you? Come back, come back soon."

A miracle happened. First he heard the neighing of the mare and in a few seconds it approached its master. Chand moved ahead extending his hand and the mare neighed in joy! The Fakir happily watched the reunion of the master and the mare!

Chand enjoyed heavenly bliss. He had found God on earth!

Chandani was happily grazing and the Fakir asked Chand to drink some cool water and take rest.

The Fakir lifted his wooden club and hit it hard on a rock. A jet of water spurted and flowed like a brook. Chand was speechless! He was fascinated with delight with this strange experience in life!

The Fakir now took his clay pipe. He took out a little tobacco tied at the end of his shoulder-cloth and filled his pipe with it. He lifted his club again and struck it on the rock. A flame rose high. With this, he lighted the pipe.

Chand drank the sweet water. The Fakir smoked the pipe and gave it to Chand to puff it. Both of them happily smoked.

Smoking over, Chand asked timidly – "Lord, please come with me to my house". He had a secret desire that his family members should be blessed.

The Fakir knew it and said – "Why not?"

Chand accompanied by the Fakir and the mare returned to his village.

3

FROM DHOOPKHED TO SHIRDI

$\mathcal{C}$ hand Patel was a popular person in Dhoopkhed. The news that he is returning to the village along with a Fakir caused a commotion among the villagers. Everybody knew that he had lost his mare four months back and they felt sorry for it. Chand Patel was popular with the people for his friendly nature. Now people were happy that he could trace his lost mare.

Chand and Fakir entered the village. Chand introduced him to everyone – "The Lord is here. Allah has showered His grace on me!"

The Fakir emphatically reminded – "Chand, I told you I am not God! I am a poor Fakir, a mere slave of God!"

Chand could no longer hold his patience. At once he told the villagers about the miracles performed by the Fakir. More and more people came to meet the Fakir and Chand kept narrating the miracles performed by the Fakir to them.

This made the mare panicky, and it could not move forward as a lot of crowd had gathered around. Chand carefully dismounted the Fakir who by now was furious! The Fakir picked up stones lying around and flung them randomly anywhere and at anyone. People ran for life and the road was cleared so that the horse could move and they could go to Chand Patel's house.

In this commotion, a stone hit a small child – a lame boy who was sitting at his door step watching the crowd from a distance. On seeing this his mother quickly rushed towards the boy. The boy was quiet as if nothing had happened to him. On seeing his mother, the boy got up and walked towards her. The boy had never walked earlier and now he could easily walk! The mother was happy and exclaimed – "It is his grace. Come, let us go, and touch his feet!" The mother pulled the child to Chand's house.

A girl who was mentally unsound and deaf and mute was also hit with the Fakir's stone. The stone hit her forehead and blood oozed out of it. Her mother ran towards the girl, who said, "Ma, God has come to our village." For the first time this girl had uttered some words in her life. Her mother was astounded and so were the neighbours. The girl talked to everyone. All of them happily rushed to Chand's house to have the Fakir's darshan.

Another victim of this confusion was a blind man who was hit in the eye resulting in his sight being completely restored!

A very large crowd had gathered outside Chand's house. It was a calm and disciplined crowd. The Fakir who was furious a few minutes back was now in a very happy mood. As one by one, the villagers touched his feet, he blessed them saying, *Allah Bhala Karega*.

The villagers considered the Fakir as the God walking on earth and chanted *Jai Jagadisha Hare, Shiva Shambho Mahadeva*.................

Five days passed like this. The entire village was in a bliss.

Today they all looked sad! Their Lord was leaving. He was to accompany the wedding party of Chand Patel's nephew who was betrothed to a girl in Shirdi. Chand had spoken to the Fakir – "My Lord. The marriage party will leave for Shirdi early morning tomorrow. Please join us?"

"Why not? I love Shirdi! It is my Guru's place. I will certainly join you."

Since early morning the entire village started coming to Chand's place. Elders, youngsters, children, none of them wanted to miss taking the blessings of the Fakir.

A caravan of carts was ready at Chand's door, ready with the luggage. The Fakir came out with Chand. The crowd shouted spontaneously – *Fakir Baba Ki Jai*. Quickly one by one they touched his feet. He smiled and stood in silence till all of them had finished bowing to him. He declined the garlands brought by the villagers. He made them put those garlands around the bullocks and also tied a few garlands to the cart.

Greeting them again the Fakir entered his cart and one more spontaneous shout of praise went into the air!

The carts moved. The cart with the Fakir led the caravan. Day and night the caravan moved.

The wedding party members dozed off. The Fakir was awake. He was alert and as the caravan neared Shirdi, his ears heard from a distance a mingled music of *shehnai* and tolling of a bell from a temple. He was pleased with the harmony of their combination. He enjoyed it because he knew that one came from a Muslim house and the other one emerged from a Hindu temple. *Shehnai* was played at Noorbhai's house whose daughter was betrothed to Chand's nephew. The bell tolled in accompaniment of the morning aarti Mhalsapathy offered at the Khandoba temple. It was a perfect harmony of musical notes irrespective of the place they emerged from.

The Fakir mused - "That is my Mission! Mission of Love! Mission of Brotherhood! Unity of souls!"

The Fakir was lost in a reverie! He came out of it as the rising sun cast its rays on the village which was still a little away from there. He woke up Chand and told him – "Chand, We are now in Shirdi! I will live here forever to bless everyone – even after I give up my body!"

The Fakir summarised his mission in short.

Noorbhai was already there with members of his family and a large number of Hindu villagers to receive the marriage party. A marriage in the village – whether Hindu or Muslim - is the affair of the entire village. Hindus and Muslims lived with unity and happiness in this village.

The caravan stopped near Khandoba temple. The priest, Mhalsapathy finished his prayer and came out. He was wonderstruck at what he saw!

The young Yogi who had disappeared four years ago was there again! Though clad as a fakir now, Mhalsapathy's alert eyes recognised the divine person who had now come with a Muslim marriage party.

The Fakir came out of the cart followed by Chand Patel. He looked at Mhalsapathy. Their eyes met! It was a look of deep recognition! In a hurry Mhalsapathy rushed ahead calling out excitedly, "Come on Sai, Come on Sai Baba!" He prostrated flat on the ground in reverence.

"Sai – Sai Baba!" Only two words! Their divine vibrations vibrated through the cosmos. "Come on Sai – Sai Baba!" was an invitation to come. The Fakir instantly accepted it and turned to enter the temple, saying, "Yes, yes, Braga, I am coming to you! Coming to you!"

"To the temple? But Baba……." Mhalsapathy faltered.

The Fakir told him – "Why not? You invited me!"

Mhalsapathy took courage to speak. He said, "But Baba, what will people say? A Muslim in a Hindu temple? A thing which is never allowed…."

"Muslim?" Baba shouted with rage, "Come on Chand, and tell me the caste of your Allah? Tell me, to which community your Khandoba belongs?"

Fuming with rage, he continued, "You have no answer! God has no caste, no community, and no religion! Why should you observe it?"

None could find an answer! All kept mum and pondered. Baba broke the silence. He said, "All right, do not worry! I will go to a mosque instead." Baba named his permanent abode.

With his curt decision Baba turned around to leave. No one dared to stop him. He went a few steps ahead, stopped, turned, and spoke, "Listen Bhagat, my mosque will be a temple – a temple of Lord Krishna! It will be Dwarakamai! Mark my words, not you alone, but the Hindus, the Muslims and others will come there to pray! It will be a shrine of universal love!"

A great proclamation indeed! With it the fakir walked briskly towards the mosque. The villagers ran after him calling, "Sai Baba, Baba, Baba...."!

Baba reached the mosque and turned towards the dais at the other end. Heaps of rubbish had made the place shabby. This mosque was not in use and in a dilapidated condition. No one prayed there as the Muslims had another one in the village.

Sounds of heavy footsteps of Sai Baba scared the rodents which hastened to their holes. A snake too disappeared into a hole!

Ignoring all this, Baba climbed the steps and sat on a wooden log lying there. Villagers gathered around him. Some Muslims requested him to go over to the new mosque but He declined. So they began to clean the place.

Baba took out his clay pipe and began to fill it with tobacco. Chand hurried and brought some water. He soaked the pipe-cloth to wrap it around the pipe. Taking his club Baba got up and struck it hard on the log on which he was seated. The dry wood instantly caught fire. He lighted the pipe and started smoking and went into a reverie! His mind was somewhere else!

The villagers were dumb founded with what they saw. They decided to keep the fire burning forever! In no time they collected firewood. They placed some over the burning log. Thus started a fire in this mosque.

This is known as Sai Baba's Dhuni!

4

GOD BEGS FOR ALMS

"Give me roti, mother!"

Bayja heard Sai Baba's familiar call for alms in his own style. He had come on his daily round for begging which he had started since the second day of his arrival. Bayja had baked two rotis for Baba and gladly offered it to him.

Eight days had passed since Baba came to stay in Shirdi. Ever since his miracle of fire which he produced in the mosque the villagers considered him as an incarnation of God and visited him in large numbers for guidance.

At that time, a saint by the name Devidas also arrived at Shirdi. He lived in chawadi, a place near the mosque where Sai Baba stayed. Devidas had many followers in Shirdi prior to Baba's arrival. But due to Baba's popularity people visited Baba and started ignoring Devidas. Baba did not like it. He had great regards for Devidas and had started visiting him in chawadi. Similarly Devidas also started visiting Baba in the mosque. The discussions between the two saints enlightened the village folk and they started realising the importance of universal love and brotherhood.

Bayja was opposed to Baba's begging for food. She openly expressed her resentment. She told him – "Baba, you should not beg. I can feed you every day. You are God indeed in human form."

Baba just smiled at her words, even though he did not like the 'I' feeling she had while claiming that she can feed him. He did not listen to her. He would not compromise on his ideas.

One day, after her husband left home for his work, she arranged all sweets and savouries nicely in a clean brass plate, covered it carefully and asking her son Tatya to wait till she returned, she went to the mosque. Her son Tatya, though hungry, simply obeyed his mother.

Baba politely refused the food. He said, "Mother, what use is this rich food to me. I am after all a poor fakir. To beg for a roti or two and eat it when desired is my routine! Take this good food and offer it to an uninvited guest in whichever form he appears at your door. Believe me, He is God!"

"No, No!" Bayja declined, "You are God yourself! Please eat this food instead of begging for it from door to door and it is already late. You must be terribly hungry – I can see that."

Baba told her earnestly – "Mother, do not be angry with me. Believe me I am not at all hungry, neither I am used to such rich food. If you are so particular, feed those two pigs," pointing out two pigs opposite the mosque. He continued – "I am no different from them."

A great truth Baba tried to explain though it was beyond Bayja's understanding. She ignored him and vehemently told Baba – "No, no! I will not take this plate back nor will I feed the pigs."

Baba lost his temper. He went near the *dhuni* and started putting firewood into it. Flames rose high and touched the roof. Villagers watched it with fright. They thought the mosque would go into flames!

Bayja too was terrified. She regretted that she was the sole cause of Sai Baba's wrath! Her eyes filled with tears.

Baba was least concerned with Bayja's fear or what the villagers felt. He shouted abuses and went on throwing more and more logs into the dhuni.

Baba watched the leaping flames. With the orange glow cast by the fire his figure attained a golden glitter. With her head down, Bayja knelt down before him. She said, "Excuse me, My Lord. I will not repeat this mistake."

She touched Baba's feet. The villagers too came forward and put their heads on Baba's feet, one by one! Baba's wrath melted into compassion!

Baba picked up his wooden club, looked at the leaping flames, hit the club on the ground and shouted at the fire to come down. To everyone's surprise the flames obeyed Baba's instructions and came down step by step with every stroke of Baba's hitting. The villagers breathed a sigh of relief.

Baba smiled and looked at Bayja. Everybody knew that it was not the fire but the ego in Bayja that was tamed down by him. Relieved of her tension, Bayja lifted the plate to take it home. Baba snatched it from her and fed the two pigs outside the mosque. Everyone watched this astounding sight.

Baba looked at Bayja again. Her eyes were filled with tears of gratitude. Baba was visibly moved! He handed back the empty plate to her and said – "Go home mother, do not be unhappy. When I come to your door, do not give me more than one roti. Now go home and feed your son, Tatya. He is hungry and waiting for you. Instead of feeding him first, you came rushing to feed me. Remember God is not only in me. He is at your home, He is in Tatya, and He is in you, in all living beings. Feeding a hungry soul brings God's blessings. Remember this forever!"

Bayja hurried back home in haste. She was sorry that she had kept her son, Tatya hungry. She took a vow that she would never insist Baba to take food from her. But three days later, she found Baba at the house opposite to her with his begging bowl. That house belonged to a Brahmin and Baba was waiting for alms. Brahmin's son scoffed at Baba – "You will not get anything here. This is a Brahmin's house. Get lost as we do not feed Muslims."

Baba did not get humiliated. He affectionately told the boy – "Listen dear, never say 'No' to a beggar! Tell your refusal in a polite manner!"

The boy's mother appeared with a roti and some curry in a plate. She scolded her son – "Ram, how many times I told you not to abuse anyone who comes at our doorstep? You are just like your father! You do not know in what form God will appear at our door to test us one day!"

Turning to Baba she begged earnestly - "Forgive us, Baba! My son is ignorant. He does not know what he talks! Please accept this little food."

Baba expressed his happiness, "Allah will be kind to you" after putting the roti into his shoulder bag and pouring the curry into the tumbler. Blessing the woman Baba went to Bayja ma's house.

Bayja ma was waiting with her offering and had watched everything. She was a little touchy at the child's behaviour. She wondered as to why Baba should beg from a house where he is insulted, while she alone could feed him every day. She knew that her ego was cropping up and Baba did not like it. However her thoughts betrayed her as she was offering food to Baba.

"Baba, why do you go to that house? That boy insults you every day. Come here – I alone can give you as much food as you want!"

"Bayja ma, Bayja ma, What have I to do with your food? The roti you give me in charity is enough." Baba controlled her ego on time.

"Then why do you beg for food in five houses every day?" Bayja ma asked.

"Mother, do I beg to fill up this small belly?" – Baba queried.

Bayja ma could not understand as to why then he begged! She simply stared at him. Baba himself clarified – "Listen Mother, by making you give charity, you are achieving merit which will be recorded with God! Uninvited guests, ascetics, sadhus, beggars – all those who come to your doorstep should be given alms in whatever little measure you can afford. Thereby you achieve 'Punya' – merit! Charity reduces your misery and sufferings. Always bear this in your mind!"

Bayja ma innocently asked Baba – "Then take full alms from me alone. Let me get full merit myself." Baba told her - "Mother, to me all are equal." That mother in your opposite house is a great soul. Because of her merit, the entire family is doing well!" Bayja ma went on – "Her husband is very cruel! Though he is a Brahmin – Kulkarni and a physician himself, he is a miser and counts every pie. He has no consideration for poor and needy. His son is also just like him….."

Baba stopped her, "Enough, enough. I want them to be happy and that is why I go to their house for alms. Now give me my food….."

"But Baba, you took curry from that house in that tumbler. Now you want me to pour this chutney also into it. How can you enjoy their different tastes?" Bayja ma exclaimed.

"Why should a fakir bother about taste, Mother?" Baba asked. "All the food goes to the same place gets mixed up. All blood and dirt are alike. Why should the palate be tended so much?"

Without further argument Bayja ma poured chutney and vegetable into the tumbler and roti into the sack. Baba blessed her heartily.

Baba left for the next house. He visited five houses. That was his rule. Of course women in all houses awaited his arrival on his begging round. Those mothers from whom Baba accepted charity were very fortunate.

While Baba was on his begging rounds, two or three dogs followed him wagging their tails. The mothers who happily offered food to Baba never even once bothered about those hungry dogs! Baba was aware of this!

On reaching the mosque, Baba would lovingly call the dogs, the birds and the pigs that watched him from a distance. He would pour the contents of his sack and tumbler into a stone bowl kept at the entrance. The dogs and pigs would rush and the birds swooped to feast on these free-for-all meals! Baba moved away to light up his 'chillum' while these creatures barked, growled and clamoured – but ate together their daily fare which they got without any effort. Baba watched it all as he smoked but never chased them away.

Satisfied with the feast, the animals moved away leaving only a little for Baba. Baba then came near the bowl and ate the leftovers. With that he satisfied his hunger – as he did in those early days!

Baba was 'God in human garb' and practised what he preached. He believed that the divinity is present in all creatures. To show disrespect towards them is like disregarding the divinity that existed in each of them!

5

MIRACLE OF LAMPS

*L*ife in Shirdi moved on. Since Baba's divinity was proclaimed on the first day of his arrival at Shirdi, villagers watched all his moves, listened to his words and observed his actions carefully. They were secretly looking forward to another miracle by Baba. But there was none thereafter.

Baba's begging rounds evoked a lot of commotion in the beginning. Now it was a matter of routine. The eyes which were fixed on Baba when he started from the mosque with his bag and the tumbler, now turned away in resentment with his sight. This was more so because Baba was begging twice or thrice a day and going to the same house at times. People began to consider him mad. Even those mothers who awaited his begging rounds eagerly lost their faith and no more cared for this man of miracles!

However, Bayja ma was an exception! She would always be restless if Baba failed to appear at her door! She used to wait for him eagerly without taking food for hours together with a few rotis and chutney ready for him. She waited just to have a glimpse of Baba and then have her food.

Baba was aware of her love and devotion! But he deliberately avoided her so that she did not develop ego that she was offering him food every day.

If Baba failed to come on any day, this extremely perturbed Bayja who would then herself go to the mosque even on a scorching afternoon and secretly place a couple of freshly baked rotis and chutney in the bowl outside. Such was her selfless love towards Baba. As if the birds and animals were aware of it, they never touched the offering to respect her sentiments for Baba! Though Bayja ma took this liberty she also remembered the wrath of Baba! She always recollected as to how Baba beat her when she had a severe abdominal pain which vanished subsequently!

What happened actually was that one day, Bayja ma had a severe pain in her abdomen. She spent the entire day lying down on the bed after her cooking. Her husband and son had food and left for their farm. Bayja ma was too restless and so dozed off. When she woke up, it was already evening. Her abdomen was still griping and the pain was unbearable. On inquiring from the neighbours, she came to know that Baba had not come to her house that day. This pricked her maternal instincts. She guessed that Baba must have starved himself that day. Unmindful of her condition, she got up, baked two rotis, took some vegetables, and rushed to the mosque.

In the mosque, Baba was furious since morning. He was gabbling to himself! He was flinging and tossing things at random – at anyone! Everybody was frightened and no one dared to go near him. Baba would go into this type of temper-tantrum, just to relieve someone's misery. Bayja ma saw this and guessed that her own agony must have been disturbing Baba. She moved ahead and offered food to Baba. On seeing her, Baba rushed forward with his club to hit her. Bayja ma ran in fright! Baba too chased her and ultimately flung his club at her. People thought that she must have been hurt badly. But to her it was a boon. Her abdominal pain had totally disappeared! It never troubled her again! That was Baba's way to drive away his devotee's illness! So

Bayja ma's entire family had implicit faith in Baba and her mind always hovered for his glimpse and grace!

One day villagers could not refrain from watching Baba who left the mosque for begging in the evening. It was quite an unusual time for Baba to beg! He had not done it before! He went to Nandu's shop.

"What can I do for you, Baba?" Nandu politely asked. "Oh! Give me a little oil! That is all!" Baba extended his tumbler.

"Oil? At this hour?" Nandu Marwadi hesitated! According to his custom, giving oil in the evening was considered inauspicious. Baba assured him – "It is all right Nandu! Lakshmi will come to your doorstep! Believe me!"

Without any argument Nandu Marwadi poured some oil in Baba's tumbler. Baba left the shop without paying anything. This disturbed him as he expected Baba to pay him at least two *paisas*. He grieved that Lakshmi has not favoured him at the auspicious hour.

"Nandu, there is a deal of two thousand rupees worth supply of jaggery! Would you like to accept?" Nandu Marwadi was taken aback to hear this from his friend Raja Bhai. Raja Bhai, a merchant from Kopergaon had come to him and explained him that, "I cannot accept the deal myself. My hands are tied up. This is a good deal and I am sure you will make good money."

"Oh, you Raja Bhai!" Nandu became excited. Jubilantly he said – "Who will lose this chance? Come, have some tea!" So Lakshmi indeed had favoured Nandu at this hour of the evening. As he lighted a lamp in his shop, Nandu's mind made a quick calculation of how much profit he could make in the deal of jaggery, which Raja Bhai offered. He thought – "The mad fakir's words have really come true."

Why Baba needed oil today – all traders pondered. Baba had approached them all. There were four of them in Shirdi! However they all gave him a little oil willingly.

So far only a single lamp was lighted in the mosque. Appa Jogale daily used to supply oil for it. Today he had gone out of the village. Even so, instead of one, Baba lighted four! Four earthen lamps in four corners of the mosque!

Today was the day of *amavasya* – the new moon day on which every Hindu lighted a special lamp in his house. Many had forgotten this tradition.

He continued getting oil from the shopkeepers and kept the wicks burning throughout. The grocers gladly gave oil to Baba. They did so because to give oil in charity in the evening time is now considered auspicious! Even then, there was one man who wanted to put an end to the good deed of others!

That was Kulkarni – the village physician who was jealous of Baba getting oil gratis every day for burning four lamps in the mosque. He always wanted to harm Baba's popularity and to stop free oil supply to this mad man!

Whenever Kulkarni saw Baba in the street, he always used to mock at him in disgust. Baba was never disturbed at his silly behaviour. He had his own plan of transforming Kulkarni. He wanted to win his heart. Baba was planning to make Kulkarni an instrument to prove once again his omnipotence with a dazzling miracle of all times!

The next day was Deepawali. The entire Shirdi village was geared up to celebrate the festival of lights. As usual, Baba went to Nandu Marwadi's shop to get some oil. Kulkarni physician was already there to buy some items. On seeing Baba, an evil thought cropped up in Kulkarni's mind and he decided that on the day of Deepawali, Baba's mosque will be in darkness. Not only that but Kulkarni wanted that from that day onwards Baba should not light a lamp in the mosque. As soon as this devilish idea shaped in his mind, Kulkarni executed his plan. Right in the presence of Baba, he asked Nandu Marwadi – "Nandu, does this fakir pay you for the oil?"

"No, no! We never ask for it!" Nandu explained, "It is not fair to ask money for that little oil! All grocers gladly give it to him!"

"Excellent business practice! Very wise of you! Free supply of oil!"

With this remark, Kulkarni left the place. A spark can light the fire. Same thing happened with Nandu. He gave Baba his usual quantity of oil and saw him off. Baba went to other shops and got oil for lighting the lamps.

As Nandu watched Baba leaving his shop, he went to the shop next to him and spoke to his co-businessman, "Deepchandji, tomorrow is deepawali? Should we give charity oil tomorrow also?" He bluntly asked.

"Why not? What is the harm?" Deepchand asked with surprise. "No, no! Not that way! Tomorrow every house will light the lamps. We have more demand for oil. How can we afford to give it free to Baba?"

The devil worked! Deepchand said – "You are right Bhaiya! We will think about it!" Nandu opened up his mind, - "If I alone stop this free supply of oil to Baba, it is not right! We must unitedly take a decision."

Deepchand agreed with him – "Yes, yes, let us stop this oil to Baba from tomorrow!" He instantly got up and said – "Come Bhaiya, let us meet Kewalchandji and Bhagchandji. We will discuss with them too!"

All the shopkeepers agreed to stop oil to Baba from next day onwards!

The next day dawned. It was deepawali, the festival of lights! Day of worshipping Lakshmi, the goddess of wealth!

Everyone was in a festive mood. They wore new clothes and visited temples. Many came to Baba.

The first one to visit Baba was Kashiram, the village tailor. He had come with a green coloured gown and a cap to Baba. He had worked overnight on his sewing machine to stitch this new dress for Baba. He prostrated to Baba and offered his gift. Baba was moved by his love and affection. Although Baba did not like to wear coloured clothes but He accepted Kashiram's loving gift. Kashiram also took a promise from Baba that he would wear that green-coloured dress on that day at least, discarding his torn clothes.

The villagers were happy to see Baba in his new dress on that auspicious day. But more joyous was Kulkarni. He was certain that his plan would work and the shopkeepers will not offer oil to Baba! With delight, he waited for the nightfall to see total darkness in the mosque, when the entire Shirdi glittered with lights! He mused at the fun he was going to watch!

Bayja ma prepared some sweets and snacks and went to the mosque. She also took some oil and poured into his tumbler. She was happy that Baba had put on a new gown today! He happily enjoyed the sweets brought by Bajya Ma. He was moved by her affection, as she had brought some oil, which she poured it into his tumbler. A bright idea to illuminate the entire mosque struck Baba. He went straight to Vaman, the village potter.

"Vaman, I want earthen lamps!" Baba asked him. "Have as many as you want, Baba!" Vaman put a big basket before him. He was extremely happy that Baba had visited his shop on an auspicious day!

Baba took around hundred lamps and returned to the mosque. Not knowing Baba's plan to celebrate Deepawali by illuminating the entire mosque, the villagers wondered as to why Baba had brought over a hundred lamps. They knew that Bayja ma had brought very little oil and the Marwadi shopkeepers may not offer adequate oil for all those lamps!

Baba began rolling wicks for all the hundred and odd lamps. He skillfully rolled them. The little boy, Abdulla came running and assisted Baba. Abdulla wanted to celebrate Deepawali in his house, but his mother objected. He came running to the mosque and seeing Baba rolling the wicks, started assisting him in rolling the wicks quickly – one after the other.

Abdulla's mother came to the mosque in search of her son. She was shocked to see Baba rolling the wicks to illuminate the mosque to celebrate a Hindu festival. She was aware that the Muslim community in the village did not like the way Baba behaved. They were sore that Baba had started a permanent fire dhuni in the mosque and was lighting four lamps in four corners of the mosque. But they kept mum as they were aware of his super-human powers. Abdulla's mother went back home and informed her husband that Baba was rolling the wicks to celebrate Deepawali.

The few Muslims in the village gathered. They had a discussion and wanted to put an end to all the Hindu activities in the mosque. Noor Mohammed led the mission and spoke to Baba - "Baba, we do not like the burning of lamps in our mosque like the Hindus!"

"Why not? What is wrong?" Baba queried. "Not like that, Baba!" Noor Mohammed expressed his discontent, "First you started a permanent fire in the mosque, and you call it dhuni. Later every night you light four lamps. Now you are celebrating deepawali – a Hindu festival right in our mosque!"

Baba listened to them and quietly answered – "Noor, to me Hindus and Muslims are one and the same! We are all children of Allah. Whether Muslims or Hindus, we all live under the same sky. The water you drink – they also drink! The fire that cooks for you cooks for them also! Where do you then differ? Hindus attend your 'Tabot' on the Moharam day?"

The Muslims had no reply. They returned as they came!

Only Abdulla stayed behind to light the lamps! He had no other thought. He saw that the wicks were ready and put into lamps. Undisturbed Baba had completed the job. But where was the oil? Already there were some onlookers and all eyes were fixed on Baba. Baba got up. With his tumbler he went to Nandu Marwadi's shop. Some villagers followed him to watch the fun! "Nandu, I am lighting many lamps tonight! Give me a little more oil today! You all must fill up this tumbler," Baba spoke with his poise and confidence and extended the tumbler in his hand.

"Very good! Happy deepawali at our cost!" Nandu exclaimed, "Baba, we cannot afford to give you oil free of cost every day. Moreover, today I am out of stock. You know every house celebrates Deepawali." Nandu spoke plainly and uttered a blatant lie. He was the first amongst the shopkeepers whom Baba visited every day and moreover, it was his mind which was set on fire by Kulkarni.

Baba did not utter a word! He knew that none of them would give him oil that day. However he went ahead to test others. The other three traders – Deepchand, Bhagchand and Kewalchand – lied that they had no stocks.

Baba returned to the mosque undisturbed and empty handed! The villagers and the shopkeepers too followed him to watch Baba's next step. Kulkarni too came and stood a little away from the mosque to watch the fun. They were all eager to see what Baba would do without oil!

Baba took the tumbler which contained a little oil that Bayja ma had brought in the morning. He drank every drop of it. Poured water in it from the earthen pot kept in a corner of the mosque and drank it all again. Everyone watched eagerly. Poor Abdulla was scared and stood in a corner!

Once again Baba filled the tumbler with water from the same pot. Quickly he poured it in all the hundred and odd lamps in which he had rolled the wicks. He then called Abdulla - "Light up all these lamps! Illuminate the entire mosque! Let us celebrate Deepawali here! Come, be quick! Place the lamps in every nook and corner of the mosque!"

Baba gave vent to his wrath! Little Abdulla was frightened! Yet he obeyed! He was doubtful as to how the lamps will burn with water. However he drew out a matchstick! He lighted the first lamp! Then the second! Thereafter even the third! Doubts and fear gone, he lighted all the hundred and odd lamps, dancing with joy – lighting them one by one! One after the other!

On hearing this great miracle, Bayja ma rushed to the mosque. She picked up five lamps and placing them on a plate waved an aarti around Baba – who now was all in smiles – blessing devotees.

The lamps burnt throughout the night. People kept awake to watch this divine brilliance! Shouts after shouts went high in the horizon in praise of Baba! Message spread to neighbouring villages and in the next few weeks, people came rushing to the mosque to have a glimpse of Baba.

6

RARE YOGIC FEAT

*D*azzled with the miracle of lights, the villagers shouted *jaikars* to Baba. While everyone rejoiced, only one person - Kulkarni was smeared with his own sin. He quietly retreated to his home.

Stealthily he entered his house and went to bed. He was restless and fuming with his self-created humiliation! He regretted that with this miracle, Baba's popularity has reached a great height while he has lost the regards of the villagers forever! He knew that everybody would now curse for instigating Nandu Marwadi to stop giving oil to Baba. He was rolling in bed restlessly.

The first to curse Kulkarni were the shopkeepers themselves who had realised their blunder. Nandu Marwadi was sorry that he listened to Kulkarni and had offended Baba, forgetting Baba's greatness.

Next morning Nandu Marwadi and the other three shopkeepers reached the mosque, touched Baba's feet and surrendered to him – "Pardon us Baba! The devil in Kulkarni misled us. We could not see God amongst us! Please forgive us." Baba spoke to them in his usual humility – "I tell you again that I am not God! I am 'Yaad-e-huque', one who remembers Him! Brothers, you told me a lie yesterday. I am here to lead you on the path of righteousness, but you took the lane of untruth. Why? Just to earn a few coins. You have been exploiting these villagers all along! Remember God is watching you! Do not utter lies! Truth alone brings you peace and wealth!" There was a murmur among the crowd. People wondered as to why they are getting less for the price they pay!

The shopkeepers took a vow of truth and righteousness. They promised Baba of fair business practices! That changed the outlook of all in the village! All began to have faith in God! Love among Hindus and Muslims developed and this resulted in everlasting peace!

Abdulla who lighted the lamps on Deepawali, settled down in the mosque to serve Baba forever! His parents permitted him to stay there to have Baba's grace. Every day he cleaned the mosque, attended to Baba's service, lighted the lamps, and did other errands till Baba's mahasamadhi!

Next day Abdulla lighted the usual four lamps. In fact, he desired to illuminate the entire mosque next day too. But Baba did not permit it. Instead, he fed Abdulla with sweets and snacks that Bayja ma had brought to the mosque. Abdulla relished their taste and soon went to sleep!

The night fell! The festival of lights soon dimmed covering the village in total darkness! The shrill sound of the crickets created a weird atmosphere. A sleepless night on the previous day and the happiness of witnessing a great miracle soon lulled the village into deep slumber. Though everyone was enjoying a good night's rest, Baba was wide awake. He was thinking of Kulkarni and how to appease his disturbed mind?

Indeed Kulkarni's mind was on fire! He wished to set the mosque on fire and burn Baba alive! As such, he too was wide awake! Both his wife and son who were sleeping nearby were in deep slumber!

Making certain that none of them watched him, Kulkarni got up from his bed. Stealthily he came out and started walking towards the mosque. He had a wicked plan! The ever-burning 'dhuni' in the mosque was to be the cause of a devastating fire in it! He had carefully thought out a plan to make the police and the villagers believe that the fire was accidental. It was possible!

Baba too had a plan ready with him to deal with the devil! God is ever careful in every move!

Kulkarni approached the mosque and from outside glanced at the elevated platform at the other end on which Baba slept. The dhuni was burning peacefully. Abdulla was fast asleep. Firewood logs were there. The four lamps were burning. The unlighted hundred and odd lamps were lying at random, scattered carelessly. The water pot was uncovered with its lid lying aside. Baba's clay-pipe, his club, his new green dress lay by his side. Kulkarni felt that all belongings of Baba stared at him!

Kulkarni was determined to execute his plan! He carefully planned his way out after setting the mosque on fire. He sneaked in through the entrance which was always open.

Keeping an eye on the sleeping figure of Baba facing towards him, looking at the 'dhuni' and the heap of logs lying beyond, he cautiously walked with silent steps in the direction of Baba – never once removing his eyes away from him. The place was strangely quiet!

Suddenly Kulkarni stopped! He had stumbled over something! He looked down in horror! It was Baba's severed head lying below! He shuddered and saw sideways! Baba's separated limbs – hands, legs and a headless trunk scattered all around!

With a terrified look, Kulkarni glanced in the direction he had first seen Baba sleeping. Now Baba was not there! The four lamps burnt calmly and Kulkarni could see everything clearly. The pipe was there, the club was there, the gown too! Everything in its own place! Only Baba was not there!

Kulkarni shook to the core, realising that Baba has been slaughtered by someone else! He trembled from head to toe! What he had desired has at last happened, but he was afraid that as he hated Baba, people would suspect him for this murder! Frightened as he was, the whole mosque was spinning! He traced back his steps. Feeling dizzy he was unable even to reach the exit! He stumbled here and there and finally reached his home!

Lying in his own place where he was sleeping, Baba was enjoying this fun! After Kulkarni left, Baba too went to sleep!

Frightened first but overjoyed afterwards that Baba has left this world forever; Kulkarni soon embraced a peaceful slumber!

Next morning, Kulkarni had a message from Baba. He had called him to the mosque. The message from Baba froze Kulkarni to the core! He was waiting since morning for the happy news of Baba's murder! Having slept peacefully, he woke up early for the news. He was happy and pleased. But a message from the murdered man rocked him from top to bottom!

"Baba calls me?" Kulkarni stammered as he questioned. He looked as pale as snow! His wife saw her husband nervous. She saw Ganapat Rao Kote Patil who had brought the message from Baba. She was surprised that of all people, Baba would call her husband to the mosque. She made sure that the message was for Kulkarni only. She asked her husband to meet Baba and seek his blessings. Otherwise she warned him everyone is devoted to Baba, patients may not come to him and he would lose his medical practice!

Kulkarni also had second thoughts. Wisdom dawned on him! He decided to meet Baba. He accompanied Ganapat Rao Kote Patil to the mosque. But what he saw there made him speechless!

Baba himself was washing the wounds of a leper. The leper's body was full of wounds – bleeding and oozing pus! They were stinking too! It was an advanced case of leprosy. But Baba was lovingly attending to the wounds. Kulkarni felt nauseated and kept two steps backwards. Ganapat Rao Kote Patil announced his arrival, "Baba, Kulkarni is here". "Ask him to wait," Baba answered, continuing his service to the leper. Kulkarni waited.

The mosque was crowded. In the crowd were Baba Saheb Dengale and his brother Nana Saheb Dengale from Neemgaon. A boy having his eyes tied up with a bandage was also present with his mother. He was a patient of Kulkarni who had tied up his eyes on the previous day.

Baba Saheb Dengale was Baba's ardent devotee. He considered Baba as God. However his family members did not share his view. After hearing the miracle of Baba lighting lamps with water on Deepawali, Baba Saheb Dengale's brother Nana Saheb Dengale too accompanied his brother today. Since he had no children, he secretly desired for progeny.

Recently, during the last five days, Baba had undertaken the mission of service to the sick and disabled. He would visit them, treat them, and nurse them at their homes with herbs and medicinal plants. Sitting near them he would reassure them with his sweet and compassionate words. His loving behaviour made them happy and their bodies and minds recovered in no time!

The miracle on the day before, on Deepawali, attracted many villagers from the neighbourhood to seek Baba's blessings and to get divine healing for many incurable diseases and other miseries. This leper had come for cure!

Having washed his wounds, Baba cleaned his hands and took out a fistful of ash from the dhuni. He applied it liberally over the leper's wounds. The patient who was groaning with pain felt much better.

The leper expressed his gratitude. He was an outcaste in the society. He had found someone giving him real love. Baba assured him that his leprosy would be cured and sent him home with ashes from the dhuni. For Kulkarni, cure of leprosy with ash was ridiculous.

Baba looked at Kulkarni and asked him – "Panditji, tell me about anacardium". Kulkarni quoted a verse from Ayurvedic medicine listing the beneficial effects of nacardium in treatment of leucoderma, dysentery, and fever. Everyone appreciated Kulkarni's learning. But Baba hardly listened to him and he was busy removing the bandage from the eyes of the boy who was treated by Kulkarni the previous day. The boy's eyes were swollen and red. Baba told Abdulla to mash a nut of anacardium. He rolled it and plastered into the boy's eyes. Kulkarni was aghast and tried to prevent Baba putting Anacardium plaster into the eyes of the boy. Kulkarni announced that the boy would be blind forever and left the mosque.

Those who had faith in Baba's miraculous powers quietly watched. Few sympathised for the loss of the boy's eyesight.

Baba Saheb Dengale too was losing his faith. His brother Nana Saheb Dengale was feeling sorry for having come all the way from Neemgaon!

"No! You have not come in vain!" Baba loudly replied to his thought, "Go home! Allah has granted a son to you!" Baba blessed him in advance – even before he disclosed his innate desire! As he spoke, Baba suddenly removed the bandage on the eyes of the boy. His eyes were clear! There was a sigh of relief from everyone present.

Nana Saheb Dengale bent down in reverence, his head on Baba's feet.

And one year later, his wife gave birth to a son!

7

DEVOTION OF MHALSAPATHY

*M*halsapathy was very much disturbed! He was restless because he had stopped Baba entering Khandoba temple when Baba arrived with the wedding party along with Chand bhai Patel. He repeatedly questioned himself – was it wrong to stop a Muslim fakir entering a Hindu shrine? Had he allowed him, the temple would become unfit for Hindus to worship! The villagers would have been upset and perhaps an enmity between Hindus and Muslims would have resulted in a communal clash!

But the subsequent events made Mhalsapathy repent deeply for not permitting Baba to settle down in Khandoba temple! Baba had proved his divine identity. His miracles had drawn people from all over! Such miracles were witnessed for the first time in Shirdi. Naturally Mhalsapathy was fascinated with them just like others. He felt that he should overcome all his inhibitions in meeting Baba and decided to have Baba's darshan!

Mhalsapathy was a goldsmith by caste and profession. He was an uneducated young man. Khandoba was his family deity. With his own money he had built a temple for Khandoba at Shirdi. He led a life of poverty but always remained contented, with implicit faith in God. He was possessed with the spirit of Khandoba and when he was in trance he solved many problems of the villagers. He was detached to worldly pleasures. This led him on to a spiritual path and made him highly respected by the villagers.

Mhalsapathy too heard of Baba lighting the lamps with water on Deepawali. His thoughts were focussed on Sai Baba, but he was afraid to meet him as he thought that Baba would still be angry with him for not permitting him to settle down in Khandoba temple. The villagers also had told him about Baba's rage. Mhalsapathy thought that his very sight would flare up Baba.

Actually it was Mhalsapathy who made the people aware of Baba's divine powers. When Baba arrived four years ago at Shirdi, it was Mhalsapathy who had his divine vision. It was because of Mhalsapathy, a shrine was unearthed below the neem tree, which had benefitted many when they took a vow to burn incense on thursdays and fridays. When Sai Baba arrived along with Chand Patel's wedding party, it was Mhalsapathy who welcomed him with the call 'Come - come on, Sai, Sai Baba' and as such Mhalsapathy is credited for giving a name to this 'Loving God'.

Mhalsapathy, who had erred in stopping Baba to settle down in Khandoba mandir got isolated from him. Even Baba did not bother to send a word to him to come to his mosque. Mhalsapathy was deprived of both Baba's darshan as well as blessings, in spite of his implicit faith in Baba. He began to blame himself, as his ego had prevented him from calling on Baba! He now felt that if he continues to keep quiet, he will be committing another blunder! So Mhalsapathy decided to visit Baba immediately.

Baba was not in the mosque. Abdulla told him that he has gone to the well for taking bath. Mhalsapathy started towards the well but Abdulla prevented him, saying, "Uncle, Baba has told me not to send anyone there". Mhalsapathy hesitated but ignored Abdulla's word.

This deserted well outside the village was not frequented by the villagers. As such Baba found it convenient for his wash. He went there almost daily taking care that no one came that side while he bathed. But Mhalsapathy was in such a state of mind that he would throw away all barriers so that he could meet Baba! He reached the well and had a rare sight to see!

Sitting near the well, Baba had completely taken out his intestines and was washing it like a piece of cloth. He was rubbing it inside and outside to clean it. Seeing this strange sight, Mhalsapathy stared at Baba with a transfixed gaze! He had heard about the *dhothy-pothy* yoga which Baba was now practising. None of the mendicants who had told Mhalsapathy about this yoga had ever practised it themselves. It is indeed a difficult practice which only ancient *rishis* in India did to have a long radiant life!

Today Mhalsapathy had the privilege of seeing Baba practising this! Looking at this facet of Baba, Mhalsapathy was thrilled and prostrated in veneration although Baba was sitting far away from where he stood!

Baba was very well aware of this. He knew that Mhalsapathy would be coming to him. Since he desired to clean the mind of God-fearing Mhalsapathy, he made him witness this strange yogic practice!

Quickly Baba put the intestines back into his abdomen and came in front of Mhalsapathy. Mhalsapathy was unaware of this, as he had closed his eyes and still contemplating on the strange vision of Baba practising dhothy-pothy yoga.

"Bhagat, why did you come here?" Baba's stern voice brought Mhalsapathy to senses. Opening his eyes, he saw Baba standing in front of him. "Did Abdulla not prevent you from coming here?" Baba asked.

Seeing Baba in anger Mhalsapathy was scared! He remembered that he had violated Baba's orders and even though Abdulla pestered him not to go near the well, he was in a hurry to have Baba's darshan. He got up. His feet trembled as he faced Baba! "Pardon me, my Lord! I have come to beg for your forgiveness. On that day, I prevented you from entering your own shrine. That is why I have come to ask your mercy on me!"

Mhalsapathy earnestly prayed – "Abdulla repeatedly told me not to go near the well. But I have come here, as I could not wait long without your darshan." Baba was moved with Mhalsapathy's pure heart! He said, "It is all right, bhagat! What you did that day was not incorrect. You only followed the tenets of your religion. And moreover, if a person sincerely repents, God definitely forgives him." Baba kept his hand on Mhalsapathy's head and told him – "Do not worry! Allah will shower his grace on you!"

Mhalsapathy was relieved of his tension. He kept his head on Baba's feet. Baba made him get up and said – "Come! Let us reach Dwarakamai fast!"

"Dwarakamai? Where is it?" Mhalsapathy was perplexed. "Bhagat, have you forgotten? Did I not tell you my mosque will be Krishna's Dwaraka?"

"Yes, yes, Baba I remember it now!" Mhalsapathy replied. "Come, let us reach there quickly. Abdulla is eagerly waiting for me!"

They rushed to the mosque hurriedly. When they reached the mosque they saw a strong built Muslim fakir having a tiff with Abdulla. Abdulla was quite angry and shouting at this stranger – "All this belongs to Baba! How dare you throw them away?"

The fakir wanted to throw away all the articles of Baba – his club, bed, begging bowl, etc. Abdulla was giving him a tough fight. He had firmly held the fakir's hand in his tender fist. Surprisingly the strong-looking fakir was finding it impossible to snatch it away from Abdulla's grip. Some villagers had started gathering while the scuffle went on.

"Well, Bade Bhai Jawahar Ali, what is the idea?" Baba's melodious voice made the fakir Jawahar Ali look back. Encouraged by Baba's presence, Abdulla flung back Jawahar Ali's hand with a sudden jerk! Since it pained him, cursing Abdulla, Jawahar Ali spoke to Baba, "you know my name?" "Why not? The entire world knows Jawahar Ali's name, Sir", said Baba politely. "Listen, you little chap! Did I not tell you?" Jawahar Ali proudly told Abdulla. "I am a far greater man than your Sai Baba. The whole world knows my name! Do you understand? Now remove all these things like a good boy! Or else, I will throw everything out – including you!"

"Well brother, what makes you displeased? These things belong to me," said Baba with same humility. "Then remove them immediately! I am going to stay in this place." Jawahar Ali spoke rudely.

"Stay here happily if you like! I will stay outside." Saying this Baba called Abdulla. "No, no Baba! You should not go out! We will see how this Jawahar Ali stays here!" Mhalsapathy raised his voice. He moved towards Jawahar Ali. Other villagers too stepped forward. Jawahar Ali was frightened. He gathered some courage and said, "No, no! I – I – I meant.........simply asked as to who started this fire here!"

Mhalsapathy spoke of what he was convinced – "Our God who stands before you started it with his powers."

Jawahar Ali asked sarcastically, "So you mean this fakir is God?"

Nandu Marwadi said – "Of course, he lighted lamps in this mosque with mere water." Kashiram tailor said – "Not only that he showed us four burning lamps beneath the neem tree there." Appa Jogale added – "He cured the swollen eyes by plastering marking nuts."

Jawahar Ali said with mischief in his tone – "Yaa Allah! He must be a magician!" The villagers explained – "No! He is not a magician. He is God! God Almighty!"

"No, no! Brother Jawahar Ali. I am a mere Yaad-e-huque! Servant of God! They all love me – respect me! That is why I am staying in this village." Baba explained with his usual humility.

"Then I will also stay here!" Jawahar Ali declared his intenton. "By all means! This is Allah Miya's mosque! A shelter for all! Come! We will both stay here!" Baba put an end to a bitter episode!

The villagers left with Baba's permission. Jawahar Ali chose a more comfortable corner of the mosque to spread his bed.

After this, Baba went on his begging round. He collected food from five houses, fed Jawahar Ali and Abdulla, fed the birds and animals and ate a little and rested for a while. Abdulla went to meet his mother.

Jawahar Ali was a common fakir, but he knew *Quran* by heart. He was a good conversationist. Besides Quran, he had studied *Ramayana, Gita*, etc., from which he used to quote profusely and had won arguments with many scholars. This had made him very proud! However he was now convinced that his usual tricks will not work in Shirdi. Therefore he started scheming! He thought that Sai Baba was an ordinary and immature fakir and as such could be easily controlled!

One evening many devotees had come to meet Baba. Baba treated a few patients with his herbal medicines. Jawahar Ali watched all this. He started inquiring about Baba through his devotees. Then he began to believe that Baba knew some witchcraft and he wanted to learn this from him!

After the devotees had left, Abdulla lighted the lamps in the mosque. Baba kindled his ever-burning dhuni, shared food brought by the devotees along with Abdulla, Jawahar Ali and the animals and prepared his bed to retire. Abdulla slept off and Baba and Jawahar Ali kept talking for a long time. Jawahar Ali wanted to learn witchcraft from Baba while maintaining superiority over Baba. He worked out a scheme to achieve this.

Jawahar Ali spoke to Baba – "Tell me, my boy. Do you know our holy Quran?" Baba shrewdly replied – "Yes! Just a little!"

Jawahar Ali tried to trap him – "Why little? Why not fully?" "If you teach me, Sir, I will learn fully!" Baba knowingly offered him an opportunity!

"Yes, yes! Why not?" Jawahar Ali impatiently said, "But for that you will have to serve me and do all my menial jobs – like a servant." In rapid succession, Jawahar Ali put forward his conditions.

"Oh, sure! I will be glad to serve you. Who will miss this chance of a life time to learn the holy Quran from a learned person like you?"

Jawahar Ali decided to leave Shirdi next morning for Rahata with Sai Baba in the early hours. Baba had already given his consent. To achieve his own end Jawahar Ali had planned to separate Baba from his devotees in Shirdi.

Next morning Baba's devotees came as usual for his darshan. They were shocked to find that Baba had left with his belongings with Jawahar Ali! Abdulla was unable to throw any light on this mystery!

8

THE EGO MELTS

The villagers of Shirdi were shocked to find that Sai Baba has left their village even without informing them, while those in Rahata were surprised to see him in their small town in the company of Jawahar Ali – a common fakir! Leaving Shirdi these two had come to stay at Rahata.

Rahata is a small town three miles away from Shirdi on the main road to Ahmednagar. There is a Veerabhadra temple in this town. Close by is an idgah or mosque for the Muslims to carry out their prayers. This idgah was built by Jawahar Ali in those days. After leaving Shirdi, Sai Baba came here along with Jawahar Ali. Now Jawahar Ali prided himself as the master and Sai Baba as his disciple! But he considered Baba as an all purpose servant!

A few months back, Jawahar Ali had come to Rahata from Ahmednagar and had chosen a deserted place near Veerabhadra temple for his stay. He had a few followers along with him. Both Hindus and Muslims were impressed with his learned talks on religion and looked up to him as a spiritual master and willingly contributed to build an idgah. However, Jawahar Ali got into problem with the local people for throwing meat near Veerabhadra temple. The enraged people drove him away. Even the few followers abandoned him. So all alone, he went to Shirdi where also he got into trouble. From there he had come back to Rahata along with Sai Baba.

In bringing Sai Baba along with him, Jawahar Ali had two-fold objectives! He wanted to isolate Baba from the villagers of Shirdi. Secondly, his being associated with Sai Baba will enhance his public image. Baba's fame had already reached Rahata. A shopkeeper Chandrabhan Sait and a few others from Rahata were already devotees of Baba and had visited Shirdi on several occasions. Jawahar Ali knew these things.

In the morning, people in Rahata were delighted to see Sai Baba amidst them. They could not believe their eyes, when they saw Baba making trips for water to a well carrying it to the idgha. Their delight changed into anger when they saw Jawahar Ali commanding Sai Baba to do all his menial jobs. They were more shocked to see Baba obeying him like an ordinary servant.

With a lightning speed, word went around that Sai Baba is in Rahata. People rushed to the idgha for Baba's darshan. Chandrabhan Sait and others rushed ahead and prostrated before Baba while he was busy washing Jawahar Ali's clothes. Baba said, "Brothers, why do you prostrate before me? Touch my Guru Jawahar Ali's feet! He is there!"

"Is Jawahar Ali your Guru? Impossible, Baba!" Chandrabhan Sait angrily looked at Jawahar Ali and spoke. "Yes! I am his disciple and servant too!" Baba explained. "No, no! This is impossible! You are God Almighty yourself! We know!" Chandrabhan Sait expressed the feeling of all!

"This Jawahar Ali polluted our deity in Veerabhadra temple! Yesterday we chased him out of Rahata," said another man.

Sai Baba tried to pacify them – "Brothers, how can God be polluted like that? Why are you angry with him? If an idol gets polluted so easily, then it is not God! It is a mere stone – a piece of rock! Just throw it away!"

"That is what I told them!" Though scared Jawahar Ali was now bold enough by Baba's intervention. "You are perfectly right, Guru Maharaj!" Baba took Jawahar Ali's side. The villagers kept quiet.

"Go home, brothers, let me serve my Guru." Baba pleaded.

The villagers left helplessly.

They had to! But they were restless! Their devotion, veneration and love for Baba made them very uneasy! They were sorry that they were unable to serve their God even though he was now in their village. Forgetting his grudge against Jawahar Ali, Chandrabhan Sait returned with food for both. Others too accompanied. Chandrabhan Sait said, "Baba, we will serve Jawahar Ali, do all menial jobs – but you should come with us and stay happily in my house," He argued – "We do not like you to do such menial jobs!"

"No dear ones! I have accepted him as my Guru! I have given him my word! Even Lord Krishna had to serve his Guru Sandipini and Lord Rama served Vashishta! To serve my Guru is my duty."

"But Baba" – Chandrabhan Sait wanted to argue. Baba stopped him and said – "And no work is low in service! While serving, we must do well, speak well, and act well!" Baba explained the path of righteousness.

Chandrabhan Sait had nothing more to say. He fed Baba and Jawahar Ali. However people felt that Jawahar Ali has played some sorcery against Baba. That is why he is completely under Jawahar Ali's spell. After Baba and Jawahar Ali had their food, Chandrabhan Sait and others left.

Jawahar Ali stretched himself and asked Baba to massage his feet.

After some time, a group of villagers came to the idgha. They brought along with them, a wandering mendicant Devidas. The disappointed visitors met Devidas, who was on his way to Shirdi. Devidas had great regards for Baba. So he immediately walked to the idgha along with the villagers. Seeing Devidas, both Sai Baba and Jawahar Ali got up and offered their greetings.

"Sainath, what are you doing here?" Devidas asked humbly. Jawahar Ali answered him rudely – "He is my disciple! What has that to do with you?"

"It has to do everything with him. You are ignorant! Do you know who he is?" Devidas raised his voice. "I know only one thing. This boy is my disciple! My attendant!" Jawahar Ali also spoke in a high pitch.

"Jawahar Ali, you do not know. He is God Almighty! Anal Huque! Do you understand?" Devidas replied. "Surprising! A Muslim who does not even know the holy Quran can be Anal Huque?" Jawahar Ali threw a sarcastic look at Baba and questioned!

"Devidas ji, I tell you again and again – I am not 'Anal Huque'! Please do not intervene. Let me offer my service as he wills!" Baba requested Devidas. "It is alright! I will leave – but I will see what I can do about it!" Devidas left abruptly followed by the town people.

Devidas reached Shirdi and was on the job. Settling himself in the Maruthi temple, he went to each and every house in the village. He called a gathering of all villagers at one place. He told them that Sai Baba is at Rahata and advised them to bring him back!

When Devidas met him, Jawahar Ali sensed trouble and so decided to run away from Rahata along with Baba by evening. So he collected all his belongings and handed the bundle to Baba to carry and both started to leave Rahata to an unknown destination.

Unfortunately for Jawahar Ali, the villagers of Shirdi had already reached the idgha and were joined by their friends from Rahata. On seeing this big crowd Jawahar Ali lost his courage. He became nervous! On seeing his pitiable condition, Sai Baba himself faced the crowd. The villagers were happy to see their Master.

Mhalsapathy said emphatically, "Baba, we have come to take you back!"

Baba calmly said – "Bhagat, I must go with him wherever he takes me. I have accepted him as my preceptor!" Baba did his best to persuade and pacify the villagers. But they were in no mood to listen.

Bayja ma took a firm stand. "No! I will see how he takes you. Come on brothers! Let us carry Baba back to Shirdi."

The crowd stepped ahead. Jawahar Ali entreated with a pathetic tone – "Please, please! Do not take Baba alone. Take me also along with him."

The crowd opposed, but Baba was moved with pity. He took Jawahar Ali with himself. Chandrabhan Sait had brought his own *tonga* to enable Baba to go back to Shirdi. Baba respectfully asked Jawahar Ali to sit first and then he sat near him. In the procession from Rahata to Shirdi, people shouted jaikars to Baba and danced to the tune of devotional songs with accompaniment of bells and drums. They reached Shirdi before dusk and everyone expressed joy at the home-coming of Baba.

It was a Thursday. Bayja ma's vow under the neem tree to burn incense for the safe return of Baba was answered!

Devidas was happy that Sai Baba had come back to Shirdi. However he did not like the idea of Jawahar Ali staying with him and calling himself the Guru of a divine personality! He decided to put an end to this.

Destiny also desired it! Jankidas arrived in Shirdi after four days. He was also a great saint like Devidas. While in Shirdi, Devidas stayed in Maruthi temple and Jankidas stayed in Mahadev temple.

With the arrival of Janakidas in Shirdi, Devidas thought of a plan. Since four days, Devidas had watched Sai Baba serving Jawahar Ali like an ordinary menial. Jawahar Ali's arrogance had come down but his boasting had increased. He would never miss an opportunity to exhibit his learning of the Hindu and Muslim scriptures.

Today Devidas decided to put Jawahar Ali's knowledge to test. He invited Jawahar Ali to take part in a debate between Janakidas and himself on spirituality. Devidas invited villagers from Rahata and other places to attend it. The open place outside chawadi was selected as the venue. Jawahar Ali, whose knowledge was only limited to vain boastings, was confident of winning over Devidas and Janakidas.

The ground in front of the chawadi was filled today to capacity with crowd from different places apart from the local public. For the first time, Shirdi had seen such a vast gathering. The platform was the verandah of the chawadi. Even the dogs which accompanied Baba on his begging rounds occupied their seats in advance under the verandah.

Almost at the same time, but from different places, arrived Sai Baba with Jawahar Ali, Devidas from Maruthi temple and Janakidas from Mahadev temple. The session began! Jawahar Ali was given the first opportunity to speak. He was an eloquent speaker, quoted profusely from Quran, Gita, Ramayana and other classics and tried to prove the superiority of Islam religion and Quran above all. The audience was spellbound by Jawahar Ali's lecture and people wondered as to how Devidas would defend!

Devidas challenged Jawahar Ali in the beginning itself. He said, "One who has not understood his own religion has no right to meddle with other religions and their scriptures!" Jawahar Ali was furious! He shouted – "What? You want to talk about our holy Quran?"

"Yes, about Quran and Islam! I want to clearly point out as to how you have misunderstood your own religion." It was an open accusation by Devidas.

"That is fine! I want you to teach me Quran now so that I understand it!" Jawahar Ali spoke to ridicule him.

One after the other, Devidas quoted from Quran in Persian language and interpreted in an impressive manner. He compared them with references to Gita, similar thoughts in Buddhist scriptures and hymns from the *Bible*.

In a very simple and lucid style, Devidas explained the tenets of Islam in a very convincing manner. For the first time, the rustic villagers were exposed to an intimate knowledge of various religions. The Hindus among the audience learnt about Islam and realised as to how they had misunderstood their Muslim brothers. Similarly the Muslims felt elevated to learn the noble principles of their religion from a Hindu saint and also had a clear insight into Hinduism.

Devidas spoke for two hours. He was shining with a divine luster. People were deeply immersed in his discourse. They came to reality only when Devidas completed his speech.

Everyone turned to see how Jawahar Ali would defend himself. To their surprise, he was not there. He had already sneaked away!

It was no more necessary for Janakidas to say anything in support of Devidas. Sai Baba watched this drama calmly with a pleasant smile!

9

BABA ACQUIRES A STONE SLAB

*B*ayja Ma was very much worried today as the usual time for Baba's begging round was already over. He had not come to beg that day at all. This made her unhappy as she felt that Baba has remained without food. In fact, in the last eight days, even though Baba begged in other houses, he had not come to Bayja ma's house. Even though Baba had suppressed her ego that she alone was feeding Baba, he could not suppress her motherly heart which made her love him as her son! She did not feel sorry that Baba had not come to her house in the last eight days but what made her unhappy was that he had not begged for food at other houses also! But still she had no guts to carry food to the mosque, fearing Baba's anger!

It was already noon now! Her husband and son had left for the farm. Though hungry, she waited for Baba. She became restless and ultimately baked two rotis and hid the bundle under her saree lest Baba on seeing food may scold her. Reaching the mosque she found Abdulla alone. Baba had gone out! Abdulla told her that Baba has gone to the forest.

"Oh my God! Did he eat anything?" she asked him. "No, mother! Baba did not beg for food today." Abdulla told her.

Bayja ma decided to take risk and go to the forest to feed Baba at any cost. She started, took few steps and suddenly realised that Abdulla also must be hungry. She knew that Baba always fed him after his begging round. She returned and asked him, "My boy, did you have anything to eat?"

"No mother! Baba asked me to go home for it. I will go after Baba comes, as I cannot leave this place unguarded!" He innocently explained.

"My God! You too are hungry yourself! Have this! Do not starve!" she handed over the bundle to him.

After reaching home she baked two more rotis and left for the forest with a vessel containing drinking water. In feeding Abdulla she had done the right thing! Baba would not accept her food if she had left Abdulla starving at the mosque. This loving God, having oneness in all, never liked anyone to starve or fast. She recollected the day when she took food to Baba without feeding her son Tatya at home, for which Baba had scolded her.

It was a hot afternoon! Even the animals had sought shelter of the green shade. Bayja ma went through thorny paths in the forest with the vessel of drinking water in one hand and a bundle of rotis in the other. She walked on and on in the forest and became totally exhausted. Her only intention was to locate Baba and feed him. She was out of breath and sat down under a tree. The scorching sun had sapped all her energy. Suddenly she saw her loving God a little away in deep meditation! He was sitting on a big slab of rock.

Seeing Baba, Bayja ma went and stood in front of him. The vibrations of her restless mind made Baba come out of his meditation. He spoke to her – "Bayja ma, you did a very nice thing in feeding Abdulla before coming over here! The child had not gone home for food even though I had asked him to do so. He was more concerned about guarding my things than for his food!"

"Yes Baba, he did not go!" Bayja ma affirmed, "He is a nice boy!"

"You are also nice! You care so much for me! You have trodden thorny paths in the entire forest trying to locate me! How nice of you! Come, give me my rotis!" Thus Baba revealed everything that happened far away from where he sat in meditation. Bayja ma was familiar with his clairvoyance. She was happy that Baba asked for food himself. Quickly she opened the food bundle, plucked a big leaf from a nearby tree and served the rotis.

Baba admired everything she did and said - "Bayja ma, why do you take all this trouble?" "My Lord, I feel most unhappy when you are without food!" Bayja ma replied. "But Mother, I will be coming here every day! What will you do then?" said Baba. She innocently asked - "You will come every day? For meditation?"

"Yes mother, I intend doing it here!"

"Well, well! Can you not do it in the mosque itself?" Bayja ma wanted to discourage Baba treading this thorny path.

"One can meditate anywhere, mother! But this stone fascinates me! The moment I sit over it, I go into trance! Sitting on this I come to know everything. Leaving my physical body here, I go and serve the suffering souls wherever they are!" It was an exposition of Baba's omnipresence! To Bayja ma it was Greek and Latin! She admitted her ignorance and said – "My Lord, I do not understand a word of what you say! All I can do is that if you like this stone, we will shift it to your mosque."

Baba laughed at her simple suggestion and said – "It is too heavy!

"Let it be! The entire village is at your service! Come, finish your food."

Baba ate the rotis with the vegetable and chutney that Bayja ma had brought. He was extremely happy at her selfless love. He said – "Bayja ma, send your son Tatya to sleep in the mosque from today. He will sleep in my company till he gets married." Remembering his plan to grace this family, Baba thought of giving his divine company to her son.

Bayja ma felt happy and elevated. She instantly agreed.

Bayja ma made the villagers shift the stone slab from the forest to the mosque. The ever burning dhuni at one end and the stone slab at the other end made the mosque vibrate with Baba's mission.

Tatya started sleeping in the mosque as desired by Baba. Next day, Baba asked Mhalsapathy also to sleep in his company. Mhalsapathy also agreed.

Just as Baba wanted to shower his grace on Tatya, he also wanted Mhalsapathy to attain *moksha* in this life also. Of course, Mhalsapathy was already a detached soul. He had three daughters and a son. The son was always sick. With his worldly worries, Mhalsapathy had no attraction towards domestic life. Baba wanted to give him the highest joy of divine bliss. Hence he called him to sleep in his company.

Tatya was a practical person. Baba desired to shower the success of material life on him! Tatya and Mhalsapathy! Two travellers on the path of life treading in different directions under the guidance of a 'Loving God'!

Baba, Mhalsapathy and Tatya! A trinity of a divine, detached and a worldly being! Sleeping in the mosque with heads to East, West and North, with their legs bundled up together like a trident! They would spend their nights daily happily laughing, playing games and other pranks. Baba would tell them stories of higher attainment! While listening to these stories, either Tatya or Mhalsapathy would sometimes sleep or doze off. Baba would then sometime pull their legs or throw away their bed sheets. However none would get irritated.

But soon came a day when the sleep of not only these three but that of the entire Shirdi village was brought to an end by a mad person Rohilla, who had forced himself to Shirdi. Nobody knew from where he came and no one knew when he would leave! He was a nuisance as he would recite the *kalams* from the Quran in the dead of the night and walk along the streets of the village, unmindful of what others felt! He did not sleep nor allowed anyone to sleep peacefully!

This went on every night. Baba listened to Rohilla's recitations peacefully. Tatya and Mhalsapathy could not even sleep for a minute and would feel miserable. They could not do anything as Baba used to enjoy it.

The hard working villagers spent their nights cursing for want of sleep! Ultimately they approached Baba for help. Baba calmly listened to them but supported Rohilla. Baba pacified the villagers – "Brothers, he is the only man who takes God's name day and night! I know it disturbs you. He is troubled by his wife. To avoid it, he chants Quran. How can I stop him? He will continue doing this till he gets tired one day and will leave this place! Let us bear with him till such time and enjoy the bliss of the Divine name!"

The villagers could argue no more. Rohilla did not have any wife. What Baba meant was Rohilla's evil thoughts which would haunt him.

Soon, Rohilla too left Shirdi forever! That night Tatya and Mhalsapathy happily slept in the mosque and continued to sleep peacefully for fourteen years thereafter!

10

WORTHY MOTHER BAYJA MA

$\mathcal{I}$t was a day after those fourteen years of association of Baba, Mhalsapathy, and Tatya!

As usual Mhalsapathy got up in the early hours of the morning and left for his daily routine and worship at Khandoba mandir. In the happy company of Baba, he was compelled to spend sleepless nights sitting by Baba's side. Baba used to chat with him endlessly. But this never tired Mhalsapathy. He would never miss the morning worship at Khandoba mandir.

On the other hand, Tatya would sleep till late morning, covering himself! If Baba ever pulled his cover sheet, he would simply say, "Be good enough, Mama! Do not disturb me. I have to attend market in the morning! With this he would pull his sheet and cover up and would soon be snoring! Baba would let him sleep as long as he chose. However, on his way to the market or farm, Tatya would have *darshan* of Baba, even though he would pass the nights in his company. In all his dealings, he always depended on Baba for guidance. Baba always blessed him for his prosperity!

In case of Mhalsapathy, this was not so! Baba would create more difficult situations in his life so that he was detached to the family life and would have a spiritual awakening. He also kept him awake physically to receive his grace.

That night Baba himself remained restless. He spoke nothing and kept on tossing and turning in his bed. Mhalsapathy dared not ask Baba the reason for his restlessness. Tatya was fast asleep as usual. As soon as Mhalsapathy left, Baba got up and woke up Tatya – "Tatya, get up! Is this your father's mosque that you sleep so late! Get up lazy boy! Go home!"

Tatya had finished his sleep. Thinking it to be his usual prank he replied – "Mama! It is true this is not my father's place! But it belongs to my Mama! Why are you teasing me so early in the morning?"

With it he again pulled his covering. Baba was furious. He pulled Tatya and pushed him out! Being familiar with Baba's wrath, Tatya quietly left.

In fact, Baba would never be angry without reason! His wrath used to be a forerunner of an impending calamity or would be an occasion of grace on someone! Many had their experiences. Rarely there would be anyone who left Shirdi without having Baba's darshan. Baba's fame by now had reached everywhere between Rahuri and Kopergaon. Hence devotees from these places frequently visit Baba, some for darshan, some for medical cure, some for solution of worldly problems and a few for spiritual upliftment.

One day the mosque was full to capacity and a farmer sat near the entrance with a vessel full of water to be handy for cleaning himself whenever he went to ease himself. He was suffering from diarrhoea and would frequent the toilet every now and then. Baba was solving the problems of many devotees and was also watching this farmer. Slowly the farmer moved ahead waiting for his turn to go near Baba. As he neared him, Baba became angry suddenly. He picked up a log near dhuni and angrily rushed towards the devotees! Everyone dispersed in panic! In a second the mosque was empty! The poor farmer, already weak due to diarrhoea, also tried to sneak away. But his frail legs did not help him and he fell down! Baba held him by his hand and with abuses on his lips, made him sit on the platform. He picked up a small bundle of roasted groundnuts. He rubbed them between his palms, blew the peel and pushed the clean nuts into the farmer's mouth. Depressed with his disease and frightened at Baba's wrath, the farmer ate the groundnuts quietly. This queer treatment made him nervous. Baba too ate as he continued to abuse! The nuts were finished and so the farmer's malady! He left the mosque totally healthy!

Thus everybody knew that this sudden flare up of Baba has some secret significance, though no one can understand its cause! He was restless that something would happen today!

When Tatya reached home, Bayja ma had taken her bath and was worshipping. She was in a happy mood. She had completed fifty years of her married life with Ganapat Kote Patil. She had an ideal husband and a devout son. She had a happy and comfortable home. The sweet memories of her family life moved her emotionally. She had prepared many delicacies and sweets for this golden jubilee of her wedding anniversary. She wanted to take some food to the mosque and feed Baba. But she had an inner desire that Baba should visit her house and take food from her hands.

With such thoughts flooding in her mind, she was surprised to see Tatya returning home so early in the morning. She asked him, "Tatya, how is it that you have come home so soon?"

"Mother, Mama chased me out!" Tatya told her.

"Why? What happened?"

"Well, you know mother! You cannot gauge Mama's mind! Since early hours he is in a bad mood! Do not know what is in store for us?"

"Yes, my boy! Something strange happens whenever he is angry. Will he come to our house if he is in that mood today?"

"How do I know, mother? When he is angry he does not go for begging also. Mother, why not take food yourself if he fails to come."

With this suggestion, Tatya went to take his bath. Bayja ma was certain that Baba was unlikely to come. Still she wanted to invite him for food.

The mosque was crowded with visitors but Baba was not there. After sometime the visitors left. Bayja Ma went there again and again to see if Baba had returned. Ganapat Kote Patil had invited some guests for lunch and Bayja ma's presence was necessary.

The time for Baba's begging was also over. Bayja ma served food to all their guests, her husband and son too. She waited for Baba. She thought of searching him in the forest too! But she had now become old and did not have the capacity to tread the thorny path of the forest. Moreover since morning she had a dull aching pain in the chest. Even then she cooked and served the guests. Now the pain had increased. She did not want to take food as long as Baba did not have it.

Bayja ma took rest for some time but her mind was centred on thoughts of Baba. She recalled that ten years ago Baba had told her that she will no more have cycle of birth and death and she will be in Kailash forever! She recalled many mystic events of Baba's life!

Suddenly she heard Baba's loving call! "Bayja ma, have you kept food for me? I will take it here today!" It was an immense joy for Bayja ma that her Loving God came to her house to take food! She got up and suddenly experienced a shooting pain in her chest! Her mind worked fast, her body moved quickly! She offered a seat to Baba and served food to Baba ignoring her pain.

Her pain was great, but greater was the bloom on her face! She was very happy that Baba came for food on the fiftieth anniversary of her wedding! Baba ate to his heart's content.

Baba finished his meals and insisted that he served and fed Bayja ma with his own hands. The Loving God himself fed his devotee like a mother to her child. In that joyful state, she ate more than her capacity. She also desired that her husband and son too should witness this rare sight. Both arrived and were speechless with what they saw!

She finished her food. The couple touched Baba's feet. Tatya too followed.

"Engage him into wedlock, Patil, do not delay!" – With these curt words Baba swiftly turned to go. Suddenly he thought of something and turned back. Taking out a pinch of *udhi* he had brought from his dhuni in the mosque, he applied it to Bayja ma's forehead. He kept his thumb on Bayja ma's forehead for some time and with a transfixed gaze looked at her for a few seconds. She was in a dazed state, speechless, motionless, looking at him – eyes to eyes in trance!

Baba withdrew quickly and left abruptly. Bayja ma was still not in her senses, eyes wide open and steadfast! This frightened Ganapat Kote Patil and Tatya. They were aware of her chest pain since morning.

Tatya called out – "Mother, mother!" The pupils in her eyes flickered. She spoke in a low sunken vice – "Baba has shown me the Divine vision! Baba is Lord Shiva Himself! I saw His glorious vision! I am leaving for the abode of Shiva! God bless you both!" She closed her eyes and her body collapsed!

"Mother!" Tatya yelled piteously! He ran to the mosque to call his Mama to save his mother! But Mama was not there!

Bayja ma got salvation from the cycle of births and deaths. Ganapat Kote Patil in course of time got Tatya settled in family life. Afterwards he too joined his wife in heaven.

11

BRIEF SOJOURN WITH ALLAH

*B*aba made Tatya settle down in life. At the same he persisted to bring Mhalsapathy out of his family environment. Absolute poverty at home, progressive deterioration in the health of his son, rough post-marriage circumstances for his daughters, Mhalsapathy faced extremely difficult conditions in the home front. Even then, his implicit faith in Baba was exemplary. After marriage, Tatya stopped sleeping in the mosque while Mhalsapathy rigidly observed his practice of giving company to Baba during the night time. Besides this, he undertook several other practices too! He started performing 'Aarti' four times – morning, noon, evening and night – to Sai Baba. He firmly believed that Sai Baba was God and mosque his temple. Hence all this worship! Baba was not inclined to accept this but ultimately submitted to Mhalsapathy. Similarly the Muslims were against it but since Baba did not subscribe to any faith, they stopped opposing it.

With such a busy routine, Mhalsapathy was now almost out of his family life. His greatest pleasure was the company and worship of Baba. In fact, he was fed up as a house holder. Just for the heck of it, he did very little as a goldsmith and passed on his little earnings to his wife. She managed her household with difficulty. Their son's illness was another concern to her.

In spite of all these problems, Mhalsapathy maintained his calmness of mind. He was a detached soul! But soon came a day when he lost his peace of mind! It was neither due to his domestic worries nor his son's illness! It was the illness of Sai Baba that ruined his tranquility! Baba started getting continuous cough, followed by difficulty in breathing. It was virtually an attack of bronchial asthma. The malady became intolerable and Baba refused any treatment. Baba suffered silently.

This was a lesson in trust and an ordeal for Mhalsapathy. Baba fell ill and at the same time, Mhalsapathy's son also was seriously ill. Even then, Mhalsapathy continued to sleep in the mosque. He was in a dilemma as to whether he should attend to Baba or his own son! But his love and devotion to Baba succeeded! He stopped attending his work as a goldsmith, stopped going home, and served Baba by keeping a vigil on him, day and night! He prayed to Khandoba and vowed to fast until Baba recovered!

At Mhalsapathy's home front, his son's health was causing more and more concern. All alone, his wife looked after the son and spared no efforts to save the boy. She sent messages after messages to her husband at the mosque. But Mhalsapathy left his son's care to Lord Khandoba and stopped thinking of anything else except service to Baba and nursing him!

Ultimately finding it difficult to bear his suffering, Baba decided to cure his malady by merging with the Supreme Self! In a feeble voice, he spoke to Mhalsapathy - "Bhagat, I cannot stand this ailment any longer!"

Mhalsapathy pleaded – "My Lord, transfer your suffering to me. Live long and do good to all!" He sincerely meant what he said. He was prepared for any type of sacrifice for his Master!

Since Baba fell ill, Mhalsapathy always thought that he should take over his illness. What use is his body? He was neither useful to his family nor the village. How nice it would be if Baba transferred his illness to him? Day and night he served Baba! Now he must take over his disease!

"Bhagat, it is the law of nature! One must pass through his own sufferings! Nobody is spared! It is a divine plan!" Baba was moved at his devotion!

"Then what can I do for you Baba?"

"Just protect my body for three days. To get relieved from this illness, I am taking away my life breath, leaving behind this body here! At the end of three days I will return to this body! Guard it till then!"

Baba lost consciousness even as he was speaking to Mhalsapathy. His body became stiff and motionless while his soul merged in the Supreme Spirit! His rattling breath sounds and cough stopped! Baba's breathing too stopped! These signs of death did not deter Mhalsapathy!

Baba had kept his head on his lap. Mhalsapathy calmly watched his face. Abdulla was sleeping nearby. Since he was confident that Baba would return after three days, he did not call anyone or send word to anyone. He kept his vigil on Baba's body. It was almost a week he had not performed 'aarti' to Sai Baba neither had worshipped Khandoba.

The day broke. Abdulla got up. He looked at Baba. Thinking that he was still sleeping on Mhalsapathy's lap he started his work with pin drop silence. He did not ask Mhalsapathy nor did he tell him!

Though Mhalsapathy did not say anything to Abdulla, he could not do so for others. Soon Tatya came to inquire his Mama's health. Seeing Baba fast asleep with his head on Mhalsapathy's lap, he spoke in a hushed tone. Mhalsapathy told him that Baba is not asleep but is in trance! "He has removed his life-breath leaving his physical body in my care!" Mhalsapathy explained calmly.

"Taken his life-breath away? What do you mean?" Tatya was frightened.

"I will re-enter this body after three days – that is what Baba told me!" Mhalsapathy further said.

"Uncle, what are you saying? When did Baba abandon his body? Why did you not send word to me?" Tatya was furious and impatient!

"Tatya, do not lose your temper! Baba could not bear his illness. That is why he abandoned his body. He has asked me to guard it!"

"But uncle, why did you take it on yourself? The villagers will take you to task if something has gone wrong with Baba!" Tatya tried to convince Mhalsapathy, the seriousness of the situation! Mhalsapathy maintained his calmness and replied – "I am obeying Baba. I am not worried about others".

Tatya ran! Abdulla was frightened. He had slept in the mosque during that night. He too was partly responsible for what had happened. He also scolded Mhalsapathy!

Soon Tatya, Kashiram, Appa Jogale, Ramachandra Patil and others rushed to the mosque. Appa checked Baba's breathing and found it absent. Kashiram held a thread near his nostril and confirmed that his breathing has stopped. All accused Mhalsapathy of his gross negligence. But Mhalsapathy did not lose his composure. He had implicit faith in Baba and was confident that Baba would return to his body after three days!

But that day was indeed unfortunate to Mhalsapathy! While he was being accused of negligence, Mhalsapathy received a message from his wife that he should rush back home immediately as his son was on the verge of death. It was test! An ordeal! The villagers too induced him to go home. But under no circumstances, Mhalsapathy would budge and leave Baba!

Then came Kulkarni, the village physician. He still bore a grudge against Baba. He checked his pulse, which had really stopped. He tested his breath. It had ceased. He ascertained that the pupils had gone up. Completely satisfied with the indications of death he breathed a sigh of relief! But still he feared that Baba might come back to life, as he did earlier, when on one night fifteen years ago he attempted to set fire to the mosque, he had trampled on his severed head and seen body parts thrown all around! Hence he wanted the villagers to hurry up and dispose the body. He said, "Patil, Baba has completed his mission! Now hurry up and dispose the body."

Mhalsapathy flared up – "Never. Nobody will touch him. Baba has asked me to take care of him for three days! He will return to this body".

Kulkarni made a poisonous remark – "Bravo Mhalsapathy! You better return home and take care of your dying son than this lifeless body!"

His words convinced the villagers that Baba had really died! The entire village rushed to the mosque. The crowd too came for the last glimpse. People from Shirdi and surrounding villages were emotionally moved. The women wailed! Children cried and elders shed tears! Everybody tried to persuade Mhalsapathy but nothing disturbed his tranquility nor his decision to take care of Baba for three days, holding Baba's head on his lap!

At last the villagers yielded and they decided to wait for another two days. Most of them respected Mhalsapathy as a divine personality. He possessed the spirit of Khandoba and in his trance had guided many persons. Besides, many of them had noticed with surprise the fresh luster on Baba's face!

The third day dawned. There was no sign of Baba returning to his body. Mhalsapathy in the last three days had not even once changed his position. Seeing that he was not prepared to yield, people decided to forcibly dispose Baba's body. Muslims brought their *Kaji*. A grave was dug and preparations were made to inter Baba's body in it. Still they believed Baba to be a Muslim and everything was done according to Muslim rituals.

Mhalsapathy was praying to Baba to return to his body!

Four Muslims came ahead to lift the body. Tatya and Ramachandra Patil moved forward to control Mhalsapathy. Mhalsapathy also got ready to counter the move. He had decided not to allow anyone to touch Baba's body at any cost. He had planned to embrace it firmly if they tried to remove it by force! He was confident that they will not use force to snatch the body lest they hurt it. But deep in his heart he was praying anxiously.

It was a critical moment! Pin drop silence prevailed as everybody watched as to what will happen next. Ramachandra Patil spoke to Mhalsapathy in a stern voice – "Uncle, we want to lift Baba's body. Do not obstruct".

Mhalsapathy was equally firm. "No, never! I will not allow you to remove it – come what may!"

Ramachandra Patil signaled to Appa Jogale, Kashiram and Tatya. They were uneasy as they had to offend their great friend Mhalsapathy. But still they moved forward to control Mhalsapathy so that the Muslims could lift the body to the grave. As they approached, Mhalsapathy hugged Baba's body firmly and yelled in distress! – "Baba...... Baba.......Baba...."

This shriek rebounded, resounded and reached the abode of the Supreme Spirit where Baba's soul rested! It re-entered Baba's body lying in the embrace of Mhalsapathy. The body came to life! Baba lifted his right hand and lovingly stroked Mhalsapathy's back who still held him in embrace.

Ramachandra Patil, Appa Jogale, Kashiram, and Tatya were startled and the villagers shouted – *Sai Baba ki Jai.*

Baba's hand moved on Mhalsapathy's back who sobbed in joy with a sigh of relief. He said still sobbing in embrace – 'Baba…Baba…'

"Bhagat, you have done your duty – but I have failed in mine! Go home! You are wanted there!" – coming back to senses completely, Baba spoke!

"Tatya, Ramachandra Patil, Kashiram, and Appa – you all go with Mhalsapathy. Do not worry about me! I am all right!" - Baba said emphatically!

Mhalsapathy had never disobeyed Baba. He got up to go home. Kashiram, Appa, Tatya, and Ramachandra Patil followed him.

Mhalsapathy entered his house only to see that his son was dead!

12

MIRACLE OF PLANK

$\mathcal{S}$ai Baba giving up his body and by re-entering after three days made a sensational news! People from Ahmednagar and Manmad and other places made a bee-line to Shirdi to have Baba's darshan and seek his grace. This kept Baba ever busy and would not have rest even for a second. The mosque was always filled with people. But in this crowd, Baba felt isolated as his own man was not there. That was Mhalsapathy! In the last fifteen days never even once Mhalsapathy had visited the mosque! This pained Baba who was very much accustomed to his company during days and nights. Baba felt sorry for his wife too! The poor lady still wailed and wept in vain for her dead son! To make her happy again Baba desired that her dead son should return to her womb. On Baba's advice, Mhalsapathy now slept at home, even though his mind always hovered around Sai Baba.

Some days after Baba's resurrection, Nana Saheb Dengale brought a crude wooden cot for him. He had now become his ardent devotee after Baba blessed him with a child. Baba visited his house at Neemgaon at times as it was not far off from Shirdi. Thus a bond of intimacy had developed between the two. Nana Saheb Dengale was worried since Baba fell ill. He felt that Baba's illness was due to his sleeping on the ground. He also knew that Baba's bed comprised five or six thin bed sheets presented to him by devotees, which he simply spread one over the other. Some devotees offered a mattress but Baba would throw them out and would be angry with the person who brought it. Hence no one dared to offer him one. Nana Saheb Dengale therefore brought a corded cot which he wanted to keep in the mosque secretly. He came to the mosque when Baba had gone to Lendi baug.

Lendi baug was a favourite spot for Baba! It was a well known garden with tall trees in Shirdi with a small rivulet called Lendi. Baba used to spend hours together in its peaceful atmosphere. Baba had watered several plants and made a beautiful garden. Baba used to go to Lendi baug twice during the day. Today being very warm, he had gone there earlier. As he walked to Lendi baug, Baba watched the farmers having completed reaping and after storing the corn, the husk piled up in stacks close to their houses!

Baba was in Lendi baug when Nana Saheb Dengale arrived with the cot. He quietly kept it near the dhuni and waited for Baba along with other visitors. Baba came to the mosque. He saw the cot and was very much enraged. He started abusing, banging and tossing things around. The crowd watched him helplessly. Nobody dared to tell him as to who has brought the cot. Baba lifted it, broke it into several pieces, and threw it into the dhuni. The fire was kindled and the flames rose high!

Just then a boy came in a hurry shouting – "Kondaji, your husk stack has caught fire! Your house is in danger!"

Indeed Kondaji's house was in great danger! It was very close to the huge heap of husk he had piled up. Kondaji and his brothers were in the crowd at the mosque. They all ran towards Kondaji's house. The fire was devastating! In the mosque, Baba's temper also rose high! As Baba's anger rose higher and higher, dark clouds gathered in the sky! A stormy breeze started fanning the burning flames towards Kondaji's house. The situation was indeed critical and the house was in peril!

Kondaji was a carpenter in the village. He had two brothers Gabaji and Tukaram. They were good in their craft and as they had no competitors, they had a prosperous business. Shirdi being an agriculture based village, these brothers worked on farmers' implements like ploughs, bullock carts, house roofing. They had built their own house in the outskirts of the village and had stocked wooden logs in the house. This accidental fire would not only destroy their house but was a threat to the entire village! All the brothers were sincere devotees of Baba and regularly sought his blessings.

How can Sai Baba throw his devotees on the street? On the pretext of fire near Kondaji's house, Sai Baba protected the entire village!

With every shout of Baba, black clouds gathered in the sky, lightening struck and in a few seconds, heavy downpour began drenching the village! This extinguished the fire! Kondaji's house was saved!

But with the incessant downpour, water surged all around! Pits and trenches overflowed! The gushing water entered the houses too! People, cattle and live stock ran for shelter! It was all a chaos!

Sai Baba came out in the open drenching in the heavy rains and shouting at the sky – shouting to stop raining! His shouts thundered louder than the clouds! It stopped raining and people could see the glittering sunrays!

The villagers were astounded with Baba's control over the natural elements! It created a confidence that under his protection, they have nothing to fear.

Baba had averted two calamities. He entered the mosque to take rest. But there was not an inch of dry ground for him to sit! Baba started pacing! Nana Saheb Dengale saw that and ran to Kondaji's house to bring a thick wooden plank. He requested him – "Baba, you have just now recovered from a serious illness. May be, your sleeping on the floor was the cause of your asthma. So why not sleep on this plank. Please do not say 'no'."

Baba was moved with Nana Saheb Dengale's love! He knew that it was Nana himself who had brought that cot! Baba told him – "Nana, why do you bother about this mad fakir's well being? Sometime back you brought that cot. Now you have run to Kondaji to bring this plank! Why do you pamper my worthless body? After all I am a mere fakir in the mosque! I must be prepared to be anywhere, eat anything people offer me and sit quietly repeating Allah's name! That is all!"

Nana Dengale pleaded – "But Baba, it is all wet here! Where will you take rest? Where will you lie down? Please listen to me."

"All right, all right! Keep it there in that corner." Baba yielded. Nana Dengale kept the plank and left for Neemgaon. All visitors also left. It was impossible to sleep in the mosque and Abdulla also had gone home.

Now Baba was all alone in the mosque. He did not have anything to eat that day! He did not bother about it. He started preparing to retire for the night. He looked around and he could not even see a spot where he could even sit. The plank that Nana Dengale had brought was eight inches wide and five feet in length and hardly enough for Baba to sleep comfortably! At that time Mhalsapathy arrived at the mosque. Somehow he felt that Baba must be starving that day and so brought some food for Baba.

Baba took the food brought by Mhalsapathy. He asked him to return home. He pleaded - "My Lord, I feel restless at home! This mosque has been my home for the last fourteen years! I feel my final salvation is here only!"

"My dear bhagat, surely I will make you attain emancipation! But your wife is unhappy. For her sake please stay in your house. She wants a son – she will have the same one who died!"

"Then Baba, at least permit me to stay here on alternate nights!" Mhalsapathy pleaded with Baba.

"It is all right! Come and sleep here. I will also sleep in the chawadi every alternate day. There in the company of others, I will not miss you!"

Mhalsapathy was very happy! He saw the plank and said – "Baba, you must sleep on that plank, you must.......!"

"Yes, Bhagat, it is wet everywhere. That is why Nana Dengale brought it."

"Then why not hang that and sleep over it? Today the whole village is infested with snakes due to heavy rains. It is safe to sleep above. I will bring a rope to hang it."

Mhalsapathy left hastily. Baba took out an old worn out bed sheet and tore it into few pieces. He took out four flimsy shreds and with that hung the plank and peacefully slept on that.

Mhalsapathy returned with a rope along with his bedding. He found that Baba was peacefully sleeping on the plank hung by mere shreds. Four oil lamps burnt on the four sides. He was amazed that four flimsy shreds could bear the weight of a heavy plank along with Baba on it. Mhalsapathy watched this miracle for some time.

Suddenly his mind pondered that in case the shreds break, Baba would fall down and injure himself! He decided that he should lie down on the ground below the plank so that even if Baba falls down, he could bear the brunt of injury. He looked up and touched the plank with the tip of his finger to guess the total weight. And lo! That plank with Baba's weight was raised high like a flower! Mhalsapathy was wonderstruck! Baba's body was weightless! He realised that Baba was now in his divine Form – above physical existence! He folded his hands in prayers! He had earlier seen dhoti-pothy yoga in which Baba had washed his intestines near the well! Here is another yogic manifestation in which Baba could make himself weightless and as light as a flower! However he was puzzled as to how Baba could climb over the plank at that height!

Wondering about Baba's mystic powers, he was preparing to lie down on a make-shift bed on that wet ground. Suddenly he heard people shouting - "Snake-bite, snake-bite, Madhava Rao is bitten by a snake." Mhalsapathy stood up and looked out. Before that, Baba was already standing on the floor listening to the shouts and yells. How he climbed over the plank and alighted from it remained a mystery to Mhalsapathy.

A snake had bitten Madhava Rao Deshpande! Madhava Rao Balwant Deshponde was a teacher in the school adjacent to the mosque. He was a young man, Brahmin by caste and his house was close by. He was deeply religious and orthodox too. He had great regards for Sai Baba, whose 'darshan' he had every day before attending to his school. Anandanath Swamiji of Yeola Mutt was his Guru.

One day due to unprecedented rains, water had entered the school and some records were drenched. Madhava Rao was working in the school at night, cleaning and arranging some papers. Some teachers were also helping him. They were working in the dim light of a kerosene lamp. While they were arranging papers, suddenly a cobra bit Madhava Rao. As Madhava Rao screamed, everybody saw a black cobra moving away. As they yelled, Madhava Rao's body turned black! The snake was killed and Madhava Rao was taken to the mosque.

The moment they reached the mosque, they found Baba in a fit of fury! He had his club in his hand! The villagers brought Madhava Rao near the steps. Baba became more ferocious on seeing him. He hit the plank hanging above with his club! With every stroke he was shouting – "Get down, get down, you Brahmin! Get down, I say." The shreds holding the plank gave way in no time and the plank fell down with a thud!

Madhava Rao, who had already turned black with the deadly poison of the cobra, now became pale with fright! He was confident of Baba's help but now Baba's strange utterances ruined his hope! With Baba's hits and shuts, he retraced his steps but still his gaze was fixed on Baba. His friends thought that Madhava Rao may collapse and came forward to support him. Someone suggested taking Madhava Rao to Vithoba temple and calling physician Kulkarni over there! This enraged Baba further!

Mhalsapathy came forward. He knew Baba's strange behaviour. He understood it even now. He told Madhava Rao and friends – "Take Madhava Rao home. His work is done. Baba did not ask Madhava Rao to get down. He had addressed the cobra, which is considered to be a Brahmin. He ordered the poison to come down, not him! Have no fear!"

This indeed was what Baba meant! Now understanding the underlying significance Madhava Rao's friends took him home. The poison subsided! Poison that had entered Madhava Rao's system became ineffective!

Baba was calm once again! He took udhi from dhuni and giving it to Mhalsapathy said, "Bhagat, you also go to that school-teacher's house. Apply this udhi on his forehead and put some in his mouth. Do not allow him to sleep throughout night!"

Once again Mhalsapathy was assigned a job that would keep him awake throughout night. He took up this assignment willingly.

13

SHAMA'S NEW ASSIGNMENT

*S*ince Baba saved him from the clutches of death, Madhava Rao Deshpande became his staunch devotee! There is one more reason for it! His friends – Nandram, Bhagchand and Dagdu Bhau, who were all attached to Anandnath Maharaj of Savargaon, a village near Yeola and whom they accepted as their Guru, once went to him for his darshan. Anandnath Maharaj also joined them while they were returning and had Sai Baba's darshan. He told them – "God is right amongst you at Shirdi! Go to Sai Baba! Have his blessings!"

Thus knowing the greatness of Sai Baba through his Guru and his own experience after the cobra bite, Madhava Rao became an ardent devotee of Sai Baba with an eternal bond of love.

No doubt Madhava Rao had reverence towards Baba. But he also had his reservations. He felt a saint should not display his powers. He thought that Sai Baba's miracles are gimmicky. It took a long time for Machala Rao to realise that miracles of Sai Baba are a demonstration of his divine nature!

Baba too had a purpose in attracting Madhava Rao towards him. He wanted somebody who could assist him. As Baba's miracles began to draw thousands towards him, He needed a God-fearing, religious and sincere devotee like Madhava Rao for managing the huge crowds.

Two days after the snake bite, Madhava Rao went to Baba, a completely changed man, totally surrendered to him. Baba on seeing him, jocularly said –"Well, Shama, yesterday you enacted *Kalia-Mardana* drama! But you yourself became a victim of that black *kalia!*"

Madhava Rao prostrated before Baba. He offered a coconut and a one rupee coin as 'Dakshina'. Seeing that Baba said – "Shama, you must give me two! Not one! Two means duality! Part with that feeling! Do not think that your Guru and other saints are different! It is like differentiating the various forms of one and the same God! Do not entertain such thoughts!" On the pretext of advising Madhava Rao, the entire human race was advised by Sai Baba with a short but great truth!

"You may be devoted to your Guru but do not look at others with a sense of duality." Baba emphasised! Madhava Rao felt guilty that in spite of his accepting Anandnath Maharaj of Yeola as his Guru, he has now surrendered to Sai Baba! Baba had solved his dilemma! His mind turned calm! He realised that his Guru and Baba are one! He said – "Baba, my name is Madhav, not Shama!"

Baba explained – "Oh, dear, you know Shama means Krishna! Another name for Krishna is Madhava! Isn't it?" Madhava Rao liked Baba's explanation and since then he became Baba's Shama.

He requested Baba – "My Lord, let my devotion be as pure and unalloyed as that of Radha to Krishna! Let it be more and more day by day!" To develop his devotion, Baba gave him his constant companionship!

Hundreds of devotees were visiting Baba every day. To organise their interviews with Baba, to put forward their problems to Baba, to make them understand what Baba said and also to arrange their stay in Shirdi – were few of the responsibilities Baba entrusted to Shama.

Devotees offered money to Baba as *dakshina*. Sometimes Baba himself asked for it. This raised a question among devotees. Why Baba needs money? To fill his belly, he would beg! For covering his body he would use the same clothes over and over again though torn! For accommodation, he had the mosque and chawadi! So where was the need for money at all?

However there were reasons. This way he would make people offer charity. Sometimes he would make them fulfill their vows to other deities. To test their faith and attachment to money, he would ask for dakshina!

One day after seeing others offer dakshina to Baba Madhav Rao also did the same. Baba demanded two rupees from him. Later his mind revolted when Baba demanded thirty rupees from some other devotee. To Madhava Rao's surprise, that person gladly gave it and also prostrated before Baba in gratitude for having asked for it! Strangely Baba refused to accept the same amount from his friend, saying, "My fakir demanded it from him alone!"

As Madhava Rao was puzzled with, Baba spoke to him saying, "Shama, take them home and feed this one with plenty of sweets."

The gentleman concerned was astounded with Baba's clairvoyance! He reverentially touched Baba's feet and said with emotion – "Lord, you know everything. Please protect me forever!"

All this was new to Madhava Rao! He took them home, offered a lunch full of sweets. Madhava Rao asked one of them – "Pardon me if I am inquisitive! Baba demanded thirty rupees from your friend, which he willingly offered, while he refused to accept any from you! Similarly he asked me to give you plenty of sweets. Do these things have any significance? I am unable to understand Baba's ways!"

"Madhava Rao, this is a clear testimony of Baba being Lord Datta!" The gentleman who had given thirty rupees to Baba said, "Baba did not demand thirty rupees without a reason! In fact, I have fulfilled my old vow of offering to Lord Datta! Years back I went to Goa in search of a job. I made a vow in the Datta shrine at Sakhali. I vowed to offer my first salary to Lord Datta on getting a job. I got the job. I got increments and promotions and my salary got raised from thirty to three hundred rupees! Years rolled on and I forgot my vow. Today Baba reminded my vow and got it fulfilled. Indeed you are all lucky that Lord Datta has incarnated as Sai Baba!"

Madhava Rao was moved emotionally! How he misunderstood Baba for demanding thirty rupees from a stranger! After all it was due to him!

The other gentleman spoke – "Madhava Rao, Sai Baba is omniscient and omnipresent! People say that beyond a couple of villages around here, Sai Baba has never left Shirdi. But I had a different experience altogether! I feel He visits every nook and corner of the universe! I also belong to Goa. Sometime back there was a theft in my house and I lost my life's earnings! My own cook had robbed me of my belongings though I did not know about it. Frustrated, I was sitting in the verandah of my house. Sai Baba in the garb of a fakir came there and told me – 'Stop eating what you most like! Surrender to Sai Baba of Shirdi! You will get back your lost wealth!' I gave up sugar which I liked most! Believe me, within three weeks the cook who had stolen my wealth repented and returned everything! To fulfill my vow, I have found the way to Shirdi and here I am. I find that the fakir who came to my house is none other than Sai Baba. That is why he asked you to give me plenty of sugar which I had stopped since then."

Listening to these tales of vows, Madhava Rao remembered a long standing vow offered by his own mother. At the time of her death, she had told him – "Dear, I had offered two vows to our family deity – Saptashringi of Vani, near Chandwad. Since your father expired, I had no resources to fulfill them. Will you please do them on my behalf? When you were seriously ill in your childhood, I had taken a vow to present her an apparel and a coconut. Later, when I had a swelling in my right breast, I had taken a vow to offer a pair of silver breasts. She fulfilled my desires but I failed to keep my word! Now God is calling me and I am leaving. Please fulfill both the vows."

Madhava Rao had a brother Bapaji, who lived in Savul Vihir, a village close to Shirdi. Madhava Rao had a plan to go there, as he desired that his brother should also become a devotee of Sai Baba. Since a couple of plague cases were reported from Savul Vihir, Madhava Rao wanted his brother and family should have blessings of Baba. During his visit, he decided to discuss with his brother and fulfill his mother's vows.

The two guests from Goa left soon after lunch. Madhava Rao wanted to take rest for a while. Suddenly someone knocked at the door and came a voice – "Dada, Dada...." That was his brother's voice. Madhava Rao opened the door to see his brother panting for breath.

Bapaji could hardly speak. He told Madhava Rao – "Brother, my wife is serious. Plague has attacked her. She has two buboes in the armpit. I do not know what to do." Madhava Rao froze to the core. Bapaji was married only six months ago and own with plague.

Madhava Rao exclaimed – "Oh Lord Sainath, you alone should save this girl!" He quickly narrated his own experience of cobra bite and how he was protected by Baba. Bapaji also desired to go and have darshan of Sai Baba.

On seeing the two brothers, Baba said – "Shama, it is nice you have come now! Now you sit with me."

"But Baba, my brother has come from Savul Vihir. His wife is down with plague", Madhava Rao explained quickly.

"I know everything Shama! Why do you worry? My fakir will take care of her. Come, take some udhi from dhuni, and give it to him. That should suffice. Ask him to apply it on his body and put a pinch into the mouth" Baba said all this casually as if nothing was serious.

Madhava Rao quickly took some udhi. Baba touched it and gave it to Bapaji. He prostrated to Baba and looked at his brother expecting him to accompany him to Savul Vihir. Madhava Rao spoke to Baba – "Baba, I will go with him, see her and come back."

"No, no! It is not necessary! I want you here. These people have come here from different places. Sit here with me. If you feel like going, tomorrow morning you can go and come back immediately! Baba commanded!

Yes! It was a command. Nobody dared go against Baba's word. Bapaji left while Madhava Rao nervously watched him getting down the steps of the mosque. However he sat near Baba but his mind was at Savul Vihir! He eagerly waited for the next morning to go and see his brother's wife!

Bapaji was walking back towards Savul Vihir. He was very much frightened. When he left home, his wife was in a critical condition! That is why he wanted his brother to accompany him. Though he was astounded at Madhava Rao's miraculous experience, he was frightened about his wife. He had told his neighbours to take care of his wife. But they too had their family members down with plague. She had no other company. In fact, Bapaji was displeased with Baba for not permitting his brother to accompany him!

Savul Vihir was not far off. It would take thirty minutes to reach. It was already three hours since Bapaji had left. He was afraid that anything could happen. As he reached his village, he could hear shrieks and wails from his neighbour's house. It startled him! With a sudden jerk he opened the door of his house! His wife was unconscious! He rushed in and felt the warmth of her body. He breathed a sigh of relief! There was still life in her! Quickly he poured some udhi in water and gave it to her. In a feeble voice she asked him – "Has bhaiya come?" Bapaji curtly replied – "No" and applied udhi on her body. But his own body was perspiring profusely!

14

ASPIRANT LIFESTYLE

*M*adhava Rao could not get a wink of sleep throughout night! On the previous night he was kept awake by Mhalsapathy as instructed by Baba to avoid danger to his life. Tonight it was his brother's wife who was ill with plague! He was wondering as to how his brother could have managed the situation. He eagerly awaited sunrise and rushed to Savul Vihir.

The tales of vows which he heard the previous day also made him restless. He was wondering as to whether his own cobra-bite and the plague attack to his brother's wife have anything to do with the unfulfilled vows of his mother. He wanted to fulfill those vows at the earliest!

While his body moved fast towards Savul Vihir, his mind travelled back to Shirdi. Since yesterday he would only think of Sai Baba and nothing else. He began to wonder as to whether he deserved the faith reposed by Baba in him. Within a day Baba had become very close to him which he did not with others. Baba stroked him on the head, rapped him on the back as if they were very old friends! He was wondering as to how to behave with this Loving God! Ultimately he left it to Baba to mould him in whichever manner he liked. Baba has taken him into his fold, for which he had created events, selected an opportunity and gave him suitable thoughts! Madhava Rao realised that he has no more control over himself. He is now under the spell of Sai

Baba. He has selected him for his work! With this thought Madhava Rao's mind became calm!

He reached Savul Vihir. Peace prevailed everywhere in the village! The door of his brother's house was wide open. Having now surrendered to Sai Baba, he was not anxious about his brother's wife. As he entered, he was surprised to see his brother's wife welcoming him, holding a cup of tea in her hands. Madhava Rao was confident that with Sai Baba's grace, his brother's wife would be safe but he hardly expected her to be so well as even to prepare tea! He looked at his brother who was all in smiles!

Madhava Rao mischievously asked him, "You are a wonderful chap, brother! You simply frightened me! It kept me awake throughout night!"

Bapaji heartily laughed. He said, "Dada, it is all Baba's play! It is his udhi that did the trick!" Bapaji quickly explained everything.

The brothers were happy! They were aware of the power that saved them. It was Sai Baba – their Loving God!

Madhava Rao returned to Shirdi and straightway made for the mosque to attend to Baba's work. The mosque was full with devotees and patients. Baba had now stopped giving them medicines. Instead he was giving them udhi from his dhuni. He would now sit near dhuni. Devotees and patients would receive it or have it applied to their foreheads by Baba.

Madhava Rao made his way through the crowd and reaching Baba stood by his side. Mhalsapathy was also sitting nearby. Baba beckoned Madhava Rao to sit near him while he himself got up and went into the crowd. A leper was sitting in the corner. By his side he had a dog with him. Looking at this leper, the visitors scoffed at him and maintained a safe distance from him. They did not allow him to move forward to reach Baba.

Bhagoji Shinde was the name of the leper. Due to leprosy his family had abandoned him, he had lost his property and there was no one to take care of him. He had learnt that Baba would cure incurable diseases and helped the helpless and hence he had arrived at the mosque.

How then the Loving God Sai Baba would disregard Bhagoji Shinde who had come seeking his help? He was filled with pity when he saw others rudely behaving with him. He went to the hall and approached Bhagoji Shinde. There was a commotion in the crowd and everyone was watching as to what Baba would do now. Bhagoji Shinde had bleeding wounds. Flies hovered around those. Baba held Bhagoji Shinde by his hand and led him towards the 'dhuni'. Seeing Baba bringing a leper with him, Madhava Rao got up quickly and moved aside. Sai Baba's alert eyes noticed this. Baba went up and asked Bhagoji Shinde to sit near him. Baba then lovingly moved his hands over his afflicted hands and feet. Bhagoji Shinde felt very much comforted. For years none had given him this love or affection.

Baba spoke to Bhagoji Shinde – "Bhagoji, destiny demands that you will not be cured! Suffering is your lot! Bear it out! You are already out of your family ties. Now stay with me. Serve me and my fakir will give you salvation from the cycle of birth and death! Come, fill this pipe for me!

Bhagoji Shinde was happy even though Baba declared that his leprosy will not be cured! Here was someone who looked upon him as a human being!

Madhava Rao was feeling awkward and still stood aside. It was a jolt to his idea of health and hygiene. He could not stand Bhagoji Shinde's leprosy. Suddenly Baba asked him – "Shama, will a disease keep away from you just because you run away from it?" Madhava Rao felt guilty and nervous.

Baba continued – "It is a punishment for the sins of his earlier life. Poor man, he has to bear it! You need not run away! Having been with me for many births earlier, would you like to be away from me in this birth?"

This unexpected exposition from Baba on his unexplained intimacy with Madhava Rao enlightened him and he felt highly elated. He realised that he was in the company of Sai Baba through many lives. He considered himself very fortunate! Then why should he be afraid? He sat near Baba again.

Bhagoji Shinde lighted the pipe and handed it over to Baba. Baba had some puffs and passed it to Madhava Rao. Not accustomed to smoking, Madhava Rao found it difficult and returned it to Sai Baba. By now, he had forgotten that Bhagoji Shinde had filled the pipe. He realised that for Baba's company, one should be above a loathsome feeling for others, a mind clear of anger, jealousy and pride, disgust for poor and above sexual attractions. Looking for the divine in every living creature is to be practised.

The pipe was circulated four or five times. Those who first scoffed Bhagoji Shinde were now unmindful to sit near him just to have a puff from the pipe. Even the dog of Bhagoji was amused at his master getting a place of honour.

Bala Saheb Mirikar from Kopergaon freely participated in this pipe smoking. He was a Mamaltadar, a position of prestige in the Government. His father was Kaka Saheb Mirikar of Ahmednagar, whom the British Government had given the title *sardar*. Kaka Saheb Mirikar was a great devotee of Sai Baba and had written to his son, Bala Saheb Mirikar to have darshan of Sai Baba at Shirdi. Now Bala Saheb Mirikar was posted at Kopergaon and was on an official trip to Chitali, close to Shirdi. Thus while going to Chitali he had dropped in at Shirdi for Baba's darshan.

After he had three or four puffs, unexpectedly Baba asked him – "Do you know anything about Dwarakamai?"

Bala Saheb Mirikar was bewildered, but he hastily said – "Yes, yes, Baba! That is Lord Krishna's Dwaraka! Am I correct?"

"No doubt, Krishna had Dwaraka as his capital. But this one is our mother! One who sits on her lap has nothing to fear!" Baba said. Mhalsapathy told him that Baba had named the mosque as 'Dwarakamai'.

Bala Saheb Mirikar could not grasp Baba's words. He just said 'yes' to everything. As it was getting late for going to Chitali, he got up and touched Baba's feet. Baba took out a fistful of udhi, dropped it in Bala Saheb Mirikar's hands and raising the same fist he shaped it into a cobra hood, saying "Do you know this long Buwa!"

"Oh! A snake!" looking at the shape, Bala Saheb Mirikar answered.

Baba continued in his mystic tone – "Yes, yes, a snake! Why bother when we are under the protection of Dwarakamai! We have no fear of him."

Neither Bala Saheb Mirikar nor others could make the head or tail of what Baba was telling. Mirikar did not seek a clarification also, as he was in a hurry. As Mirikar reached the front door, Baba called Madhava Rao and asked him to accompany Bala Saheb Mirikar to Chitali.

Madhava Rao went behind Mirikar and told him that Baba had asked him to accompany him up to Chitali. "To accompany me? What for?" Being ignorant of Baba's intention, he said – "My Boss is arriving there. May be I will have to stay overnight at Chitali! Why should I trouble you?"

"All right! I will inform Baba" Madhava Rao had no courage to disobey Baba, at the same time could not insist on Mirikar to take him along. So he went back to Baba and Bala Saheb Mirikar waited at the entrance.

"Baba, Bala Saheb Mirikar says that it is not necessary for me to accompany him. He does not want to trouble me." Madhava Rao told Baba.

'All right, all right! Do not go! Here God proposes and man disposes! What can you do? Do not worry! Stay here." Baba told Madhava Rao.

Bala Saheb Mirikar heard what Baba said. He had some apprehension. So he signalled Madhava Rao to accompany him. Madhava Rao did not take a decision but sought Baba's permission – "Baba, Mirikar has changed his mind. Now he wants me to accompany him. What shall I do?"

"Go! Shama, Dwarakamai will not fail her children even if they disregard her!" Baba lovingly said.

Devotees knew that Baba's words were always significant! They expected some sort of danger and were moved with Baba's love for his devotees.

Madhava Rao quickly collected a pair of clothes and bedding and got into the tonga of Bala Saheb Mirikar. There was a peon also.

The tonga passed Rahata and turned towards Chitali. An old man was carrying bamboo sticks. Madhava Rao purchased one! Mirikar jocularly remarked as to whether Madhava Rao was going to fight with someone!

They reached Chitali after three hours. It was evening. Bala Saheb Mirikar's boss had not yet arrived. So they decided to camp in Hanuman temple.

The night was warm and sultry. The peon had lighted a lantern. Mirikar had brought some eatables. They shared it. Then both spread the beddings. The peon slept in the verandah and soon was snoring. Mirikar was reading a newspaper. Madhava Rao was chanting *om namah shivaya* by turning his rosary. Even though he had two sleepless nights, his vigilant eyes were on Mirikar. Suddenly he saw a big cobra spreading its hood, gazing at Mirikar, about to charge him. The situation was very dangerous and tense.

Madhava Rao, with his presence of mind threw his chaddar on Mirikar and in a split second took his stick and precisely hit the cobra on its head. The hit did the job. Mirikar stood up and moved aside. He was saved.

The peon also joined Madhava Rao and hit after hit, killed the cobra.

Mirikar still trembled with terror! He was sweating profusely. He now remembered Baba's words 'Lambu Buwa', Dwarakamai's protection etc.! Realising their significance now he was in tears, tears of gratitude!

Bala Saheb Mirikar embraced Madhava Rao and both clasped themselves for minutes together – thinking of Baba and nothing else on earth!

15

MYSTERY OF FORM

*D*ay and night Madhava Rao's mind thought of nothing else, but Sai Baba! To him Baba was God, Baba was his family deity Saptashringi and Baba was all in all and everything! And this thought brought a complete tranquility to him! To experience such a calm mind, it requires implicit faith. Next morning, he purchased a pair of silver breasts from the jeweller. He took it and offered it to Baba. He narrated the vow taken by his mother and as he considered Baba his family deity – Goddess Saptashringi, he requested Baba to accept it.

Baba patiently explained – "Shama, it is not like that! Your family deity has her own reverential place in your domestic life. You have to observe some family practices to get her grace. Therefore go over to Saptashringi and offer this pair of silver breasts to her."

Baba's explanation satisfied Madhava Rao and so he decided to visit the shrine of Goddess Saptashringi at Vani near Chandwad in Nasik district. But indeed it was Baba's will as someone from that place yearned to visit Shirdi for Baba's darshan! Who was he? His name was Kakaji Vaidya! He was the priest of Saptashringi temple at Vani.

Kakaji Vaidya was a devout person who looked after the needs of visiting pilgrims and a great devotee of Saptashringi. He had lost his peace of mind due to several domestic problems. He prayed to the Goddess for relief. She gave him a dream vision and directed him to go to Baba. He was at a loss to guess who this Baba was! He thought it was Lord Shiva and hence decided to go to Triambakeshwar near Nasik and worship the 'Jyotirlinga'.

Kakaji Vaidya spent two weeks propitiating Lord Shiva. The peaceful, beautiful and sacred Triambakeshwar had no effect on this unfortunate soul.

He observed rigid rules and fasts and prayed earnestly to Goddess Saptashringi. She gave him a dream vision again and said – "You fool, I asked you to go to Baba – Sai Baba of Shirdi! Not to Triambakeshwar!"

Once again Kakaji Vaidya was in a riddle! He did not have complete instructions. He had not heard of Sai Baba nor Shirdi. He yearned to visit Shirdi and asked many people about Shirdi and Sai Baba. Kakaji Vaidya's earnest thinking of Sai Baba must have reached him and as such Sai Baba advised Madhava Rao to visit this remote place.

The noon aarti was in progress when Madhava Rao and his family members reached the shrine of Saptashringi. To the Jaikars of 'Jai Jagadambe, Jai Saptashringi Mata', one solitary voice – 'Jai Sainath, Jai Shirdinath' was added. It was Madhava Rao's!

This new acclaim to 'Shirdinath, Sainath' thrilled Kakaji Vaidya! His mind was emotionally inspired! That was the beginning of a peace of mind he so much sought! He took Madhava Rao and his family to his house and made their stay comfortable. Madhava Rao was also thrilled to hear from Kakaji Vaidya about his dream vision and the instructions of the Goddess to go over to Sai Baba. He realized that Baba is Lord Shiva himself.

Kakaji Vaidya was stunned at this miracle. The Goddess not only directed him to a loving God but also arranged a close devotee of Sai Baba to take him to Shirdi. In fact he had no more disturbed mind. Throughout the day Madhava Rao was relating to him miracles after miracles of Sai Baba!

Next day Madhava Rao reverentially worshipped Goddess Saptashringi. The brothers fulfilled the vow of offering a pair of silver breasts, cloth, and coconut. They were happy and relieved. Kakaji Vaidya prepared for the journey and they all left for Shirdi.

Reaching Shirdi they straightaway made for the mosque. A South Indian family of pilgrims was giving a performance of Rama bhajans. Sitting on his stone, Baba was listening to this devotional music. While melodious bhajans were sung, the woman was shedding profuse tears! She was witnessing a vision of Lord Rama in place of Sai Baba!

At the same time, Kakaji Vaidya's eyes also shed tears of joy. He was seeing 'Shanthi' – peace embodied Sai Baba! Peace of mind lost for several months! The divine peace on Baba's countenance, his lustrous complexion, his kind eyes, the sweet smile – all showered flowers of peace on Kakaji Vaidya! The mystery of Goddess Saptashringi sending him to Baba became clear to him! The very vision of Baba enchanted him!

While Baba showered peace on Kakaji Vaidya, he showered grace on the South Indian woman. She saw him as Prabhu Ram while all others saw him as Sai Baba. This miracle changed her completely. She had come to Baba as she had heard that Baba gives lot of money to musicians and other artists. Baba blessed her but gave her only two rupees saying – 'Allah will give you ample!' But that blessing did not satisfy her greedy husband. He was sorry that Baba had appraised that lovely music session for a paltry two rupees. For him the meaning of two rupees – 'Shraddha and Saburi' was worthless! He pulled his wife and children to the Hanuman temple for passing the night and leave Shirdi next day early in the morning.

The greedy husband did not accept his wife's vision of seeing Lord Ramachandra in Sai Baba. He ridiculed his wife's divine experience.

Was it ever likely that one who visited Shirdi would leave without carrying implicit faith in this Loving God? The greedy husband had a dream in the early hours of the morning. He found himself with his arms tied back and held by a chain by a policeman. Baba was watching the fun. The man was frightened and bowed to Baba. He pleaded – "Baba, I came for your darshan and here I am arrested for no offence." Baba replied – "Oh! It must be a punishment for your evil action in your earlier life!"

The greedy husband pleaded – "Your darshan must have burnt my earlier *karma* to ashes". "Do you have that faith?" Baba asked him. He nodded.

Baba asked him to close his eyes. As he did, he heard someone fall down with a thud. He opened his eyes and saw the policeman lying dead. He was terrified and told Baba that he would be charged for murdering the policeman. Baba again asked him to close his eyes. When he opened his eyes, the policeman was not there and he was free again.

Baba asked him again – "Now what do you desire?"

"Baba, I would like to have darshan of Samartha Ramdas".

'Look Behind!" Baba commanded. Standing behind was Swami Samartha Ramdas. The greedy husband flung himself before him and touched his feet. When he looked up, he saw Sai Baba in his place!

The dream was over! Somewhere a cock crowed announcing the advent of dawn. The South Indian was now a transformed man! He agreed with his wife that Baba is

Almighty - a Loving God! The family stayed for eight more days at Shirdi and every day they sang with devotion and the woman was blessed with vision of Lord Rama!

Kakaji Vaidya too returned to Vani with a blissful peace of mind.

16

BLESSING FOR PROGENY

*K*akaji Vaidya was drawn to Baba through Goddess Saptashringi! But Baba had many ways to bring his devotees from various places. To some he would give a dream vision. To some he would meet in person in a far off place without leaving Shirdi. Sometimes he would call a person through a personal message even though he is not known to Him. To some he would attract through his photograph. For some he would create difficulties which would lead them to him seeking solace. The overall fact was that Baba's will alone bring them to his feet. Some may have faith in God and saints and even those who came without faith left with implicit faith in him. Man needs merit to come across a 'Loving God' in human form!

Years passed! Baba's promise to Mhalsapathy was fulfilled. Mhalsapathy had a son. His wife forgot her sorrow. But this made Mhalsapathy more attached to Baba. In Baba's company, Mhalsapathy forgot his worldly afflictions and progressed spiritually. He once again started giving company to Baba during nights, alternately at the mosque and the chawadi.

Sakharam Aurangabadkar of Sholapur lost his wife, when his first son was born. A decade later he married again. Many astrologers told him that his second wife will not be able to bear a child. Sakharam's wife tried taking a lot of treatments for this but to no avail. Then, she learnt that Baba had blessed progeny to a few. She expressed her desire to her husband that she will pray to Baba for a child. Accompanied by her step son Viswanath, she reached Shirdi.

The lady's problem was very delicate! She could not open her mind in the presence of her grown up step son! Least of all before any stranger as with her age people would laugh at her! She stayed in Shirdi for over two months and at last met Madhava Rao and told her agony. She requested him to intervene on her behalf for the blessing of a son.

Madhava Rao told her – "Well sister, we will try. Baba is never alone as his countless devotees always surround him. If Baba wills, everything will be all right. Now from today you make it a point to sit in the verandah with a coconut and other offerings while Baba takes his noon food. The moment I call you, come up and have his darshan. Baba is great! He will surely bless you!"

Aurangabadkar's wife was happy and confident that Madhava Rao would surely help her! Baba had now stopped begging as his devotees visiting him would bring ample food for him as offering. He could not displease them. So after finishing the forenoon session, Madhava Rao would send away all and give food to Baba. Then Baba would have some rest.

As already planned, Aurangabadkar's wife went to the mosque alone with a coconut, camphor, incense and flowers and waited outside while Baba ate. Three days passed and nothing happened! On the fourth day, Madhava Rao seized an opportunity. Baba had finished taking his food and was washing hands. Madhava Rao poured water on Baba's hands and then offered a cloth to wipe them. While he did so his face came very close to that of Baba's. Baba lovingly pinched him on his cheeks and pulled them out with affection. Though happy, Madhava Rao pretended annoyance and said – "What is all this? Baba! You are pulling my cheeks. Does it not hurt me?"

Baba said – "Why do you make an ado over nothing? We are associated with the last seventy-two births and have I pinched even once?" Baba too was mischievous. Madhava Rao was free and frisk – "We do not like a God who merely pulls cheeks for a show and gives nothing!"

"Ask anything you want!" Baba offered the entire wealth of the world!

"Nothing more, my Lord! I want your devotion – your love! That is all!" Madhava Rao too asked God's greatest grace.

"For that only I am here, Shama! You demand – I will give!"

Madhava Rao signalled Aurangabadkar's wife. She came up, offered the coconut to Baba and put her head on his feet. Baba took the coconut and struck it hard on the wooden railing. It did not break! Baba said – "This coconut rattles empty! What does it say?"

"It wants that this woman's womb should rattle with a baby! Cast that coconut into her lap so that she gets a child!" Madhava Rao straightaway opened the topic.

"Have you gone mad, Shama! Does a coconut ever bring a child?" Baba asked. Madhava Rao insisted – "My God, If you will – not one but a chain of children will be born to her. Give her that coconut as your *prasad*!"

"No! We will break it and eat!" Baba said.

"No! We will not! Offer it to her" Madhava Rao pleaded.

At last Sai Baba gave her the boon – "Well, she will have a child."

"When? Tell it first!" Madhava Rao demanded.

"After twelve months!" Sai Baba declared. Madhava Rao immediately broke the coconut and offered half to Aurangabadkar' s wife. He said – "Listen sister, you are a witness to what he has said! If you do not have a child after twelve months, I will break a coconut on this God's head and throw him out of this holy shrine."

Only a great devotee like Madhava Rao could declare a decision of driving away the divine! The lady prostrated before Baba, looked at Madhava Rao with gratitude and left. Looking at her, Baba ate the sweet kernel of coconut and once again pulled Madhava Rao's cheeks.

After eighteen months the Aurangabadkar couple returned with a bonny son – a boy of six months! The impossible had taken place. Sakharam Aurangabadkar was dumbfounded with Baba's power and still more with Madhava Rao's devotion!

Similar to re-birth of a son to Mhalsapathy, another unhappy couple, Sapatnekars got back their dead son back. The husband, who had criticised Baba in his college days, was drawn to him through his wife's dream. Baba appeared in her dream which made the couple trace their steps to Sai Baba. Sapatnekar was a successful advocate in Akkalkot in Sholapur district. He had criticised Baba while studying for his law degree. Just before the examination, Sapatnekar and his friends compared their preparation for the final examination. One Shewade was not up to the mark but was confident that with Baba's grace he would pass in the ensuing year. Sapatnekar mocked his faith and advised him to take his study seriously! However, Shewade was undisturbed and said – "Yes, I pride myself being after that Fakir – Sai Baba. That God has told me that I will not pass this year. But next year I will definitely pass and get the degree too!" Shewade blurted out his mind and left the place. Shewade's faith paid him dividends and he became an advocate as prophesied by Baba!

Years rolled thereafter! Shewade and Sapatnekar both progressed on the path of life. Shewade's faith kept him peaceful and contented in life. Sapatnekar amassed wealth but lost his peace of mind due to domestic calamities. He lost his only son and to console his wife, he undertook extensive pilgrimage to Kashi, Rameshwar, Badrinath, and Kedarnath. Extensive worships and rituals were observed but he did not get peace of mind.

Life was miserable at the loss of only son! The vibrations of Sapatnekar's wife reached Sai Baba. He gave her a dream vision. In the early hours of the morning, she had gone to a well to fetch water. On her way, she saw a fakir under a neem tree. He offered to carry water for her. She got frightened and turned back home. The fakir followed and the dream ended!

She narrated this dream to her husband. Immediately, Sapatnekar remembered Shewade's fakir in the mosque at Shirdi. Without wasting any time he went to Shirdi along with his wife and brother Pandit Rao.

Sapatnekar's wife was astounded as she stepped into the mosque and saw Sai Baba. Here was the fakir of her dream vision right before her! Devotees would go near him, bow down to his feet and Baba spoke lovingly to one and all. She repented for having run away in her dream from this fakir! She told her husband – "Indeed he is the fakir I had seen in my dream!"

Sapatnekar himself was in bliss on seeing Baba. His disturbed mind had attained tranquility. He waited in the line for his chance to touch Baba's feet. Madhava Rao was regulating the crowd. First it was Sapatnekar's wife. Seeing her eyes full of tears, Baba offered her udhi and asked her to sit nearby. Then Sapatnekar touched Baba's feet and placed his head on them. Baba suddenly shouted – "Get out!"

All were surprised with Baba's sudden anger! Madhava Rao was also puzzled. Sapatnekar thought that Baba mistook him for someone else. Again he moved forward and tried to touch Baba's feet. This enraged Baba and he again shouted

– "Get out". Madhava Rao asked Sapatnekar to go back. Sapatnekar was sad and he went near the entrance and waited. Baba was unkind to him alone. His brother got up and joined Sapatnekar. His wife too got up to go near him, but Baba asked her to sit there itself.

Just then a rustic woman started massaging Baba's feet. Baba told her – "Mother, Indeed my feet were aching. Your massage has given me relief! I get pain in my abdomen, back, hands and in fact, everything pains."

The rustic woman just said 'yes, yes' to whatever Baba told her. Sapatnekar's wife listened to this conversation and felt that Baba described her complaints. She was feeling better now and felt as if Baba is narrating her story. While she was thinking like this, Baba concluded – "Mother, it was all due to my drawing water from the well."

Sapatnekar's wife now knew for certain that it was indeed her tale. She felt relieved that her disease will disappear without any medicine. She happily looked at her husband who beckoned her to come near him.

She went near him and explained everything. Sapatnekar felt very unhappy. The Loving God who was kind to everyone had asked him to get out. Someone suggested that they should try to see Baba through Bala Shimpi. Bala Shimpi was a tailor and a close devotee of Baba. He advised them to buy Baba's picture and with that once again they went to the mosque in the afternoon. Bala Shimpi took the photograph from Sapatnekar and giving it to Baba said in a friendly manner – "Baba, whose picture is this?"

"You know it is his Master's picture" Baba said pointing to Sapatnekar. Everyone laughed. Engaging Baba in this conversation, Bala Shimpi asked Sapatnekar to bow down to Baba's feet quickly. Baba took back his feet with a 'get out' as before. Madhava Rao asked Sapatnekar to go behind.

Sapatnekar broke into tears! He returned with his family to the lodgings. He placed a garland around Baba's picture and bending before it expressed- "Baba, pardon me! Now I have realised why you are angry with me! I had condemned you before Shewade and ridiculed him for his faith in you. This is a punishment for that!" Sincerely he prayed before the picture and went to Madhava Rao's house. Hiding nothing he told him everything.

Madhava Rao reassured him that Baba simply wanted to correct Sapatnekar. Now that he has repented for his misdeed, Baba will shower his grace on Sapatnekar. He asked him to meet Baba next morning when he was alone.

With this a new hope was born in Sapatnekar. Next morning he went to the mosque. Baba was alone. He noticed Sapatnekar and how nervous he was. He called him – "Come up! Do not be nervous! Remove the wall between us." Baba's loving attitude made Sapatnekar bold enough. With his wife and brother, he went up. Still feeling nervous and shaking hands, he carried a garland and he could not properly place it around Baba's neck. Baba himself took the garland and put it around his own neck. Sapatnekar held Baba's feet and placed his head on them. His tears flowing profusely, he virtually bathed them. Baba said, "Listen, how can you go away from these feet. They are time-honoured!" Sapatnekar held them fast! Baba stroked his head! Sapatnekar felt he had achieved everything he desired.

Just then Madhava Rao entered. Baba said to him – "Shama, this man says that I have killed his son! Tell me, did I kill his son? Do I not give whatever my devotees demand?"

Madhava Rao explained – "Baba, he is unhappy that you asked him to get out every time he tried to bow down to your feet."

"That was not for him!" Baba explained. "It was for his ego." Sapatnekar was now thoroughly reformed. Baba raised him up and said "Do not lament! Your desire will be fulfilled! Your dead son will be reborn to you! Go mother! Be happy!"

Baba placed a coconut in her saree which was spread before him. Both brothers tried to touch Baba's feet simultaneously and hit their heads. Baba smiled and said – "It is enough! It is enough! Have this udhi!"

Sapatnekar gave one rupee as dakshina. A sweet-looking poor girl with a box was standing nearby. She opened the tiny box and asked Baba to put that one rupee into her box. Baba lovingly pulled her near and said – "Young mother, do I owe anything to your father? Every morning you come and ask for money!" Baba placed one rupee given by Sapatnekar in that box. Sapatnekar watched something of what happened to the vast dakshina that Baba received from devotees.

Devotees offered money as 'dakshina' and n many occasions Baba too had demanded it. In fact, Baba never needed it himself. Whatever money he collected during day he distributed it all before night. The regular recipients were that little girl Ani, Kondaji's wife Jamli, Lakshmi who baked rotis to Baba, Tatya Kote, Bade Baba! Some visitors also got their share.

Thus this Fakir from a mosque at Shirdi, whose income was more than a Governor, was a pauper again at night, as he rolled his hard bed of chaddars! However to him, it was a bed of wealth – wealth that was a bliss divine!

17

ADORATION OF PERSONAL GOD

*S*apatnekars returned home with memories of Baba which made them immensely happy. Soon a son was born to them. He was named Muralidhar. Sapatnekars had two more sons – Bhaskar and Dinakar. Their greatest joy was their repeated visits to Shirdi. The lawyer who once condemned Sai Baba was now totally surrendered to him!

There are many in the world, who condemn even saints. Sai Baba targetted such persons and would transform them.

Swami Somadev of Haridwar was a 'Sanyasi' wearing saffron robes and was a spiritual aspirant. He had heard about Sai Baba and decided to meet him in person and therefore planned a trip to Shirdi.

Changing trains at Manmad, he reached Kopergaon. There he joined a group of four persons bound to Shirdi. They took bath in Godavari river and in their conversation spoke high of Sai Baba.

While travelling to Shirdi, from a distance, Swami Somadev saw the white flag flying on the mosque. He thought that Baba must be a publicity-oriented man and spoke caustically about him. His co-passengers told him that Sai Baba did not need a flag but his devotees out of affection have put the flag on his abode. They told him that Baba is being taken on a palanquin procession by his devotees.

Swami Somadev lost his temper completely. He almost shouted – "A procession of a Sadhu? Does your Sai Baba consider himself a King? No, no, stop the tonga here! Let me get down! I have seen many such imposters!" Without even thinking of the consequences, Swami Somadev jumped from the moving tonga. The result? He sprained his leg! With a groan he sat down on the road!

Those accompanying him felt that Baba has punished Swami Somadev. However being Baba's devotees they stopped the tonga and rushed to his help. He was not prepared even to sit back in their tonga. They tried to convince Swami Somadev – "Swamiji, if you do not have faith in Sai Baba, you need not see him or kneel before him. But please do not stay on the roadside with your injury! You can take treatment at Shirdi and then leave for your home town. Come, let us go." Ultimately Swami Somadev accepted their wise counsel and travelled with them on one condition that he will not enter the mosque nor have darshan of Baba. He would wait outside while they met Baba and returned and they could look after him afterwards.

Swami Somadev was very much hurt. He could not even stand. But still his ego refused to have darshan of Baba. It was an embarrassing situation for his co-passengers to leave him outside and just go in for Baba's darshan. They knew that this would invite Baba's wrath. In fact, in an earlier visit, these three people avoided visiting the Datta shrine near Kopergaon as they thought it would delay their reaching Shirdi. On the way one of them had a thorn prick. When they went to the mosque, Baba took them to task for not visiting the Datta shrine and indicated the thorn-prick as a punishment. Remembering this they felt, if they leave Swami Somadev uncared outside the mosque, Baba would not like it. By now, Swami Somadev also had calmed down. He requested them to carry him to Baba's presence.

They knew it to be Baba's plan. They took Swami Somadev on their shoulders and entered the mosque. Baba began gabbling in his own style – 'He is here, he is here. He likes to tear my flag so dear!' Then he applied udhi to a young boy with a disease in the bone of his right leg!

On seeing Swami Somadev, Sai Baba shouted – "Throw out this sanyasi, who wants to throw away my flag! What use are saffron clothes to a sanyasi? What use is a horse to a fakir? Why should a fakir be taken in a procession? Not a fakir, but a sanyasi needs a ride in procession!"

Baba's comments continued as he continued to apply udhi to the boy's leg. He was reassuring the boy in between. Swami Somadev's ego completely melted. Baba's divine power illumined his dark heart! Now he did not want to leave the mosque. In Baba he had a vision of affection and anger at the same time – anger for himself and affection for the patient boy! Baba addressed the boy's mother – "Mother, do not worry! Your boy is cured! Stay in Shirdi for four more days and then go home." The boy and his mother bowed to Baba in gratitude and left.

Swami Somadev had just witnessed as to how lovingly Baba healed the boy. His pain was also increasing and wished that Baba cured his pain too! In a whisper he expressed his desire to his companions. One of them took courage and told Baba – "Baba, this Swami Somadev is hurt as he fell from the tonga!" Baba corrected him – "No, no! He jumped into the pit of ego".

Baba spoke plainly! This removed the last trace of ego in Swami Somadev. He himself spoke – "Baba, pardon me! I have commited a blunder."

"The mistake is not yours. It is of these saffron robes! Ego must be discarded before putting on the garments of a 'sanyasi'! For this you must give up your attachments. Now go home and take rest." Baba answered. One of Swami

Somadev's companions thought that Baba has forgotten about the injury. He reminded – "But Baba, his leg......" Baba was clear in reply – "what is wrong with his leg? He walked the wrong way and suffered! Now ask him to walk the right way, he will be alright."

Swami Somadev walked to their lodging. By the time they reached, the swelling and pain had disappeared and his mind was full of devotion to Baba. So Swami Somadev who condemned Baba and who wanted to return even before reaching Shirdi, now became his devotee!

This is how Baba would attract his own people. Healing the boy of his infection in the leg bone was in fact an excuse to pull another devotee. That boy's uncle was a doctor in government service at Malegaon. The Doctor and his colleagues did the best to treat the boy's malady. Even a surgical operation was done. Everything was a failure. At that time, somebody suggested taking the boy to Sai Baba.

We know that right in the presence of Swami Somadev, Baba healed the boy. On learning this miraculous cure, the doctor expressed a desire to go to Shirdi on his way to Mumbai during his leave and accordingly planned it. But when he reached Manmad, the doctor met some people who were prejudiced against Sai Baba. After talking to them, the doctor cancelled his visit to Shirdi and proceeded straight to Mumbai.

At Mumbai, one of his relatives was laid down with fever. This doctor treated him for four days, spending sleepless nights. The patient did not improve. On the fifth day he just dozed and heard a clear voice – "You still have doubts about me." The doctor woke up and dismissed it as a piece of imagination. But he heard the same voice repeating the same words for two more nights. The doctor surrendered to Sai Baba and secretly vowed to go to Shirdi if the patient's temperature dropped to normal on that day.

Surprisingly the temperature became normal soon
after. The doctor's reputation remained aloft! Baba got the
devotee pulled to Shirdi! When he had darshan of Baba,
the doctor was happy. When he returned home, by Baba's
blessings, he learnt about his promotion to a higher post!

Merely using his voice in the doctor's dream, Baba
brought him to his feet! Likewise he transformed a non-
believer into a sincere devotee with appropriate change in
his own voice.

Kaka Mahajani was an ardent devotee of Sai Baba at
Mumbai. His contacts were very wide and it was his practice
to tell his friends about Sai Baba's greatness and take them
to Shirdi. However, one of his friends who did not have any
faith told him that he would join him for a trip to Shirdi but
will neither bow down to Baba nor offer him any dakshina.

Kaka Mahajani knew well that such people ultimately
will surrender to Baba and therefore told his friend that
nobody will force him to bow down to Baba nor ask him to
offer dakshina.

At Shirdi, when they entered the mosque, Kaka
Mahajani's friend heard a voice from Sai Baba which
startled him. That was his dead father's voice – "What
brings you here, my dear!" At the time of his death. His
father had assured that he will be with his son always! He
forgot his earlier decision of not bowing down to Baba. He
went ahead and fell flat at Baba's feet!

Then Baba asked Kaka Mahajani – "Kaka, when are
you leaving?"

Kaka Mahajani replied – "The moment you want me
to go, I will leave". Baba told him to leave soon after lunch.
Kaka Mahajani and his friend who wanted to stay at Shirdi
for sometime felt disappointed. But no one can ignore
Baba's instructions.

While leaving, Baba sought a dakshina of seventeen rupees, which he gladly offered. His friend was unhappy that Baba did not ask him any dakshina. Baba told him – "Since you did not want to offer dakshina, I did not ask you! You did not even like to bow down! If you still wish, you can offer me dakshina!" With Baba's omniscience, Kaka Mahajani's friend surrendered completely. He also offered seventeen rupees. Baba blessed him and said –"Remove the wall of duality between you and me! I am in you, you are in me! Go home quickly and come back leisurely."

Madhava Rao intervened and said to Baba – "The sky is overcast with clouds. It is sure to rain and these people will be drenched."

Baba told them that they will not be drenched in rain. They had a hurried lunch and soon after left in a tonga. A stormy breeze, lightning, and thunder greeted them on their way to Kopergaon. Although signs of heavy downpour were evident, it did not rain till they got into the train!

Kaka Mahajani's friend reached home and opened the door of his house. Two sparrows which were trapped inside the house flew out eagerly. Seeing this he was shocked! These two sparrows which were dear to his father would have starved to death unknowingly! They had built a nest in the house and his father at the time of his death had asked his son to take care of the sparrows. He always respected his father's feelings. But by mistake he got the sparrows trapped inside the house. He could now realise as to why Baba sent him back in a hurry. He was moved to the core of his heart with a feeling of relief and gratitude to Sai Baba!

18

YOU GET WHAT YOU DESERVE

*O*n reaching home, Kaka Mahajani found a message from his office waiting for him. His presence was urgently required. In fact, his office had already sent a telegram to Kaka Mahajani at Shirdi. Even before it reached his hands, Baba had made him leave for Mumbai along with his friend.

In sending back Kaka Mahajani's friend, Baba had saved two sparrows and brought out a staunch devotee in him! And for this reason, he had sent back Kaka Mahajani to pull another devotee to his feet! He was the owner of the Solicitor's firm where Kaka Mahajani worked as the Office Manager and his name was Dharamsi Jethabai Thakkar. He was called Sethji by his subordinates. He depended on Kaka Mahajani for day to day functioning of his firm but he was prejudiced about Kaka Mahajani going to Shirdi quite often and spending much time with Sai Baba. He could not replace Kaka Mahajani as a suitable person was not found all along. Now that he was able to get a suitable replacement in one Ratibai, he had decided to terminate Kaka Mahajani's services. He was looking for an excuse. When Kaka Mahajani came to the office, Sethji thought of taking strict action against him. He asked Kaka Mahajani as to whether he got his telegram sent to Shirdi! He was not aware of it as he had left at Shirdi at 11 am on the previous day. When Sethji checked the register, he found that the telegram was sent around 2 pm. Then he asked that Kaka Mahajani prolongs his ' leave by staying at Shirdi for days together and how come on this occasion he had come back to Mumbai so soon. Kaka Mahajani replied that Baba asked him to get back the moment he landed at Shirdi. That made Sethji think as to whether Baba knew in advance that he would be sending a telegram to Kaka Mahajani . He toned down considerably and said – "Kaka, I do not like your madness to go after Sai Baba! I want to come to Shirdi personally to meet him. Tell me when you are going there next time."

"But Sethji, why did you call me back?" Kaka Mahajani asked him.

"Oh, I wanted that Laud advocate's notice, which I could trace after I sent you the telegram" Sethji replied.

"Then Sethji, I will return to Shirdi. My leave is still there. Moreover the courts are also closed." Kaka Mahajani replied.

"Then I will accompany you. Let me see for myself your Sai Baba. Only thing is that you must come back with me." – Sethji commanded.

Kaka Mahajani replied – "That is not in my hands. I can return only if Sai Baba permits!" Sethji was irritated but he wanted to take a final decision of terminating Kaka Mahajani's services only after meeting Sai Baba. So he asked Kaka Mahajani's assistant Ratilal to accompany them. All three of them left for Shirdi on the same night. On their way they met Baba Saheb Tarkhad in the train. He was an ardent devotee of Sai Baba. Sethji could not keep quiet and he asked him – "Tarkhad Saheb, our Kaka Mahajani says that your Sai Baba is a divine personality. He thinks Baba reads every thought in our minds. Is it true?"

"Cent per cent correct!" saying so, Baba Saheb Tarkhad narrated his own experience. That itself is an example of Baba's omniscience!

Baba Saheb Tarkhad held an important position in a textile mill at Mumbai. He belonged to Prarthana Samaj and did not believe in idol-worship. But his wife and son worshipped many deities in their home shrine and Baba Saheb Tarkhad did not object to it. There was a photograph of Sai Baba in their shrine, which was worshipped with much adoration by his wife and son. Though he did not worship, Baba Saheb Tarkhad believed in God!

Every day his wife and son would perform worship and offer *naivedya*. At lunch time all of them used to partake this Prasad. This went on throughout.

And even if they had any sickness, the practice would not break. None of them had gone to Shirdi and one early morning, Tarkhad's wife had a dream in which Sai Baba asked her to visit Shirdi and feed him with a medley of rice and *daal*!

Baba Saheb Tarkhad on hearing the dream happily agreed to her going to Shirdi, though he himself was not in a position to accompany her. Therefore he asked his son to go along with her to Shirdi. The son was reluctant as there would be a break in Baba's worship if he goes with his mother. Baba Saheb Tarkhad promised his son that during his absence, even though he belongs to Prarthana Samaj and does not worship idols, he will continue Baba's worship as done by his wife and son until they come back from Shirdi. On this assurance, the mother and son left for Shirdi!

Next morning, Baba Saheb Tarkhad got up early, had his bath and performed worship to Sai Baba as done by his wife and son and sincerely prayed that he should accept his worship. He also offered sugar candy to Baba. He took this prasad during lunch time.

This went on for two days. On the third day, Baba Saheb Tarkhad performed all the worship but forgot to make the offering. When he came home for lunch, the cook told him that he had forgotten naivedya. Baba Saheb Tarkhad felt very bad. He prostrated before his picture and repented for his mistake. He wrote an emotional letter to his son requesting him to seek pardon from Baba. To atone his mistake he fasted the entire day!

At Shirdi, the mother and son visited Baba in the mosque. He made them sit near him and blessed. On the third day, he told them that he visited their residence at Bandra in Mumbai. He could not get any food and had to return hungry. The son immediately realised that there was some lapse on the part of his father while worshipping Baba. He was upset and decided to return to Mumbai. Baba told him that he could worship him at Shirdi itself! However, the son wrote a letter to his father expressing his unhappiness!

As directed in the dream vision, the mother prepared medley of rice and daal. Baba accepted it happily and told her to continue to stay in Shirdi for four more days and daily feed him with the same food. So the dream was not a mere dream at all!

The letter from Mumbai reached Shirdi next day and the son's letter from Shirdi also reached Baba Saheb Tarkhad next day and Baba's omniscience proved to be a proof of divinity!

Baba Saheb Tarkhad shed tears of joy while narrating his divine experience to Sethji. But this had very little effect on Sethji. He still itched for his own experience! All of them got down at Kopergaon.

Kaka Mahajani purchased a basket of grapes. Sethji detested grapes with seeds. But Kaka Mahajani convinced him that Baba would accept anything given with devotion.

As soon as they landed in Shirdi, Kaka Mahajani wanted to have Baba's darshan. But Sethji was more concerned about his accommodation and lunch. Kaka Mahajani was helpless and had to look after him. He took him to the common mess and explained Sethji's requirements to the cook. Then he took Sethji and Ratilal to the mosque and kept the basket of grapes in front of Sai Baba. While Kaka Mahajani sat near Baba, Sethji sat watching. Madhava Rao told Baba – "Baba, this is Kaka Mahajani's boss, Seth Dharamsi Jethabai Thakkar!"

"Kaka's Boss! No, no! His Boss is standing there. Look!" All looked in the direction Baba pointed. The cook whom Sethji had just met was standing there for Baba's darshan. Baba spoke – "Shama, he has not come for me. He came for Appa, that cook! He has already met him!" Sethji was non-plussed!

Baba took the grapes and started distributing them amongst the gathering. Baba's comments had pleased Kaka Mahajani, because Sethji would always remind him that he was the master and Kaka Mahajani his servant!

On the other hand Sethji was a little embarrassed! But now he looked at Baba with reverence as he had pointed out that he had gone to the cook first. He was impressed with Baba's clairvoyance! While he was thus thinking, Baba stood before him and offered him a few grapes. With reluctance he accepted them and put it into his mouth. He did not know as to what to do with the seeds and kept them in his hand. Again Baba came and offered him grapes. He put the seeds into his pocket and took the grapes. He wanted to pass on the grapes to Ratilal. Baba noticed it and told Sethji – "They are for you! Eat them!" Sethji ate them and to his great surprise, they were seedless! He enquired Baba Saheb Tarkhad who also received the same grapes immediately after him as to whether they contained seeds. He replied in affirmative! It was for Sethji alone that Baba had performed a miracle of transforming grapes with seeds in to seedless ones! Still Sethji wanted one more confirmation. In his mind he wanted Baba to distribute grapes again from Kaka Mahajani first. Baba turned round and even though Kaka Mahajani was a little away, he started another round by giving first to Kaka Mahajani. Sethji's ego completely melted and he bowed down to Baba's feet!

After the aarti, all went to lunch. Sethji was happy at the food. Next to him sat an advocate from Nasik, S.B.Dhumal. Sethji had the experience of omniscience of Baba. Now he wanted to test the omnipotence of Baba. He asked Dhumal – "Dhumal Saheb, you come to Shirdi every now and then leaving your court work. You also stay here for eight to ten days at a stretch and do not leave without Baba's permission. How do you manage?"

Very innocently Dhumal replied – "Sethji, you will be surprised with my experience! I had a court case at Niphad, very close to Shirdi. So I thought I will have a glimpse of Sai Baba and then reach Niphad before noon. Both I and my client came here. Baba did not permit us to leave that day. Not only that day, but for the next ten days, Baba detained us here! Tell me what could have happened to the court case?"

It was unthinkable for Sethji. Leaving the case and without seeking court permission, both the pleader and the client stay in Shirdi indefinitely! Dhumal himself explained further – "Sethji, we won the case. During our absence, the case was postponed four times. First day the magistrate had pain in the abdomen. Second day he had fever, third day diarrhoea and on the fourth occasion, some other problem. We were with Lord Sainath at Shirdi leading a carefree time. He managed everything and we won the case."

Now Sethji too realised that during Kaka Mahajani's stay at Shirdi, his court cases automatically got postponed. He now remembered many occasions of Baba's omnipotence!

In spite of all these experiences, Sethji felt that he should not seek Baba's permission to leave and he was bent upon taking back Kaka Mahajani to Mumbai along with him. He told both these things to Kaka Mahajani in advance. They went to the mosque and sat in the presence of Baba.

Madhava Rao spoke to Baba – "Baba, Sethji is leaving by the evening train." Baba replied, "Let him go! Send Kaka Mahajani also along with him". It was a great relief for Sethji! He had his permission without asking for it. And so did Kaka! It was all what he desired! Now he was impatient to leave immediately. But Sai Baba asked them to leave leisurely. Since everyone asked him not to be in hurry, Sethji sat down and he was detained in the mosque for two more hours. He knew for certain that the train would have left! He decided to spend the night at the railway station rather than at Shirdi. Kaka Mahajani and Ratilal had to obey him and all three of them left for Kopergaon in a tonga. Throughout, Sethji was blurting that Baba had ruined his plans of reaching Mumbai next morning! As they reached Kopergaon, they were in for a surprise. The train was detained there due to some mechanical trouble. As soon as the three of them got in, the train left! Sethji's ego completely melted on seeing Baba's control even at the train timings!

Kaka Mahajani reported for duty on expiry of his leave after four days. He was not surprised to see a beautiful picture of Sai Baba adorning his boss's cabin!

19

THE COURT OF ENQUIRY

$\mathcal{M}$any years had rolled past since Sai Baba manifested himself at Shirdi! The ninteenth century was on its way out! During these years, many had sought refuge at the feet of Sai Baba! Many were cured of illnesses, those desiring mitigation of poverty were blessed with material gains, issueless couple progeny, those in distress got peace of mind! Even though thousands were blessed by Sai Baba, many more missed his grace!

In those days of slow communication, Sai Baba desired to reach his devotees quickly even before they came in personal contact with him. It is indeed true that only his will brought devotees to him whether they had faith in him or not! Devotees like Kaka Mahajani propagated Sai Baba's teachings and messages amongst their friends and relatives but it was too insignificant as compared to the vastness of its need!

Sai Baba chose two persons to propagate his teachings and ideas so that more people would come to him! The first one was Narayana Govinda Chandorkar while the other one was Ganesh Rao Dattatreya Sahasrabuddhe. Both belonged to Brahmin caste. Chandorkar was a graduate working as a deputy collector for the British government. The other one was not educated enough and was working as an orderly under Chandorkar. Characteristically he was more critical of others and more orthodox! Both were pious, deeply religious and observing Brahminical discipline and rituals. Chandorkar because of his education and position would not have blind faith in saints and sages. The other one, for lack of education behaved as a rustic workman, was rude and outspoken. The first one moved in higher society while the second one took pleasure in cheap company who praised his poetic compositions written for the rustic stage and catering to their low taste! However Baba needed them both. Though both had heard about Sai Baba, they cautiously kept themselves away from him. But Sai Baba knew that they were the right persons to be his apostles. So he decided to send a direct word to Chandorkar. He knew that Ganesh would follow him!

To call Chandorkar to Shirdi, Sai Baba chose the village accountant of Shirdi, Appa Kulkarni. He was a young man and a great devotee of Sai Baba. Due to ill luck, he was charged with embezzlement of Government money and was required to report to the collector of Newase. When Appa Kulkarni sought Baba's blessings, Baba advised him to go over to the temple of Goddess Mohini Raj, the presiding diety of Newase town and seek her blessings prior to appearing before the collector. When Appa did like that, he was exonerated of his charge and declared innocent! Appa was always grateful to Baba for this help. He was required to go to Kopergaon on official work quite often and every time he left Shirdi, he used to take permission of Baba.

One day Baba told Appa Kulkarni "Appa, call that deputy collector to Shirdi." Appa replied – "Baba, he will not come. He is very proud. It is no use calling him." But still Baba persisted – "Tell him, I have called."

Appa Kulkarni did not want to convey this message. He knew that not only Chandorkar will not come but will also ridicule Sai Baba. If someone abuses Baba, Appa also will be enraged. On an earlier occasion in the revenue office, a clerk spoke ill of Baba and Appa Kulkarni slapped him on his cheek. This silenced the clerk but he in turn concocted a false charge of embezzlement of Government money against Appa Kulkarni. With this background, Appa Kulkarni was avoiding talking about Baba in his official circles. But today he was helpless as Baba himself had asked him to approach the deputy collector!

Appa reached Kopergaon and met Nana Saheb Chandorkar's orderly just outside his office. This was Ganesh Rao Dattatreya Sahasrabuddhe – the second person whom Baba had selected to be his apostle. Appa Kulkarni asked him to convey Baba's message to Chandorkar – "Ganesh Rao, tell Nana Saheb that Sai Baba has called him to Shirdi!"

Ganesh Rao heard that message and roared with laughter. He spoke with mischief in his voice – "Sai Baba? You mean that mad fakir in your Shirdi?" Appa Kulkarni fumed with anger! He felt like slapping this arrogant man! But he controlled himself because of his earlier experience. Moreover, Ganesh Rao was well built like a wrestler! He calmly told him – "Ganesh Rao, you simply convey this message to Nana Saheb! That is all".

Ganesh Rao told him – "Kulkarni, my boss will not meet such cheap fakirs. Give this message to Sai Baba. Moreover he is not in the office at this moment. You will not be able to meet him also. So you can go!"

Appa Kulkarni reversed his steps and he saw Nana Saheb Chandorkar entering the office. So he went near him and spoke – "Nana Saheb, Sai Baba has called you to Shirdi". Nana Chandorkar asked him indifferently – "What for?" Appa Kulkarni replied "I do not know." Nana Chandorkar left the place curtly saying – "Tell him, I am available in my office."

Nana Chandorkar must have given such a reply because of his position. Appa Kulkarni was furious. He knew that Baba will not visit a government office under any circumstances. As he was going back to Shirdi, Appa Kulkarni remembered as to how Baba completely ignored an arrest warrant of a Dhulia court to testify as a witness in a theft case!

It was an interesting case. The railway police had caught a common thief who had stolen some jewellery in the train. He gave a statement in Dhulia court that Sai Baba had presented him those jewels. Dhulia court issued summons to Sai Baba to appear in person to give testimony. Sai Baba was furious when he received the summons. He tore it into pieces and put it into the dhuni right in the presence of the court official who issed the summons.

With this direct insult, Dhulia court issued an arrest warrant for Baba.

An officer of the court with a policeman reached Shirdi to arrest Sai Baba. Actually this officer was preparing to go to Pandharpur for Lord Vittal's darshan. But he was intercepted and sent to Shirdi for arresting Sai Baba. He was in an angry mood and wanted to complete the assignment very fast. When this court officer entered the mosque, the noon aarti was in progress. Sai Baba planned to give him a glimpse of his divine form. The court officer had a glimpse of God Vittal in place of Sai Baba! He was stunned and moved with emotion. The Lord of Pandharpur was right in front of him! He shoved the arrest warrant into his pocket and with folded hands kneeled down in reverence! Later he looked at his companion – the police constable. He was lost in the vision of Lord Rama! Both were extremely happy in their own experiences but unhappy at the official task assigned to them. However they met an advocate known to them and on his advice returned to Dhulia along with the lawyer – but without Baba.

The magistrate heard the story and heeded to the advocate's counsel. A special commission was appointed to go to Shirdi and examine Sai Baba on the spot. The accused charged with theft was also taken along.

The commission was headed by a judge. The mosque was crowded as usual when the commission reached there. Baba was engaged in stitching a torn gown. There were a few legal luminaries among the crowd. Baba got up and offered a chair to the judge. While he sent away a majority of devotees, the legal luminaries stayed back thinking that they could be of some help. But does God need anyone's help. He permitted them to watch as to how God deposes in the court of humans.

The judge asked his first question – "Your name?"

"They call me Sai Baba" – The loving God told him as to how humans address him. The judge too felt that after all God has no name! The judge asked the next question – "Sai Baba, what is the name of your father."

Everybody became alert! But Is not Sai himself the mother and father of this universe? He just said – "My father's name? Of course Sai Baba!" Ordinarily a judge would have lost his temper. But here the judge was a learned Hindu and a Brahmin by caste. His name was Joshi. He went to the next question – "Who is your Guru?" Sai Baba replied – "Venkusa." Baba always talked in a mystic manner and kept his earlier life a secret.

The next question was – "To what faith you belong?" Asking Baba his religion, Joshi Saheb had to decide on which Baba should take oath on Gita or Quran. Baba replied – "Where is the question of my caste or community? I belong to Kabir's class." What a reply indeed! With it Baba again kept himself out of any religion or community on earth! Was not Kabir's birth too a mystery? He grew up in a Muslim weaver's family, picked up Islamic culture, yet believed in Ram and Rahim!

The next question was – "What is your profession, Baba?"

"Profession! Oh! The one of Almighty Protector!" What an answer! Any other person would have bowed down to Baba! But Joshi did not do it. Hence he quickly asked him – "What is your age?"

A silly-looking but a real reply came – "Saheb, you want to know my age? Sir, it is countless! It runs into millions of years!"

The judge was still unable to decide on which Baba should take the oath of speaking the truth as per court rules. So he put a direct question. He said – "Baba, here we are sitting in a court! So you have to be sure that whatever you speak is truth and nothing but the truth!"

Baba replied – "Truth? Why, every word I utter is truth! Nothing less, nothing more!" Those who have an insight into Hindu philosophy knew that every word Baba spoke was true to its core.

Joshi Saheb asked an important question – "The accused who is sitting here, is he known to you?" Baba said in affirmative.

"Baba, this accused says he stays with you. Is it true?" Sai Baba replied on a spiritual level! He said – "Cent percent true! Because I stay with everyone! Everyone is mine!"

"But this jewellery? It was found with him. He says you gave it to him."

"Right! I gave it. Joshi Saheb asked Baba again – "Baba, you just said you gave this jewellery to him. Then tell me how it came to you?"

With this question Sai Baba flared up! How will God ever like being questioned as to how a particular thing came to him or created. He had all along replied on human plane but now he was disgusted at the way he was implicated by a mere statement of a common thief. In fact, the accused had not visited Shirdi at all. He gave Sai Baba's name just because he heard it in the train from co-passengers. How can God testify against his own child? Sai Baba was angry and said, "How do you involve me in this? It is for you to find out from the accused. Why do you ask me?" Baba got up and left the place.

The judge was considerate. He recorded the statements of a few villagers and residents. None of them had seen the accused at Shirdi. He also verified the record of visitors to Shirdi and his name was not there.

By then Baba returned to the mosque. The judge told him – "Baba, we have completed our investigation! We find that the accused never visited Shirdi. Therefore it is impossible that he has got this jewellery from you."

"That is right! I have nothing to do with it," Baba replied.

The accused also confessed his crime and was later punished appropriately!

With these thoughts, Appa Kulkarni entered the mosque. Baba was distributing udhi from his ever burning 'dhuni' muttering a poem – 'Here comes Ram with bags of udhi, a remedy par excellence for every malady'. Baba was distributing udhi as a panacea for every illness!

On seeing Appa Kulkarni, Baba remarked – "Your anger does not help, Appa! Why do you shout at a mad chap? I will look into his accounts! I have everyone's account with me! Nana and Ganu – both will come here to settle their accounts! When you go over to Kopergaon again, give Nana the same message! Tell him I have called him here!" Appa Kulkarni realised that it is Baba's will that makes Nana and Ganesh Rao to reach Shirdi. He decided that he must keep on reminding Baba's message to Nana.

20

TAMING NANA SAHEB

*W*ith Sai Baba's permission, Appa Kulkarni went to Kopergaon. When he reached the revenue office, the deputy collector was preparing to leave on an official trip. Ganesh Rao was overseeing the loading of luggage into the tonga. During such trips, he would always accompany his boss. As Appa Kulkarni approached them, both had taken their seats in the tonga. Seeing Appa, Ganesh Rao mischievously asked him – "What Kulkarni Saheb? Are you here with one more message from Sai Baba?" Ganesh Rao used to take liberties with his boss. Both belonged to same caste and were deeply religious. Ganesh Rao was prejudiced against Sai Baba that he was a Muslim and still Hindus worshipped him. He had a grudge against Appa Kulkarni that he had slapped a clerk for speaking against Sai Baba. Moreover he knew that Nana Saheb hated Sai Baba as a Muslim fakir and had a feeling that the Dhulia magistrate had given him undue importance by appointing a commission to record his statement instead of dragging him to the court. Appa Kulkarni was aware of all this but because of his strong conviction that he must do Sai Baba's work, he ignored Ganesh Rao's rude behaviour. He just said – "Nana Saheb - at your convenience, Baba wants you to come and see him".

Nana curtly replied – "Kulkarni, I have already told you. If Sai Baba has some work with me, let him come and see me in my office. I am leaving on an official tour today. Let him see me on my return."

Appa Kulkarni noted the clear indifference on the part of Nana Saheb. He was of a strong mettle and was not easily discouraged! He just said – "Nana Saheb, it is all right. I will meet you again on your return. It will be nice if you meet Sai Baba once."

Nana Saheb's tonga started and Appa Kulkarni also left for Shirdi. The first halt for Nana Saheb was Harishchandragad – a hill close to Kopergaon. There was a Devi shrine on the top of the hill and Nana Saheb wanted to visit that temple on that day. It was a difficult terrain but both Nana and Ganesh Rao were confident of climbing. It was summer and the heat was unbearable.

As they started trekking up the hill, they felt the unbearable heat! They could not even see a single tree! It was all rocks and climbing through zigzag turnings. Both were exhausted and even the water they carried was over. Thirst, exhaustion made Nana Saheb tremble and he started gasping. His throat was dry and he almost fainted! Both were frightened as nowhere near they could get water.

In a feeble voice, Nana Saheb spoke – "Ganesh, could this be because we were indifferent to Sai Baba?" Ganesh Rao curtly dismissed it. He said – "Saheb, you are an educated person, why should you give importance to that mad fakir! It is only the scorching sun! Let us rest for a while"

But Nana Saheb was feeling guilty. His mind was thinking of Sai Baba! Without a drop of water to quench his thirst, he was sinking! He felt that his end was near! He started thinking of Appa Kulkarni and Sai Baba!

This was enough. Sai Baba at Shirdi visualised Nana Saheb's condition. He just told Appa Kulkarni who had returned from Kopergaon that Nana Saheb was dying for water. Appa offered as to whether he could run for his assistance. "No, no – Nana Saheb is far away from here. Let me see what I can do." He also advised Appa Kulkarni –

"Go home and take rest. Think of God! Think of God now!"
Appa wondered on Baba's advice!

On the Harishchandragad, Ganesh Rao was also
worried at the difficult situation. The condition of Nana
Saheb was critical! Neither he could go up nor could he
descend the hill. Ganesh Rao too was exhausted and could
not carry Nana Saheb down! As he was in this predicament,
he saw a Bhil tribal who came near them and looked at
Nana Saheb. In a sunken voice, Nana Saheb asked for water.
The tribal was about to go and bring water, but Ganesh Rao
commented to Nana Saheb that the tribal is an untouchable
and how can he accept water from him.

The Bhil turned back in fury! He said, "You brute, this
man is on the verge of death for want of water and you are
thinking in terms of touchable and untouchable. Only you
people are dividing man and man! God did not intend any
division". He curtly turned to go! Both felt that was not an
ordinary Bhil tribal. Must be God in that form!

Ganesh Rao offered his help "Saheb, I will go with him
and fetch some water. Have courage till then!" But Nana's
courage had left him and he collapsed. Ganesh Rao called
the Bhil. He turned and saw Nana's condition. He said –
"Remove the boulder on which your friend is lying. There
is water below it. Give it to him!"

Ganesh Rao quickly moved Nana Saheb aside and slid
the boulder. And there was a spring of water! He quenched
Nana's thirst and then drank it himself! Both felt that they
regained their life! They now remembered the Bhil tribal
and wanted to thank him. He was nowhere to be seen even
though the view of the hill was clear on all sides!

Indeed there was a turning point in Nana's mind. From
that moment onwards, he kept looking forward to Appa
Kulkarni's visit to Kopergaon!

Appa Kulkarni heard that Nana Saheb had returned from his official trip. Even though he was running very high temperature, he decided that he should visit Kopergaon and remind Nana Saheb about Sai Baba's message. When he went to seek Baba's permission to leave for Kopergaon, Baba spoke in a mystic manner – "Appa, be careful! Thieves have entered Shirdi. They will attack your house first! Why do you want to go?"

Appa Kulkarni was in a haste to go. He did not bother as to why Baba had spoken like that! He told him – "Baba, you look after my house. I will return soon after conveying your message to Nana Saheb. I do not know as to whether I will be able to do it later!"

Baba permitted him to go but said – "All right, all right! Go if you must! Think of God! Think of God now!" Baba got up from his seat and saw off Appa Kulkarni till the entrance of the mosque. Everyone was surprised at this strange behaviour of Baba!

Appa Kulkarni reached Kopergaon. He was running very high temperature. Without any hindrance, Ganesh Rao ushered him into the cabin of Nana Saheb. Appa Kulkarni noticed a change in the behaviour of both of them. On seeing Appa Kulkarni, Nana Saheb told him – "Kulkarni, you have come again and again with Sai Baba's message. Sai Baba must be having some important work with me. Please tell him that I will come soon."

Nana Saheb's words brought immense happiness to Appa Kulkarni. He felt greatly relieved that he has fulfilled Baba's assignment. As he happily got up and turned to go, he collapsed. Ganesh Rao rushed ahead to support him to rise up. When he placed his hands under Appa's armpit, his fingers almost scorched! He found two plague buboes! Taking Baba's name on his lips, Appa Kulkarni left this world!

The plague epidemic had started its havoc in Shirdi. Unfortunately Appa Kulkarni was the first victim. Madhava Rao, Tatya Kote and others carried home his dead body. His young wife wailed with grief! Appa Kulkarni had endeared himself to everyone! Nana Saheb promptly sent a medical team to Shirdi to prevent the epidemic. He felt sorry for Appa Kulkarni who had come thrice with Sai Baba's message. He thought as to how happy he was when he told him that he will meet Sai Baba soon. He decided to visit Shirdi as soon as the epidemic came under control.

At Shirdi, the entire village had assembled at the cremation of Appa Kulkarni. Baba too came there. Appa's wife lamented loudly! Baba pacified her – "Dear child, what was destined could not be avoided. I could see his end and that is why I told him to think of God. He would have been most unhappy if he had not gone to Kopergaon. Now he is relieved of the cycle of births and deaths. Do not cry my child. Your husband is not the only victim. Six more are going to be targets of this disease! That is Allah's will! The death has arrived and he will have his say!"

Baba's word came true! In the next seven days six more persons died! Shirdi bore a deserted look. The doubtfuls evacuated to safety and those with faith in Baba continued to stay there.

Soon life was normal again in Shirdi! Those who had evacuated returned and the villagers forgot their sorrow in the company of Sai Baba!

Nana Saheb Chandorkar wondered as to how he could visit Shirdi in the absence of Appa Kulkarni. He would never come to call him again. He also had received his transfer orders. He was being transferred to Pandharpur. So before going there, he had decided to meet Baba. He wanted to keep his word given to a dying man.

The next morning Nana Saheb Chandorkar and his orderly Ganesh Rao reached Shirdi. Sai Baba was busy preparing a medley of rice and daal in a big vessel kept on hearth for himself.. For this he had purchased from Nandu Marwadi's shop items like rice, pulses, salt, chillies, ghee, etc. Without taking anyone's help, he cleaned the rice, cut onions and chillies and poured all the ingredients into the vessel.

The villagers had gathered to receive prasad from Baba. He was also muttering a song to himself – "I go to Pandharpur, to live in Pandharpur, I go to Pandharpur." The vast crowd responded to Baba's singing and they too joined in chorus. The song went on as the water in the vessel boiled! As the song was in progress, Nana Saheb and Ganesh Rao entered the mosque. Madhava Rao took them near Baba and made them sit. Both were surprised at the song of Baba and were watching his cooking. They were also amazed that Baba put his bare hand right inside the boiling mixture and began stirring the medley as one would do with a ladle! When Baba took his hand out, nothing had happened to the hand. Baba's miracle brought down Nana Saheb's ego.

Covering the vessel with a lid, Sai Baba spoke to Nana Saheb – "So you have come at last – that too because you are going to Pandharpur!" Nana folded his hands and humbly offered his respects! Ganesh Rao did nothing of the sort.

Baba spoke – "Nana, that day at Harishchandraghad, you refused to accept water at my hands. Today you can accept this porridge. The entire village will be dining here." The whole village had come to dine. People expected a little prasad at the hands of Baba!

Nana Saheb was dumbfounded! He was thrilled with Baba's reference to Harishchandraghad where he had almost prayed to him for help and Baba had come in the guise of a Bhil tribal! Nana's ego completely melted and he kept his head on Baba's feet! Ganesh Rao too followed his master!

The mass lunch began. More than a thousand devotees had a sumptuous meal with only a little cooked medley prepared in a small vessel! The food lasted till everyone had to his heart's content!

Nana Saheb and Ganesh Rao did not partake it. Their orthodox practice came in their way!

21

GANGA FLOWS FROM BABA'S FEET

*N*ana Chandorkar was impressed with Sai Baba on his first visit to Shirdi. The very next day he took his wife and daughter for Baba's darshan. Ganesh Rao too accompanied them.

When Nana's daughter Maina was presented, Baba lifted her and made her sit on his lap and applied udhi on her forehead. The usual blessing 'Allah will be kind to you' was missing and Nana Saheb became restless. Time alone was to throw light on its significance.

In the meanwhile, Nana's wife offered her salutations to Baba. At home strict orthodox procedures were observed and Nana's father was furious that his son was taking his wife and daughter to a Muslim saint and had created a scene when they left for Shirdi!

An astrologer had predicted a bad future to Nana Saheb's daughter. She would become a widow in her young age and there is danger to her own life also after marriage! Having heard high about Sai Baba, Nana Saheb's wife had come to him with the hope that Baba will change her daughter's destiny. She insisted on her husband taking her and Maina to Baba in spite of opposition from her father-in-law. But Mania did not have Baba's blessings and nobody dare ask Baba about the significance of his applying dui on her forehead. Baba made them sit near him and spoke to Gnash Rae – "Well, constable Saheb, having very high plans!" Gnash Rae realized that Baba called him a constable as he was joining police service soon after. Similarly he also had a dream of rising to a sub inspector's post!

Baba spoke – "Gnu, you will join police force but you will become a cheap show-man! A Tamashawala! Why a Brahmin like you should become a policeman?" In these words Ganesh Rao witnessed Baba's omniscience! He had not even allowed Nana Chandorkar to know his fancy for 'Tamasha'! But Baba had exposed his innermost secret!

Nana Saheb intervened - "Baba, I have recommended him myself for a police job. He has been after me for quite some time." Baba told him – "Nana, you have done your duty, but Ganu will face a lot of difficulties. We do not want such a service for him"

Ganesh Rao was afraid that Nana Saheb may now intervene and may even stop his joining the police service. Hastily he pleaded – "Baba, I have already received my orders to join the police department. I cannot refuse it now. Soon after returning from Prayag, I will join my new posting."

"Going to Prayag? What for?" Baba asked. Ganesh Rao explained – "It is a very important place of pilgrimage for us, Hindus. Once I get into police service, I may not be able to get leave to go there."

"That is all right Ganu! But the entire world is a holy place. A man should bathe in this 'Tirtha Raj'. He should follow his own faith; he should observe the religion of humanity that brings him peace and prosperity! Why then he needs only a dip in Ganges?"

Ganesh Rao tried to explain the tenets of Hinduism and the special importance of taking bath in Ganga. But Baba tried to convince them that a Sadguru is the real destination of man's worldly pilgrimage! Ganesh Rao asked Baba – "If one does not go to Prayag where else he should go?"

Baba answered – "They reside in the lotus feet of a Sadguru." Ganesh Rao had a grudge that Sai Baba considers himself a 'Sadguru' as many Hindus bow down to his feet and he had a conviction that a Muslim cannot be a 'Sadguru' and bluntly asked Sai Baba – "How can these sacred rivers be in your feet?"

Baba calmly replied – "When you say 'Guru Brahma, Guru Vishnu, Gurudevo Maheswara' you confirm that Guru is Brahma, Guru is Vishnu and Guru is Maheshwara. There is another meaning that Brahma is Guru, Vishnu is also Guru and Maheshwara too is Guru! Brahma, Vishnu, and Maheshwara – are three different forms of the same God!" He gave a new meaning!

Baba continued – "Yesterday you saluted me considering me a form of God! At that time, you did not bother about my caste, creed and religion! Then what is wrong if Hindu devotees see in me these three forms and adore me as 'Sadguru'?" Baba put up a straight question.

Ganesh Rao now spoke bluntly – "Then your feet should be considered a sacred place of pilgrimage." Baba replied – "Right you are! That is why I say you have darshan of my feet and you will have the merit of visiting Prayag." Ganesh Rao was also outspoken – "Baba, I do not see Ganga or Yamuna in these two feet. May be I do not have the insight."

Baba happily said –"Good, at last you accept it! That is why one needs a spiritual guide!"

Ganesh Rao replied – "Baba, I will accept you as a spiritual guide, a Sadguru, provided I see Ganga and Yamuna within your feet! Your sacred feet must prove that they are 'Tirtha Raj Prayag' themselves!"

Ganesh Rao openly challenged Baba! Baba was not angry. He needed Ganesh Rao in his mission for the welfare of mankind. He decided to oblige him. The entire gathering of devotees got up to watch! There was now pin drop silence in the mosque! All eyes were fixed on Baba's feet. Baba stretched them and said – "All right Ganu, watch this pair of feet very carefully now! Look!"

The moment Baba uttered the last word, water gushed out from both the toes of his divine feet! Distinctly two different streams of Ganga and Yamuna! As their water flowed both the currents mingled into one and looked like the confluence of the great Ganga and Yamuna at Prayag! A wave of joy passed over the entire gathering which happily shouted jaikar to Baba.

The first to drink this sacred water was Nana Saheb's wife, followed by his daughter. Nana Saheb was amazed at this miracle and he was convinced of Baba's divinity but enslaved in rigid orthodox principles he just applied that water on his eyes and sprinkled over his head. Ganesh Rao did not even touch. But being convinced with Baba's divinity, he accepted him as his Sadguru. He visualised him as God Vithal of Pandharpur. Extempore, he composed a song on the glory of Sai Baba –

"Pandharpur, Pandharpur, Shirdi is my Pandharpur

Sainatha Sadguru, Ramaakant wonderful

Come one, come you all

Rush to his feet, where lies salvation

Ganu prays in his heart –

'O Sai, Sai Baba, let me never part from you'"

All devotees rushed forward to take the holy water. Madhava Rao, Tatya, Mhalsapathy regulated the crowd in a disciplined manner.

Ganesh Rao accepted his defeat. Now he prostrated to Baba's feet accepting him as 'Sadguru' – "Sainath you are my Sadguru indeed! Please initiate me into a 'Mantra' and accept me as your disciple."

Baba told him – "No! Never! Dear Ganu, I have never initiated anyone in a 'Mantra'. My own Guru has never done it! For twelve years I served him. He loved me and protected me. When I asked him for a 'Mantra', he called a barber and got my head shaved! Shaved my head and shaved my ego, and asked me for two copper coins! I wondered as to why he required two coins when he knew that I was penniless! How can I pay him? I was perplexed! He saw that. He told me that he does not need the money but the coins of *shraddha* and *saburi* – faith and patience! He clearly suggested that I should have these two qualities. Immediately I gave him what he wanted. No more conversation, nothing else to give or take! He would meditate and I would watch – from near or distance, always staring at him! This exactly was his 'Mantra'. During meditation he may close his eyes or keep them wide open! But his steadfast gaze always showered grace on me. His gaze took care of me as a mother tortoise feeds her children! She does not feed them in their mouths. Her mere gaze from a distance makes them grow and guards them even if they are on the other side of the river! Likewise, even if I do not initiate you into a 'mantra', I am always with you! You will have my protection forever! Remember this much – YOU LOOK TO ME – I LOOK TO YOU!"

The devotees listened to every word of this great piece of advice with rapt attention. On account of Ganesh Rao, everybody had a feast of an important discourse by Baba! Baba's great saying – 'You look to me, I look to you' came into existence on this momentous day!

22

DASA GANU'S DEVELOPMENT

*N*ana Chandorkar decided to visit Shirdi once again next day before taking charge at Pandharpur. He reached home in an ecstatic mood. He wanted to convince his father about Baba's divinity. But when he reached home, he found to his dismay his father had left for their home town Kalyan, in protest against Nana Saheb going to a Muslim fakir. This enabled Nana to discuss freely with his wife about Sai Baba. Both were happy with their visit to Shirdi. In this mood they did not even think of the disturbing forecast about their daughter Maina. They surrendered to the will of God. This would be the attitude of whoever comes in contact with a Loving God like Sai Baba.

Ganesh Rao wanted to go to bed early as he had desired to go to Baba next morning. Generally he would keep awake late every night. When night fell, people of cheap show-world would take him to the town for their shows. He had a place of honour amongst them as he composed erotic songs and others in low taste. It brought him good income from these show people! Ganesh Rao knew that his poetic talents had no place in the higher strata of society.

Today he had an invitation for such a show. It was written by him and was being enacted that night. Returning from Shirdi, he felt like going there. But the vision of Ganga and Yamuna flowing from Baba's feet had haunted him so much that he was eager to compose a song on Baba rather than watch a rubbish play! His erotic thinking unknowingly chose words of devotional description that surpassed his earlier compositions. He completed and read out to himself. The song began with various attributes and facets, praying ultimately to Baba to save the poet from his worldly miseries. It thus began

"O Sadguru Sainath with unlimited powers
You are a saviour of all the 'living'
How wonderfully flowed those rivers
From your feet – your toes divine!
They are Prayag – the holy 'Tirtha Raj'!
You are Vishnu, the causer and the cause!"

Ganesh Rao concluded the song with an appeal to Baba –

"With such 'Leelas' like the play of Trinity,
Displays Baba with his doubtless divinity!
Even so, my mind thither wanders
I pray Thee Sai, fix it at yours
Sinner I am, yet your slave Dasa Ganu
Spare me, save me, O Saviour Sadguru!"

While humming his gifted composition in his own mother tongue, Ganesh Rao did not know when he dozed off. First time in his life he could sleep so easily, as all along his erotic poetry would only raise his passions and make him spend restless nights! The devotional composition had brought him immense peace of mind!

Ganesh Rao got up late next morning and so had to hurry through his morning tasks to join Nana Saheb Chandorkar and his family to visit Sai Baba on the third successive day. Nana Saheb who virtually refused to visit Shirdi was now eagerly looking forward to have darshan of Sai Baba!

As they climbed the steps of the mosque, a small purse which Baba used to hide, was lying open before him. It contained nine old one-rupee coins out of which six were lying aside. Three were in Baba's hands which he was busy rubbing. His continuous rubbing had made them shine lustrously. The six lying below were tarnished and dull. Once Madhava Rao had asked about the significance of Baba rubbing only three coins. Baba had told him that he is polishing the devotion of three of them – Madhava Rao himself, Mhalsapathy and Tatya! Madhava Rao was extremely happy at this, as Baba used to polish those three coins every day. Today, as Nana Saheb Chandorkar and Ganesh Rao entered the mosque, Baba took two more coins from the other dull six. Madhava Rao who watched every move of Sai Baba realised that Baba had added two more devotees!

Baba made Nana Saheb and Ganesh Rao sit near him. Then he asked Ganesh Rao as to what he scribbled on the previous night. Ganesh Rao replied that he composed a song on the previous day's Ganga – Yamuna event. On Baba's direction, Ganesh Rao sang it.

It was all new and surprising to Nana Saheb. Only yesterday he had learnt of Ganesh Rao's talents. Today when he heard his extempore song and the singing by Ganesh Rao, he was very happy that his orderly is a Master Poet and singer. Everyone liked the song. But Baba's remarks at the end of the song shocked Nana! He felt aggrieved.

Baba said – "Ganu, you are such a beautiful poet and yet you take pride in composing erotic songs for people of lower taste! What a tragedy of a divine gift?" Ganesh Rao was embarrassed! He had kept this a secret from Nana Saheb! He was afraid that Baba would now expose him.

Baba further said – "You compose erotic songs, write cheap plays and watch filthy shows! Ganu dear, God has gifted you with a gifted pen – not for writing dirty stuff, but for praising His glory through beautiful compositions. Write devotional songs and sing them with devotion! Praise and sing the greatness of saints in kirtans! My Eakir will look after your welfare! Will you not listen to me?"

Baba's appealing advice touched the core of Ganesh Rao. He was fond of composing erotic poetry. But now Sai Baba's omniscience dominated his imagination. He was a changed man! He started thinking that he was wasting his birth as a Brahmin in composing cheap dirty stuff for Tamashawallas! He decided that he should compose devotional songs and become a good Kirtankar.

Ganesh Rao noticed the sign of annoyance in Nana Saheb's face. He turned to him and told him – "Saheb, pardon me! I kept this a secret from you. Poetry is my natural instinct! I am sorry that I found a place of honour among Tamashawallas! You respected me, loved me and treated me never suspecting that I cater to low taste audiences. I dared not tell you the truth because you would not have liked it! Please excuse me! I now swear in the name of Sai Baba that I will never again compose erotic songs! Neither will I attend those filthy shows! Believe me – I promise!"

An oath in the name of Baba melted Nana Saheb's wrath! Though an orderly of his office, he had treated Ganesh Rao with respect, sought his company on his visits to temples and sacred places, participation in religious functions, never once suspecting that Ganesh Rao was a cheap show man! So this exposure had given him a jolt! But his promise satisfied Nana Saheb.

He said – "In Baba's presence you have given the promise. Stick to it." Baba intervened – "Nana, he has promised you – not me!"

Ganesh Rao said , "Baba, what is this? I am your 'Dasa' – a slave". Baba responded – "Yes, yes! I have heard that! You have called yourself 'Dasa Ganu' at the end of the song! You are Dasa – but of Ganu, that is yourself! Not of Sai Baba! Or else you would have listened to me and rejected the police job!" Baba's pun on 'Dasa Ganu' stunned Ganesh Rao. But still he was adamant. He defended himself – "Baba, let me join the police force. I have waited all these years. Now my real life starts."

Baba said – "No, no! Ganu, police service is not your life! Anyway you will not agree! Some day you will come to me, when you are in trouble."

While Baba and Ganesh Rao were conversing, a Marwari family came up for Baba's darshan. After the husband paid his respects to Baba, his wife took out the veil on her face and kept her head on Baba's feet. Charmed with her exquisite beauty, Nana Saheb fixed his gaze on her. But soon he was afraid that Baba might notice it, he turned aside and looked in some other direction. But even then he was restless and stealthily looked at her again and again! As the Marwari family talked with Baba, Nana Saheb felt ashamed and got up to move to another place. But Baba made him sit near him forcibly. Nana Saheb's condition became pitiable. He could not even look at the direction of the Marwari family. Feeling guilty, he looked down in shame till the visitors left.

However he was trying to control his wandering mind by muttering to himself a few verses from the Gita. Nana Saheb was well versed in the Gita, Upanishads and other scriptures. But vast learning alone is not enough to control the mind! On seeing his restlessness, Baba gave a hidden warning – "By and by it will be all right!"

As the Marwari family left, Baba turned to Nana Saheb and asked him – "Now tell me, Nana, How was your mother? The one who had come just now?" This question instantly pulled up Nana Saheb's fallen mind from the depth of mean thoughts to the crown of noble thinking! Nana Saheb realised that if only he had thought of that woman as his mother, he would have enjoyed the most sublime sentiment of mother's love! Baba's mode of teaching brought tears of gratitude! No anger! No reproach! No exposure!

Baba used different methods to correct his devotees in their behaviour depending on the person. To bring down Swami Somadev's ego, he used contempt, while for Madhava Rao he corrected his attitude towards Bhagoji Shinde. Seriousness for some, humour for others! A miracle for one, a dream for another!

Baba's way of teaching through humour was also unique! Anna Chinchnikar, who was past in his fifties, was once massaging Baba's right hand. His wife was sitting next to him. Many devotees would have such an opportunity to serve Baba. All were equal and they used to freely mix and render service to Sai Baba. Everybody awaited an opportunity to get a chance to sit near Sai Baba. Some would press his feet, some would knead his abdomen, some would rub his back and some would massage his hands!

Once Baba was resting near the railing of the verandah of the mosque, stretching his legs and having a pillow at the back. Anna Chinchnikar was massaging Baba's right hand. Sitting at the left was Venubai Kaujalgi, an aged widow who kneaded Baba's abdominal muscles. Without an adequate space they were virtually cramped.

This old mother Venubai Kaujalgi was popularly called 'Mausi' by everybody. Her way of kneading Baba's abdominal muscles was unique. She used to give full pressure on Baba's belly as if she was kneading the ball of flour to make papads! Because of her sincere devotion, Baba endured her massaging! Once someone remarked that she would kill Baba the way in which she is applying pressure on his belly! Baba was furious. He took his club and rested on its one end as if it is going to pierce his abdomen! Madhava Rao rushed and prevented a tragedy. The devotee who criticised Venubai Kaujalgi apologised and since that day nobody criticised her!

One day Venubai Kaujalgi was kneading Baba's abdomen in her usual manner and heaved up and down to do that. Anna Chinchnikar, on the other side, was also bending again and again in massaging Baba's right hand. As both were sincerely engaged in doing their service to Baba, unknowingly their faces were coming close to each other. Venubai Kaujalgi noticed and remarked in a lighter vein – "What Anna, you have become old but still you want to kiss me! What a shame? That too in front of your wife!"

This sparked a fire. Anna Chinchnikar was furious. He got up and shouted – "You old hog! You have lost all senses! You are talking this filth as you have a sin on your mind." Venubai Kaujalgi also lost her temper. Words clashed and voices thundered! Baba watched it all and enjoyed. At last he intervened and said – "Anna, why create a scene over an innocent fun? Why should you feel ashamed to kiss your own mother?"

The tense atmosphere in the mosque exploded with a bomb of laughter! Anna Chinchnikar felt ashamed of his act and the unnecessary fuss he created! He now realised that he should have told Venubai Kaujalgi – "O my mother, what is wrong if your son kissed you? Kiss me, mother, kiss me again and again!"

This is how Baba taught his devotees!

Nana Chandorkar wondered what answer he had for Baba's question – "How was your mother – the one who had just now come?" Baba himself said – "Nana, that mother reminded you the Gita and you muttered a few verses. Indeed Nana Chandorkar muttered a few verses from the Gita to forget the memory of that lady. Baba's question was difficult to answer and he kept quiet. Baba saw that and said – "Recite it loud, Nana! Let us hear the Gita."

Nana Chandorkar thought that Baba would not understand the Sanskrit text. But he remembered as to how Baba interpreted *Guru Brahma, Guru Vishnu, Gurudevo Maheswara* on the previous day. Hence he told him – "Baba,

I was repeating the fourth chapter of the Gita in Sanskrit. If you desire, I will explain it in Marathi."

Baba said – "No, no! Recite that in Sanskrit only! You can repeat the same stanza which you just muttered."

Nana Chandorkar recited the thirty-fourth stanza of the fourth chapter of the Gita with a free loud throat – *Tadvidhi Pranipatena Pariprasnena Sevaya – Upadesyanti Te Jnanam Jnanistatvadarshinah.*

Baba appreciated it and asked him to explain the meaning. Nana Chandorkar said – "This means that when a disciple who offers his complete life in the service of the Guru, kneels at his feet in reverence with a problematic question, the wise Guru communicates his knowledge to him as he has realised the Divine Truth!"

Baba said – "How wonderful? Let me understand the meaning of every word therein. I shall understand it better from a scholar like you! 'Tadvidhi' means with respect. This I understand. But what does *pata* mean?"

Nana said – 'pata' means kneeling down."

Baba inquired – "And what about *pranipata*. Nana replied – "pranipata also means kneeling down." Baba continued – "That means pranipata and pata mean the same, i.e. kneeling down." Nana asserted – "Of course"

Baba continued - "Nana, Vyasa must be a mad chap! When he could have managed with one word why did he put an auxiliary word before pata?"

Nana could not make out what was in Baba's mind! What point is there in analysing every word of Sanskrit? It was his feeling that Baba has no knowledge of Sanskrit. Nana himself had just studied what other exponents had explained! Baba's next question came up as Nana pondered on this – "And, Nana, what is that prasna?" Nana replied – "'Prasna' means question!" Baba asked him – "And *pariprasna* also has the same meaning!" Nana replied in affirmative.

"Same thing again! Once more an auxillary word! Has Vyasa really gone mad?" With Baba's questions coming one after the other, Nana was now perplexed! His confidence of his mastery over Sanskrit was shaken.

Baba himself continued – "Nana, 'Pariprasna' does not merely mean kneeling down with reverence. It means kneeling with reverential humility and sincerity! Just bowing down with reverence will not induce a Guru to part with his knowledge. Similarly the word *priprasnena* could not simply mean a question, but questioning with an intense urge! And that too *sevaya*, i.e. with a gratifying service! On fulfillment of all these conditions, then only a Guru will part with his knowledge."

Baba's explanation dissecting every word humbled Nana who now listened to him with complete surrender. He realised that Baba had mastery over Sanskrit language.

Baba continued – "Lord Krishna repeatedly told Arjuna that 'I am you'. When Arjuna was also a part of that great knowledge, where was the need to initiate him? Hence Lord Krishna preferred to enlighten Arjuna on his ignorance only so that he sees the Divine Knowledge within himself".

Nana Saheb pointed out – "But Baba, nowhere in this stanza there is a reference to ignorance."

Baba clarified – "Why not? Krishna has used the word *jnana*. The opposite of it is *ajnana*. If you incorporate this?"

Nana recited – "It will then mean 'Upadeshyanti te Ajnanam'."

Baba told him that now Nana was on the right track. Nana was surprised that even Shankara Bhashya, Anandagiri, Shridhar and other exponents of the Gita had missed this great truth, which Baba explained in simple words.

Baba continued – "Nana, the knowledge of divine is like pure water covered with moss. Removal of it exposes the clean water below! On that day in Harishchandraghad, I asked you to remove the boulder to find the water that was already there! The same is with divine knowledge! Guru never imparts that into you. Guru removes the ignorance that conceals Him within you. Lust, anger, pride, jealousy, attachment and delusion form the basis of ignorance. Removal of these six passions enables us to experience 'Self' within ourselves and within everyone else. It leads us to experience that blissful oneness with all – 'Aham Brahmasmi' – I am Brahma!"

Baba was feeding this nectar of spiritual knowledge to all in the pretext of advising Nana Chandorkar. Nana understood that it was for his passions. Ganesh Rao felt the advice for him to melt his ego. Everyone in the mosque visualised Lord Krishna expounding the Gita!

Turning to Nana, Baba asked him – "What did Arjuna say to Krishna at the conclusion of the Gita?" Nana replied – *Nashto Mohaha Gato Sandehaha*. Baba shook his head with a happy approval – "Nana, now you see it for yourself! Arjuna says – 'my doubts, my delusions, my ignorance has disappeared'. He has not said, 'I have acquired the knowledge'. Now you can see for yourself that Guru does not initiate a disciple but only points out to him the ignorance so that he sees the divine behind its veil!"

While Baba was busy interpreting the Gita, he was polishing two dull coins which now had acquired luster. Madhava Rao had watched it carefully that ever since Nana Chandorkar and Ganesh Rao had entered the mosque, those two coins were well polished. Nana and Ganesh Rao also felt that Sai Baba was a cent percent Hindu saint!

At that time, Baba called a person sitting in the crowd
– "Come here Anwar! Sit near me. Tell me why you intend
going to Baghdad leaving your family here?" Anwar Khan
was surprised with Baba's sudden question! Only today he
had arrived from a village in Berar. He came with a secret
desire to get initiated from Baba a passage from Quran and
then going to Baghdad. Baba read his mind and made him
sit before him. He gave him the lesson – *Bismillah Kuliya Hilo
Walka Firado Bhabudana......* Anwar Khan found it difficult to
understand it and then Baba called Abdulla and explained
him to teach it to him. Then he went near dhuni and began
to recite Quran himself.

Nana realised that Baba did not like himself to be
branded as being Hindu! In no time the mosque which
resounded with the Gita was transformed to reciting Quran,
clearly convincing that Ram and Rahim are two names of
the same Almighty!

23

TEACHING WITH DIVINE EXPERIENCES

*W*ith implicit faith in Sai Baba and pleasant memories of his three visits to Shirdi, Nana Saheb Chandorkar joined his new posting at Pandharpur. His thoughts were always hovering around Sai Baba. Due to his official position and wide network of contacts in the higher strata of society, Nana Saheb was responsible for many people going over to Shirdi to seek Baba's blessings. Baba's fame spread on a large scale among the general public.

Sai Baba wanted poor, weak, needy and the devout to come to him more as he was interested in their welfare and to get such people he wanted the services of Ganesh Rao Sahasrabuddhe.

Ganesh Rao called himself 'Dasa Ganu'. But he disregarded Baba's advice and joined police service. He had always a fascination for police uniform and the style in which they commanded respect from others. He forgot the fact that it will increase ego which will retard his spiritual progress. After coming in contact with Baba, he made an in-depth study of *Ramayana, Mahabharata, Bhagavat Gita* and others but was still enmeshed in his ego.

After joining police service he passed a departmental examination. He was looking forward to becoming a sub inspector soon. But an event happened which brought down his prospectus!

Ganesh Rao considered himself very intelligent and considered below his dignity to seek official permission for sundry acts. Once he was on duty near Godavari river and wished to visit a temple on the other side of the river which was in Nizam's territory. In spite of the advice by his colleague he did not seek permission and boldly crossed into the Nizam's territory. While returning he was shocked to see from a distance that his official superior was waiting for him to question. He could foresee a punishment of suspension from service and even imprisonment for his lapse! He remembered Sai Baba, took Godavari water in his hands and prayed to him to save him this time and took an oath that he will surely obey Baba!

Baba responded! At that moment a Munshif from Nizam territory rushed to Ganesh Rao and sought his help in arresting three thieves who were sharing the bounty under a tree. As Baba sent an opportunity, Ganesh Rao went back to the Nizam's territory and helped in nabbing the thieves. This saved him from the wrath of his official superior, as he told him that he had gone to nab a few thieves at the request of the Munshif from Nizam's territory. This also earned him a good name in the department and an award from the Nizam for nabbing the thieves! Ganesh Rao was considered a brave man and was promoted as a member of the special squad spying on the dacoits.

After some days he had to go to a place and his route was across Shirdi. As he neared Shirdi, he remembered the vow he took in Godavari river when he was in trouble in the Nizam's state that if Baba saved him on that occasion, he would obey him to the core. Hence he decided to avoid meeting Baba. If he met Baba, he will remind his oath and it would be a difficult situation. Since he had a promotion very recently, he wanted to make the best use of it.

But Baba was more than a match for such persons! As Ganesh Rao was crossing Shirdi, Baba suddenly ran towards the main road and intercepted Ganesh Rao. "Well Ganu, you wanted to avoid me?" Feeling guilty, Ganesh Rao told him that he was in a hurry. Baba reminded him about his oath by taking Godavari water. Ganesh Rao pleaded that he has just got the promotion and is about to settle in life. Moreover, he is entrusted with an important duty of nabbing a dangerous dacoit Khanya.

Baba just replied – "Ganu, you do not listen to me! I must do something myself! I must drive a peg into you. When it pains, you will come round. Go now. I will do what I want." With head bent down, Ganesh Rao left the place. Even then his ego did not diminish and he had one goal in his mind of becoming a sub inspector.

Ganesh Rao was entrusted with the spying squad for collecting information about a dacoit Khanya Bhil. As the police spied on the dacoits, they also used to watch the police movements and in the process many policemen had lost their lives. Moreover the villagers were scared of dacoits and prejudiced against the police. Mostly they were unco-operative with the police.

Once Ganesh Rao got the information that Khanya dacoit and his associates frequently visited a village, Loni Varni, where Khanya's mother lived. The village was small and as Khanya dacoit had spent his childhood there, villagers were friendly to him. Ganesh Rao and his associates disguised themselves as mendicants. Sending his associates to neighbouring villages, Ganesh Rao himself went to Loni Varni and stayed in the Rama temple there. As mendicants, travellers and visitors stayed in the Rama temple, nobody attached any importance to Ganesh Rao staying there. He was also happy that Khanya dacoit's mother stayed in a house just opposite the temple and from his place he could watch him in close quarters.

Late in the night, Khanya and his associates visited the village. He visited his mother's place and told her that police are after him and he has already killed three of them who had disguised themselves as sadhus. Ganesh Rao was terrified to hear this information as his colleagues have been killed! Khanya's mother told him that a Ramdasi is staying in the Rama temple. Immediately, Khanya came and inquired about Ganesh Rao. Though he was frightened, Ganesh Rao told him that he was a kirtankar on a pilgrimage to Kashi! Khanya wanted to verify it. He summoned all the villagers to hear a religious discourse by this Ramdasi!

The kirtan started. Ganesh Rao prayed to Sai Baba again to help him. He started with prayers to Ganesh and Sai Baba. Prose and music are the basis of kirtan. Ganesh Rao perfectly followed the procedure, style and order. At length, he narrated the advent of Datta and ended up with a reference to Sai Baba. Sai Baba's name had already spread to Loni Varni and the villagers were highly impressed by his kirtan!

While performing the kirtan, Ganesh Rao could study Khanya from a close distance! He made a very quick mental note of the special markings on Khanya's face, his peculiarities while talking, walking and laughing and all such things that go in making a police report perfect!

Khanya was convinced that he was a real Ramdasi and a Kirtankar. At the end aarti was performed. The dakshina plate was full of coins and everyone bowed to Ganesh Rao.

When Khanya placed his head on Ganesh Rao's feet, he could see the shoe mark on the feet and immediately realised that he was a policeman in disguise. He roared with anger and called him a 'police dog'. He took out his rifle to shoot point blank at Ganesh Rao. Ganesh Rao trembled in terror. He went and hugged the idol of Lord Rama from behind and prayed to Sai Baba – "Sai Ram, please save me." The villagers ran away from the scene to avoid seeing a shoot out!

Aiming precisely at Ganesh Rao, Khanya dacoit wanted to avoid hitting Rama's idol. But what he saw thrilled him. Rama's idol vanished and Sai Baba was standing there. Sai Baba was beckoning Khanya dacoit not to press the trigger! With it Sai Baba vanished and the idol of Rama stared at him with love! Khanya's heart melted. He looked at Ganesh Rao and found him already half dead with fear! He brought down his gun, prostrated before Rama's idol and warned Ganesh Rao – "Listen police dog, I leave you today! Do not come in my way! Or else, I will cut you into pieces!"

Khanya was certain that this coward Brahmin would soon give up his job with this warning. Khanya and his associates galloped away into the darkness of the night.

Next morning the villagers found that Ramdasi too had left without any traces!

24

URUS AND RAMA NAVAMI

*E*ven after he stared at death with Khanya dacoit, Ganesh Rao's ambition to become a sub inspector of police did not diminish! With that miraculous escape from Khanya, he firmly believed that Sai Baba is protecting him in all difficult situations and this enhanced his confidence! He prepared an excellent report on Khanya giving details of his physical features, his places of hiding, his accomplices, his visits to Loni Varni village to call on his mother etc.,! He mentioned as to how clearly he got him engaged in a kirtan and all that! He did not mention as to how at the end Khanya would have killed him! He had boasted that he had fooled the dacoit and slipped from his clutches to safety. Ganesh Rao's official superiors appreciated his work.

Based on the information given by Ganesh Rao, the government laid a siege with armed police around Khanya's hiding place. A fierce fight took place in which several policemen lost their lives and virtually eliminated the entire dacoit force except their chieftain Khanya himself! He absconded!

This news frightened Ganesh Rao. He knew that Khanya would slaughter him into pieces as warned by him. Therefore he sought the help of his old boss, Nana Saheb Chandorkar in getting transferred back to civil police!

Soon Ganesh Rao was transferred as an assistant officer in a taluk police station. This police station was assigned with the duties of keeping a watch on criminals, to record complaints from public, to collect fines and such other work. Being a taluk police station it was a small office with only a staff of three. A sub inspector, an assistant that was Ganesh Rao and a constable. In the absence of the sub inspector Ganesh Rao would be officiating as the master and he would behave as he liked! And he took pride in that!

Sai Baba had saved Ganesh Rao twice because he needed him for his work. Now he wished to make him resign his police job under any circumstances. Accordingly a situation arose that led to Ganesh Rao's resignation.

One day the sub inspector went on leave and Ganesh Rao was in charge of the station. Ganesh Rao was in a happy mood and went for a joy walk leaving the station to his constable. After he left, a person from a village Munshiff came with thirty-two rupees collected as fine to be deposited in the police treasury. As both the officers were not there the constable collected the amount and told the depositor that the receipt would be sent later. Since no one had seen him receiving the money the constable pocketed the amount!

After a few days it was discovered that this money was not credited in the treasury. A warrant was issued against the person who was to pay the fine. The person promptly produced the Munshiff's receipt. The Munshiff informed his superiors that the money was deposited in the police station. On further inquiry it was found that the sub inspector was on leave on that day and naturally Ganesh Rao was held responsible for the fraud. Though he did not know anything about it, he could not disown his responsibility as he was absent off the record without proper sanction of any authority. Thus Ganesh Rao was charged with embezzlement of government money. This smashed his dream of becoming a sub inspector once and for all. To avoid jail punishment he had to pay the amount and a fine also. He had to resign from service also, as there was no other option!

Ganesh Rao remembered Baba's words – "Ganu, I will have to drive a peg into you! Once that pains you will come to me!" Ganesh Rao knew that Sai Baba has arranged his ouster from police force! Ganesh Rao was feeling miserable as to what he would do without a job. Even though he did not have any children, his wife was dependent on him. At last, he decided to go to Shirdi to seek Baba's help!

At Shirdi, a large congregation of devotees had gathered to celebrate 'Rama Navami' – the birthday of Prabhu Ram! When devotees asked Sai Baba as to his birthday, he told them to celebrate Rama's birthday as his birthday. Hindus and Muslims joyously participated in celebrating 'Rama Janmotsav'.

Sai Baba had kept his religion and caste a secret. He could not be called a Hindu as he preferred to stay in a mosque. He performed 'Namaz' and taught Quran to Abdulla, and would freely use Islamic terms – Allah Malik, Mera Fakir, *Yaad-e-Huque'* etc., Even the food he prepared was sanctified with Muslim rituals. While dining with Hindus, he would make Bade Baba sit with him to remove any communal tinge to the gathering

If you consider Sai Baba as a Muslim, he was burning fire in the 'dhuni'. He would do aarti in the mosque. Hindus recited the Gita, Ramayana and other scriptures. While passing through the village, whenever he came across Hindu temples, Sai Baba would stop and fold his hands in reverence. Sai Baba made both the communities guessing that he belonged to their own community!

To strengthen the impact of non-communal behaviour, Baba attracted both Hindus and Muslims through many miracles. He was very particular that they followed their religious practices regularly, like insisting Brahmin devotees to perform 'sandhya vandana' and Muslims to perform namaz, etc.

Baba never liked conversion from one faith to another. When a Hindu devotee who embraced Islam came to him, he straightaway scolded – 'Are you not ashamed to change your father?' Even so he would encourage the Hindus and Muslims to celebrate their festivals and would advise them to participate in the functions of each other!

An excellent example of this was Gopala Rao Gund – a Hindu gentleman who thought of starting a Muslim fair, urus in Shirdi. He was childless first and by Baba's grace he got a son. To celebrate that event, he thought of starting the Urus. Many Hindu devotees like Madhava Rao, Tatya Kote, Mhalsapathy, and others supported the idea. Baba's permission was also obtained. An application was sent to the district collector for permission. They did not get a green signal since the village Kulkarni strongly opposed holding of urus on the ground that there are only two wells and one well is useless! Baba heard this, took a few flowers kept in the niche of the mosque, and threw it into the well which was considered useless. Sai Baba's blessings made the polluted water purified and water filled up to the brink!

Once again an application was made. The public health authorities checked the quality of water and found it satisfactory. Therefore permission for holding the urus was granted. Sai Baba desired that Hindus celebrate Rama Navami and Muslims urus on the same day! A committee was formed and a Mumbai devotee Amir Shukkur was entrusted with the supervision of urus, as he was well versed with the famous urus festival of Magdam Baba held at Mahim in Mumbai.

Amir Shukkur belonged to Korhale village in Kopergaon taluk. He was a butcher by profession and went to Mumbai. He earned a lot of money as a broker in Bandra slaughter house at Mumbai. He developed a disease called rheumatoid arthritis characterised with pain in all joints. After all treatments failed, he went to Sai Baba. The moment

he climbed the steps of the mosque, Baba started muttering
– "Here comes my man! Go anywhere to earn money but do
not forget your mother! You say why meet Sai Baba! I am
going to Magdam Baba! I am Magdam, I am Iswar, and I am
Rahim!" Amir Shukkur realised the clairvoyance of Baba
and surrendered to him. Baba assured him – "Dwarakamai
will make you hale and healthy! Go and stay in chawadi for
nine months! Do not come to this mosque."

Amir Shukkur who rolled in wealth stepped into the
chawadi to stay but was shocked with what he saw! It was
a dilapidated structure! The four walls were partially fallen!
The roof had a number of leakages! The floor was rough and
damp! The verandah was occupied by lepers, beggars and
fakirs! It had free access to scorpions and snakes! This was
the place suggested by Baba to Amir Shukkur for curing
his rheumatoid arthritis! In this chawadi he would have the
company of Abdulla and Mhalsapathy along with Baba on
alternate nights!

Though Amir Shukkur was nervous at first, he soon
forgot about his comforts in view of his daily adoration to
Sai Baba and the hope that this Loving God would cure his
malady in nine months!

On the very first day of his stay, in the night when
everyone was fast asleep in the chawadi in the company
of Baba, Amir Shukkur suddenly heard his shouts and
hitting of his wooden club! Baba was shouting – "Abdulla,
how could you sleep? A ghost is near my bed! Find out!" A
lantern was lit and Abdulla searched all over. Nothing was
found but Baba was still hitting with his club. It so happened
that a cobra was lying coiled near the bed of Amir Shukkur.
He was terribly frightened. The cobra was finally killed.
Baba was once again calm and everyone went to sleep. This
doubly convinced Amir Shukkur that Baba is taking care of
him.

Amir Shukkur decided to obey Baba at any cost! But it was not that easy! To pass nine months within the four walls of a dilapidated structure except for attending nature's call was indeed a punishment for Amir Shukkur! Very soon he was fed up with it. His mind revolted against his decision and then on one night, when Baba was not in the chawadi, he slipped out of Shirdi! He walked all the way to Kopergaon with the intention of going back to Mumbai. In the night, he decided to stay at a public rest house where travellers, mendicants, and beggars stayed for night!

At the entrance of the rest house, he saw an old man lying down in pain, gasping for breath. Out of pity, Amir Shukkur offered his help. He sought water in a groaning voice. Amir Shukkur saw an earthen pot with water and a tumbler in the verandah. He took a tumbler of water, lovingly took the head of the old man on his lap, and made him drink it! Next moment, he yelled with pain and died on the lap of Amir Shukkur!

Amir Shukkur was frightened! He feared that as the old man died on his lap he would be prosecuted for the murder of this innocent old man! Instantly he threw the corpse down and getting up started running back towards Shirdi with Baba's name on his lips! A few moments back he had fearlessly walked to Kopergaon. Now he was frozen with fear and ran back to Shirdi by dawn! In this tension, his joint pain too did not bother him! Villagers were in deep slumber and did not know as to when he left and returned!

Sai Baba who had taken upon himself the responsibility of Amir Shukkur's welfare was wide awake enjoying the fun of pulling him back to where he had fixed him! Next evening, Baba on seeing Amir Shukkur remarked – "Rascal, you slaughtered animals at Mumbai and now kill innocent fakir too!" Amir Shukkur was stunned at Baba's omniscience! He stayed for full nine months at the chawadi and came out hale and healthy. On Baba's advice he gave up his business in a slaughter house and took up other assignments. He visited Shirdi regularly thereafter. The villagers entrusted the important responsibility of conducting the urus to Amir Shukkur.

Under Amir Shukkur's guidance preparations for urus began in right earnest. Flags, buntings, banners all over the village, sweet-meat shops, toy shops, flower decorations, tents for stay of outstation devotees, letters to devotees, invitations to wrestlers – all such things were done meticulously! Hindus and Muslims worked in total harmony for the success of this festival.

It was the day of Rama Navami! Thousands arrived at Shirdi learning that urus will be held. Shehnai was being played near the mosque since morning. The festival was to be inaugurated with the procession of flags. Two main flags and hundred others were to be carried in procession through the village. Two main flags – one white and another saffron were gifted by Damuanna Rasane and Nana Saheb Nimonkar respectively.

Damuanna Rasane was a well known coppersmith from Ahmednagar. He had no children even after marrying two women. The astrologers had predicted no children for him. Someone suggested to him to seek Baba's blessings. Just before he arrived at the mosque, someone had presented a basket of mangoes to Baba. Baba kept aside two mangoes and distributed the rest among devotees. Nobody dared touch those two mangoes as Baba blurted out – "My Damya will come from Nagar and give those to his wife. She will eat and die!" Damuanna Rasane arrived and heard Baba's blurting. He took those two mangoes and asked Baba as to whom they should be given – the elder or the younger of his wives. Baba asked him to give them to the second wife and predicted that he will have two sons – Daulatshah and Tanshah. Even when Muslim names were suggested

Damuanna Rasane obeyed Baba's command and his faith paid him dividends.

The impossibility of getting children becoming a reality made Damuanna Rasane a devoted slave for the rest of his life. Later he would not move without Baba's advice even in his business matters. An intimate friend wanted him to invest one lakh rupees in cotton trade and promised a net profit of two lakhs! Damuanna Rasane wrote a letter to Baba seeking his concurrence. Baba told Shama to advice him not to invest. Damuanna Rasane personally came to Shirdi and while sitting in front of Baba mentally vowed that he would offer a portion of his profit to Baba. Even this thought as it reached Baba made him say – "Do not think of making me a party to your business." This settled the issue and he did not invest the money. Later Damuanna Rasane learnt that his friend incurred great loss! Damuanna Rasane's mind was filled with a deep sense of gratitude for saving him from a disaster! Similarly someone asked him to join in grain business and there also Baba dissuaded him. Therefore, throughout his life, Damuanna Rasane did no business without Baba's approval!

To express his gratitude to Sai Baba, Damuanna Rasane contributed to a portion of the expenses for the urus and also gifted a large flag.

The other big flag was presented by Nana Saheb Nimonkar. He was a hereditary officer holding rewarded estate in Nimgaon in Sangamner district. The British government had nominated him as honorary magistrate. He had earned a good name. After retirement he came to Shirdi to stay in the company of Sai Baba. Baba loved him very much! Baba would entrust the entire dakshina money to him, which he would honestly take care. Apart from this, he would work hard even with a broom in his own hands to clean Baba's mosque, chawadi and even the footpath used by Baba.

He always had Baba's name on his lips. He was unhappy that he did not study Sanskrit to understand the scriptures. He silently prayed to Baba. Baba kept his hand on his head and Nana Saheb Nimonkar from then onwards was able to understand the Sanskrit text. He imbibed the science of spirit to such an extent that in the last days of his life he could visualise Sai Baba in every being!

With those two flags gifted by Damuanna Rasane and Nana Saheb Nimonkar the urus procession started from the house of Kondaji. The drummers and pipers were at the forefront followed by Baba's Shamakarna horse, and then the two big flags held high by Amir Shukkur and Abdulla, Sai Baba walking between them, holding on him an umbrella was Bhagoji Shinde – the leper, then Bade Baba, then the other Muslim villagers. Behind them Mhalsapathy, Tatya Kote, Madhava Rao Deshpande, Ramachandra Patil, Nana Saheb Nimonkar, Gopal Rao Gund, Damuanna Rasane, villagers and thousands of devotees carried hundreds of flags, all forming the entire procession. Sai Baba had participated on the earnest desire of the devotees and also as a moral support to the unity of Hindus and Muslims.

Rama Navami – a festival for Hindus! Urus – a festival for the Muslims celebrated together on this day by both the communities! Indeed an ideal function, the first of its kind in Shirdi, which brought them nearer and nearer! This made Baba extremely happy and his joy naturally reflected on everybody's face! A lot of garlands adorned Baba as the procession passed through the village. Women came out of their houses to wave 'aarti' to Baba. Indeed it was a demonstration of a spontaneous jubilation in which everyone in the village participated.

Only one person was unhappy and that was the old Kulkarni physician! He had nursed a grudge against Baba right from the day Baba appeared in Shirdi. But his wife Parvathi, a devout woman was worshipping Baba silently, as she knew her husband's prejudice against him. Kulkarni

Physician shut all the doors and windows not to see the procession. Even then, defying her husband, Parvathi went out to wave an aarti to Sai Baba and she too joined the procession.

Kulkarni was angry that his wife went out to worship Sai Baba. He came out of his room and as he crossed the verandah he stumbled over a grinding wheel and fell down. As a consequence, he injured his head and felt giddy and could hardly see! He realised that he had lost his eyesight!

Baba blessed Kulkarni's wife. She went along with the procession till the mosque. Baba occupied his seat near the dhuni. The qawali singers started their performance. The two big flags flew high gracefully on the top of the mosque. People were in bliss by listening to the qawali and devotional music. The wrestling bout had begun in the open space outside chawadi.

Kulkarni's wife was obsessed with the fear of facing her husband's wrath. Somehow she developed courage and reached home. She was shocked to see Kulkarni injured and in a state of semi-consciousness. She nursed his injury and was sad that he had lost his eyesight. She sent a telegram to her son to come to Shirdi immediately. On her husband's direction, several medicines were tried but his eyesight was not restored.

Three days later, she requested her husband to have Baba's darshan. He yielded and at last came to the mosque. The devotees who had come for urus had left and the mosque had very few devotees. Instead of touching Baba's feet, Kulkarni wrongly touched Bhagoji Shinde's feet. When his wife pointed out this mistake, Baba remarked – "No mother, he rightly touched Bhagoji's feet! To have a universal vision of seeing God in everyone I have tried all these years! He should have seen Sai Baba, Bhagoji Shinde, this dog of Bhagoji, Shama all as one and same identity! Let him look within himself and see the 'Atman'!"

Kulkarni was moved with emotion. He begged Baba's pardon and sought restoration of his eyesight so that he could have Baba's darshan to his heart's content. Baba told him that if he restores his sight, he will fall dead. Immediately, his wife pleaded that she wanted to die as a 'Sumangali' before her husband and requested Baba to lengthen his life giving back his sight. She wanted her husband to have the vision of Baba and to see the world with a new insight. Baba blessed her and as he applied udhi to her forehead, she collapsed and breathed her last. Kulkarni got his sight and saw Sai Baba as Lord Shiva. He also saw his wife passing into the other world!

25

FROM POLICEMAN TO KIRTANKAR

*I*t was on the morning of one such Rama Navami that Ganesh Rao Sahasrabuddhe reached Shirdi after resigning from the police service. Since three years it was celebrated as 'Rama Janma Mahotsava' along with the usual urus! The idea of celebrating the 'Jayanthi' of Lord Rama on that day occurred to Krishna Jogeshwara Bhishma!

Three years back in the early hours of Rama Navami, a thought occurred to Krishna Jogeshwara Bhishma that why not celebrate Rama's birthday along with the urus. He shared this idea with Kaka Mahajani. Both went to Sai Baba to seek permission. But in his holy presence they forgot about it!

Suddenly Baba reminded Bhishma as to what he was thinking on that morning. They sought his permission to celebrate Rama's Jayanthi. Baba said – "Excellent idea! Rama and Rahim are not different. Ask Radhakrishna Ayi to make preparations!"

The 'Ayi' Baba referred to was a young widow. Her real name was Sundaribai Kshirsagar. Baba called her Radhakrishna Ayi. Ayi means 'mother'. A widow since her tender age, she was the daughter of a childhood friend of Nana Saheb Chandorkar and was staying at Pandharpur. Nana Saheb brought her to Shirdi to stay there and serve Baba. Baba gave her shelter and some 'dakshina'. Though very young in age, she was very intelligent, able and a

proactive lady. She had endeared herself to Baba in serving
His devotees.

Every year on the day prior to urus, she would clean up
the mosque, whitewash the walls, neatly arrange the logs
and rearrange Baba's things in a neat manner. Baba always
appreciated her services. Every day, she would get up early
in the morning, would clean the mosque and surrounding
paths, before they were used by the visitors and villagers.
Her enthusiasm was so much that she would collect articles
for decorations such as hanging glass lamps, door-hangings,
mirrors, pictures and other gift articles brought by Baba's
devotees and fix them in the mosque. She had changed the
appearance of the mosque in the last five years, which no
one had done earlier. It was to this lady that Baba sent word
to make preparations for the first 'Rama Janma Mahotsav'
with a short notice.

Kaka Mahajani and Krishna Jogeshwara Bhishma
conveyed Baba's instructions to Radhakrishna Ayi. The
previous night she was busy white-washing and cleaning
the mosque but with the same enthusiasm she again
started on the new assignment. She went round the village
and managed to get a beautiful cradle and got it fixed in
the mosque before Baba returned from his usual stroll in
Lendi baug. She decorated the cradle with flower garlands
and colourful sarees borrowed from ladies among visitors
and villagers. Then she went home to prepare sweets for
distribution as 'prasad' at the end of the function. Other
women used to take instructions from her, although she was
young. Amir Shukkur and other Muslim devotees looked
after arrangements such as flags, buntings, banners, etc. So
even with a short notice, preparations were completed in no
time!

Now a Kirtankar was essential for the musical discourse
on Rama's birth. As this was not immediately possible,
Krishna Jogeshwara Bhishma himself rose to the occasion

and agreed to perform the kirtan. Kaka Mahajani offered to play the harmonium.

Baba returned from Lendi baug and was pleased with the preparations. He complimented Krishna Jogeshwara Bhishma, Kaka Mahajani and Radhakrishna Ayi.

As usual the procession of two flags of the urus arrived! They were hoisted and fixed on the top of the mosque. Baba garlanded Bhishma and Mahajani and the kirtan started. The 'Ram – Rahim' festival in the presence of Hindus and Muslims was something unique and was a memorable event. In the end, everyone offered *gulal* to the cradle and on each other as an expression of joy. In their over enthusiasm thrown at random, a few particles entered Baba's eyes. He became furious and started hurling things around! Many devotees ran away from the mosque. Radhakrishna Ayi was pained that devotees are leaving without taking food. She ran to the mosque and asked Kaka Mahajani to take out the cradle as Baba could break it into pieces. Baba did not permit taking out the cradle. Then Radhakrishna Ayi told Baba that devotees are running away without taking food. This trick worked! Baba became calm in a few seconds. He said – "Tell them I am coming to serve them food myself."

Seeing Baba calm and peaceful, devotees returned to the mosque. They had food served by Baba. The rest of the day was as usual crowded with qawali recitals, devotional music, wrestling bouts, 'sandal' procession in the night, etc. Next morning the function concluded with a keertan and *Dahikala*.

Next year, Krishna Jogeshwara Bhishma was not there and a professional Kirtankar was invited. Baba paid him handsome remuneration. Third year it was Dasa Ganu's good luck that he reached Shirdi on this very day after resigning from the police service. He was without a job and empty handed. But a bowl of fortune awaited him at the mosque.

Baba remarked – "So at last you have come! Ganu, if you had given up the job when I told you, at least your reputation could have been saved."

Ganesh Rao prostrated at Baba's feet and said – "Yes Baba – you drove the peg into me and I have come to your doorsteps. Now appoint me as your security guard! People would at least say that Ganu who aspired to be a police officer became a security guard at Baba's place!"

Baba noticed the disappointment in his tone. He said – "No, no Ganu, you are not to be a mere guard! You are going to be the guide to the golden gates of God's grace! You will be a Kirtankar! An exponent of devotion! God has gifted you intelligence, a ready witted oratory and a powerful pen! Use them and be a polished Kirtankar! That day with your kirtan you could fool Khanya dacoit. Thank Allah, he sent me on time or else Khanya would have finished you!" Saying this, Baba left for Lendi baug.

Nana Saheb Chandorkar, who also had come to the festival, could not understand Baba's last comment over Ganu's kirtan for Khanya dacoit. According to Ganu's report he had managed to give him a slip from his dangerous hideout. But Baba had pinpointed the lie! Ganu was exposed! Nana Saheb took Ganesh Rao to his room. There Ganesh Rao told him everything without hiding anything!

Nana Saheb then told him – "Ganu, everything happens for the best. I have seen one thing. Sai Baba has a hold on our lives. We are not our own masters! What he wants he gets it done, even changing our destiny. For the last two days, he has been saying – 'My Ganu is coming! Let him do the kirtan this time'. Baba pays so well that already some Kirtankars are here to get a chance. So do not lose it. Take this opportunity. I will tell Baba." Ganesh Rao pleaded – "But Saheb, I am not prepared at all!"

Nana assured him "Never mind! Baba is behind you! Be ready with my clothes. Take this turban, this outer garment, and shoulder cloth – everything that suits a kirtankar! I will tell Baba and come back immediately."

Nana Saheb went to Baba while Ganesh Rao dressed himself in that decent dress which befitted him! Indeed he looked a professional kirtankar! Nana Saheb came back with Baba's approval. Though not prepared for a musical discourse on Lord Rama's birth, Ganesh Rao left everything to Sai Baba and moved towards the mosque with Nana Saheb Chandorkar.

The mosque was filled to capacity. Even the open yard outside was crowded. Ganesh Rao was reminded of his kirtan at Loni-Varni. Even at that time, he was not prepared for a kirtan. It was forced on him. But there his audience was uneducated villagers. It was not so here. In this gathering, urbanites, educated and many learned people were there. On the rustic stage he had played as ready-witted dancing boy's role. But here the audience belonged to higher strata. One time orderly of Nana Saheb Chandorkar, later a police constable, was now a kirtankar! This itself had created a lot of curiosity. But devotees knew that Baba would not be wrong in his choice!

Baba returned from Lendi baug. Seeing Ganesh Rao specially dressed for the occasion, Baba smiled and said, "Looking like a bridegroom, eh! Want to marry again?" Ganesh Rao was confused. Baba clarified – "Ganu, why do you need this fancy dress? Remove it. A plain 'dhoti' is enough! You body is like that of a wrestler, why do you cover it?"

Without a word of hesitation, Ganesh Rao removed his garments and kept them at Baba's feet. As he kneeled down, Baba moved his hand over his head and raised his tuft erect. He gave him single-stringed *tamboori* in his hand and asked him to look into the mirror.

Ganesh Rao was astonished at his image when he looked into the mirror! The rosary around his neck, the stringed tamboori in his hand, the tuft of hair standing erect on his clean shaven head made him appear like Narada Muni in epics! Immediately he realised that it was not out of mere fun that Baba had done this – but it was to remind him of that great pioneer of devotional discourses! He too wore no clothes except a *dhoti*. Subsequently Ganesh Rao decided his costume for kirtan would be a bare body wrapped only in a dhoti around his waist!

Baba took a garland brought by a devotee and placed it around Ganesh Rao's neck. The gathering clapped. Then Ganesh Rao touched Baba's feet and started the kirtan. He prayed to Lord Ganesha, Saraswati and once again to Sai Baba. He composed a song in Marathi in which he praised Sai Baba who had made him a kirtankar. He was only a mass of mud and Baba, the sculptor.

Ganesh Rao was a ready poet, a positive writer and an extempore orator. He captured the audience in no time. For over three hours he performed the kirtan of Prabhu Rama's birth. Baba went near the cradle and sprinkled *haldi-kumkum* over it and also Ganesh Rao.

The kirtan was a grand success. Women waved aarti to Lord Rama and Sai Baba. Nana Nimonkar brought out the small cloth bag containing 'dakshina' money. Baba emptied it in the tray and offered it to Ganesh Rao. For one kirtan, Ganesh Rao had earned many months salary as a policeman. For a long time, he kept his head on Baba's feet!

Suddenly Baba got up, went near the dhuni, and placed his right hand in the flames! Women screamed and went near him. Men also rushed to him. Though Baba's right hand was seriously burnt, he kept his cool and said – "Thank God, the child is saved!"

Madhava Rao, Nana Nimonkar, Nana Chandorkar, Ganesh Rao, and all others had surrounded Baba by now. Bhagoji Shinde ran out and returned with a can of oil. Quickly he massaged Baba's hand with the oil using his worn out hands! Nobody could make out as to why Baba inserted his hand in the burning fire. Only Lakshmi asked Baba – "What have you done to yourself, Baba? Whom did you save?"

Baba replied – "Dear girl, she is just like you – a potter's wife! She left the child near the furnace and went to serve food for her husband. The child crawled over to the furnace and was about to fall in the fire! I took out my hand out of its flames and pushed back the child in time. It is saved!"

Kind-hearted Sai Baba responded to his devotees in distress. The mother of the child was an ardent devotee of Sai Baba. As she came out after serving her husband she saw the child about to fall into the furnace. She screamed in terror and in a split second Baba pushed back the child away from the flames! Such incidents occurred during Baba's life time and light was thrown on some of them proving their accuracy in time, day, and details. Some remained a mystery forever!

This was the real beginning of life for Ganesh Rao! Having personally witnessed Sai Baba's acts of benevolence, his pity for the poor and aggrieved, he could guess what a massive support he offered to his devotees. He decided that he should put his pen and poetry to acquaint the world of his mission of universal love! He wrote a number of books and a series of kirtans on Sai Baba and his greatness.

Bhagoji Shinde massaged Baba's hand with oil and wrapped it with plantain leaf and bandages. Nana Saheb Chandorkar thought that this may cause formation of pus. Without asking Baba, he sent a telegram to a famous surgeon in Mumbai, Dr.Paramanand. Baba blessed the

doctor but did not even permit him to look at the injury!
Disappointed, he left by the next train but Baba's blessings
made him a famous personality and a prominent road in
Mumbai is named after him now!

26

AS COMRADE AT TESTING HOUR

*I*t was the third day after Rama Navami. Nana Saheb Chandorkar and Ganesh Rao were walking towards the mosque. A Parsi businessman approached from the opposite side and fell flat on Ganesh Rao's feet. It was a new experience for him! He introduced himself as Seth Ratanji Pistonji and with adoration called him 'Dasa Ganu Maharaj' and invited him to his place to perform a kirtan.

Ganesh Rao was immensely happy that the Parsi businessman had honoured him in front of his onetime boss, Nana Chandorkar. But outwardly he still pleaded his hesitation that as a Brahmin he could only recite a few verses from Sanskrit and he does not have the scholarship to be a kirtankar.

Nana Saheb encouraged him – "Ganesh Rao, now I know your worth. The whole world will now sing your glory calling you Dasa Ganu Maharaj! Accept Sethji's invitation to go to Nanded. In so far as scholarship is concerned, look at Baba's grace to Nana Nimonkar. Now he recites and understands Sanskrit scriptures. Baba will surely equip you to be a great *kirtankar*!" Sethji was happy that Ganesh Rao will visit Nanded.

Nana Saheb Chandorkar invited Dasa Ganu to visit Jamner after going to Nanded. From Junnar Nana was transferred to Jamner. As we already know, from Kopergaon he was transferred to Pandharpur and from there to Junnar and now to Jamner. Between these few years, his daughter Maina was married and now she was pregnant too. But Nana was worried about his son-in-law. He was very much ill and bed-ridden which had delayed Maina's coming to her father's place for delivery.

Nana Saheb Chandorkar and Ganesh Rao reached the mosque. Both placed their heads on Baba's feet. Baba said – "Ganu, you are on the right track! Keep reading! Make it a rule. Read scriptures and write what you read. Learn Sanskrit. Stay in Pandharpur. Go for kirtan wherever you are called. Do not decline!" He poured a lot of udhi in Ganesh Rao's hands. He turned to Nana Chandorkar – "Nana, you can also leave. I will come to Jamner! Ask your daughter to stay as God wills!" Saying so Baba left abruptly.

Nana Saheb was hoping to get some udhi prasad. Moreover Baba had told him – "Ask your daughter to stay as God wills!" Was anything wrong in the offing? Who knows what was in store for her. Sadly he thought over it.

As it was time for their departure, Madhava Rao came to bid goodbye to Dasa Ganu and Nana Saheb. Nana spoke to Madhava Rao – "Today Baba told me that he will come to Jamner! Will he really come?"

Madhava Rao replied – "Nana Saheb, to tell you the truth Baba never leaves Shirdi. At the most he will go to Neemgaon to Nana Dengale – which you know is just beyond. Rarely does he go to Khushalchand Sethji at Rahata. And nowhere else! Sometimes, he calls Khushalchandji to Shirdi. He too has a queer experience of his own."

Madhava Rao then began to narrate that experience. Khushalchand Seth was a nephew of Chandrabhan Seth of Rahata. In the beginning, Baba would often visit Chandrabhan Seth. Actually Chandrabhan used to come personally in his tonga to take Baba with himself. Baba was fond of gardening. From Rahata he would bring rose plants.

Baba's Lendi baug was always full of flowers. He would give them to different shrines. After Chandrabhan's demise, Khushalchand Seth was also equally devoted to Baba. As he had not come to Shirdi for long, Baba sent Madhava Rao for him. When he reached with Baba's message, Khushalchand Seth had just got in his tonga and was about to leave for Shirdi. On seeing Madhava Rao, he said that on that morning he had a dream in which Baba had directed Khushalchand Seth to visit Shirdi that day!

There were many such experiences of Baba! While Nana Saheb was thinking of Baba's coming to Jamner, they saw Balasaheb Deo coming that way. He was also a deputy collector. On seeing him, Madhava Rao said – "Look! Here is Deosaheb! Ask him as to how Baba went to him at Dahanu."

Sharing Baba's experiences was always a happy occasion for both the narrator and the listener. Here Balasaheb narrated his strange experience to Nana Saheb Chandorkar - "Nana Saheb, Sai Baba is a strange phenomenon. Only we do not know as to when he comes to us and when he leaves. We can never anticipate. We then feel sorry and repent for not recognising him. Look at my own recent experience. At present I am posted at Dahanu. One day, casually I visited the railway station on my horse. I saw a sanyasi talking to the station master. On seeing me, the station master brought the sanyasi to me and introduced him as a mendicant running a *goshala* in Varanasi giving protection to unprotected cows. Since he was collecting funds for this task he wanted to meet me! I appreciated his work and requested him to come after six months as I was busy in some other collection drive. The sanyasi agreed and told me that he would meet me after six months, gave me a pamphlet with details of his cow protection scheme, and left Dahanu by the next train!

Balasaheb continued - "Fifteen days after this incident, my mother planned to have the concluding ceremony for a religious observance. I wrote to Baba seeking his approval.

The letter was written to Bapusaheb Jog who was staying in Shirdi at that time. When Bapusaheb Jog read out the letter, Baba expressed his joy and told him – 'Good, good. Write to Deo to fix up the date. Tell him I will come. You also come with me. We will both have lunch at Deo's place.'

"The letter from Jog made us all happy with the news that Baba will be coming for the function. And soon came that day! I took my tonga and went to the railway station. Baba did not turn up in either of the two trains... I came home and was really in an irritated mood. The whole town of Dahanu was looking forward to Baba's visit. The sanyasi who had met me earlier in relation to the fund collection drive for cow protection was standing near my gate along with another mendicant. Even though I was disappointed that Baba had not come, calmly I spoke to him – 'Swamiji, I remember having asked you to come after six months.' He said – 'You are right Saheb! Today we have come to your house for food.' I told him that it is fine and they could visit us at 12 noon.

"Accordingly they joined us for lunch along with many other guests. After lunch, everybody was given 'dakshina' and they left happily. I was sorry that Baba did not come and wrote to Jog as to how the whole town was disappointed as Baba did not come. When Jog read the letter, Baba said – 'You write to him, Jog, if he could not recognise me he should not have invited me at all for that lunch. I and one more sanyasi had sumptuous lunch with them on that day. Even he gave us dakshina that day. Has he forgotten all that?'

"This message from Baba opened my eyes. Indeed I had not recognised Baba that day. Baba has advised us over and over again that we should see him in everybody. He tells us – 'Believe me, every living being is myself! Hence love all!' We forget this. Our ego puts us into bewilderment!"

After this long narration, Balasaheb Deo told Nana that just to verify that Baba came in the form of that sanyasi, he wrote to the address in Varanasi as to whether that Sanyasi had come to Dahanu on that day. He got a reply from him that after reaching Varanasi, he has not gone anywhere else! This shows that Baba came in the guise of that sanyasi. Balasaheb Deo concluded – "Baba is close behind our thoughts and monitoring each and every action. He did not want me to be proud that Baba came merely on my writing to him and also to remind us that Sai Baba is not his only form that we see at Shirdi – he is in every being, in all forms!"

Pondering over this strange method of guidance to his devotees, Nana Chandorkar went to Jamner while Ganesh Rao left for Pandharpur. Seeing them off, Balasaheb Deo and Madhava Rao turned towards the mosque. On their way, Balasaheb Deo asked Madhava Rao several questions like what Baba has told him as to how to study *Bhagwad Gita*, how to meditate, and such other things. Deo used to read *Jnaneshwari* but could never concentrate. Madhava Rao explained as to how he had understood it. Apart from this, he also narrated as to how Baba forced *Vishnu Sahasranama* on him.

That was also an interesting experience. A Ramdasi had come to stay in Shirdi. He was fond of collecting and reading scriptures. Once Ramdasi was reciting *Vishnu Sahasranama*. Baba thought that he should initiate Madhava Rao. Baba told Ramdasi that he had pain in abdomen and wanted Ramdasi to bring some senna leaves. Ramdasi left the Sahasranama and ran to the market. The moment he left, Baba picked up the book and gave it to Madhava Rao and said – "Keep this book. Recite it daily. It will do good." Madhava Rao knew Ramdasi will make noise if he comes to know that his book is missing. But Baba insisted that he take that copy!

Ramdasi returned from market, gave senna leaves to Baba, and on not seeing Vishnu Sahasranama, asked Madhava Rao. Madhava Rao told him that it is with him, as Baba has given it to him and he will get a new book to Ramdasi. Ramdasi flared up and started making wild allegations against Madhava Rao. Madhava Rao did his best to pacify him, but he was uncontrollable. At last Baba intervened – "Why are you shouting, my boy? You know its contents by heart. Let Shama also learn it! You read so many scriptures but you have not realised God contained therein. Learn to love humans! Then you do not need these scriptures to have His grace!" With these sweet words of Baba and on condition of getting a copy of *Pancharathna Gita* from Madhava Rao, Ramdasi calmed down.

Madhava Rao told Balasaheb Deo – "This is how Baba teaches. But his method of teaching varies with every individual. When Baba himself asks someone to read a scripture or a book, it is as good as his blessing. Once you get that, even a difficult Sanskrit book can be easily understood."

Madhava Rao and Deo reached the mosque. They went and sat near Baba's seat. Baba returned from Lendi baug and occupied his place near dhuni. He called Abdulla and asked him to bring his brick. Baba was taking great care of that brick. While sitting near the dhuni he needed the brick as a rest. He took care of it in such a manner, that he did not permit anyone except Abdulla to touch it. Madhava Rao made fun of his attachment to the brick. Baba replied to him – "Shama, you will not understand it! When Lord Vishnu went to Pundalik to confer on him a boon, he was asked to wait on a brick till Pundalik completed his services to his parents! For ages God is standing on that small brick in one place, waiting to see when Pundalik will finish his service to his parents. That brick has become as important as God himself! Such is this brick! It is my Guru's! Sitting on it my

Guru would stare at me! My Guru is no more physical but his memory is! I am here because of this brick! With a mere reference to his Guru, Baba would be emotionally moved! But he never disclosed who his Guru was? Hence Madhava Rao also did not ask him about it.

Seeing Deo, Baba asked him to pay a dakshina of eighteen rupees. While collecting the money, Baba became furious. He started abusing. He was hurling things all around! This frightened the devotees and in confusion, a Parsi couple – Ratanji Seth and his wife started running out! Baba's club hit Ratan Seth's wife who he thought was badly hurt. But she wasn't injured at all. They ran back to their lodgings and were about to leave Shirdi back to Nanded! Madhava Rao anticipated their departure and so ran to their lodge and pleaded with Ratanji to stay back. Madhava Rao stated that she has received Baba's blessing and whatever they desired will be fulfilled! Ratanji and his wife returned to the mosque.

Babasaheb Deo had not left the mosque like others as he had noticed that Baba was enraged only after receiving dakshina from him. He felt that Baba's getting angry was something to do with him. Hence facing Baba's wrath he stood in his place. Baba asked him – "Have you seen a shred of any rag here?" Deo asked him – "Which shred Baba?"

"You son of a thief! Are you talking to me? Which shred?" – said Baba as He held Deo by his neck tightly and shook him. He further said – "You have come all the way here to collect shreds?" With his club, Baba hit Deo three to four times. Deo could not make out as to why Baba was angry with him. He was very much frightened! For quite some time, Baba searched for the shred and continued to abuse profusely. When he calmed down, he asked Deo to sit near himself as he sat putting firewood into the dhuni. He asked him for a dakshina of another eighteen rupees! Deo got up and said – "I will bring the money!" Baba stopped him and said – "Do not bother! You have already paid it! Sit here! Now tell me what were you asking Shama?"

Deo now understood as to why Baba was angry with him. Baba did not like his asking Madhava Rao about meditation, reading scriptures, guidance given by Baba and such other things. He therefore said – "Baba, I cannot concentrate when I meditate. I cannot understand the meaning of Jnaneshwari. Whatever I read appears to be meaningless! Without your grace, I will never progress!" Tears appeared in his eyes.

Baba said – "Why are you collecting shreds? Asking this man, that man – why? Whatever you want, ask me! I am here to give you a full length golden scarf! Why should you collect shreds? It is all right. Now go home, your wishes will be fulfilled!"

Sai Baba placed his hand of grace on Deo's head! He could now understand the meaning of Jnaneshwari. In a very short period, he made a rapid progress. He could give discourses. Baba gave him a dream vision to improve his style of discourses!

Baba called Ratanji Seth and his wife. He blessed them that their wish for not one son – many sons will be fulfilled! He asked for a dakshina of twelve rupees. As Sethji was about to offer the money, Baba remarked – "You have already paid three rupees and fourteen annas! Pay the balance".

Sethji was bewildered! This was his first visit to Shirdi. His mind was obsessed with those three rupees and fourteen annas!

27

BABA AS A TONGAWALA

$\mathscr{A}$ shocking news awaited Nana Saheb Chandorkar when he reached Jamner. It was a telegram from Maina's father-in-law informing him about the death of his son – Maina's husband. It made him dizzy! Now he could clearly understand the meaningful behaviour of Baba before his departure from Shirdi! Nana now remembered everything in detail right from day one when he took Maina as a child to Baba and how he smeared udhi on her forehead. He had advised him 'Tell Maina to stay as God wills'. An astrologer had predicted that Maina would become a widow at a young age and there is also a danger to Maina's life after marriage. Now one prediction having come true, Nana was restless that the other might also come true! However Baba's assurance – 'I will come to Jamner' reassured him! He was confident of Baba's help at any cost!

He went to Jalgaon and thence to Maina's place. Seeing him, Maina broke down. She blamed Baba that he did not save her from this disaster! Nana consoled her – "Maina, it was not impossible for Baba. But he did not interfere with the divine plan. Have faith in him. If you pass this test, be sure that Baba will always look after your welfare." Maina controlled her emotions and went to Jamner with her parents for delivery.

Maina was not able to control her emotions. Again and again her mind mused about her departed husband. This advanced her delivery and she went in for a premature labour pain. The doctor predicted a complicated delivery. A *Chandi Homa* (a common yagna in order to appease divine mother Chamundi or Durga - Lord Shiva's consort to overcome domestic calamities) was performed and Nana Chandorkar prayed to Baba to save Maina by ensuring a safe delivery!

How could this earnest prayer of Nana Saheb go unheeded and fail to reach Baba at Shirdi?

The machinery of the mosque began to move! A Gosavi by name Ramgir, a resident of Shirdi thought of visiting his relatives at Khandesh. He went to the mosque to seek Baba's permission. On seeing Ramgir, Baba himself told Madhava Rao – "Shama, write down that 'aarti' composed by Madhav Adkar on a piece of paper and give that and some *vibhuthi* to this Bapugir to be handed over to Nana Chandorkar at Jamner.

Baba would call Ramgir as Bapugir. He was a local man of Shirdi. He had closely studied Baba's miracles and was not at all surprised that Baba knew his intention to go to Khandesh without being told. Still he said – "Baba, I am going to Khandesh. I want your permission." Baba told him – Of course, you can go. But first go to Jamner and hand over this 'aarti' and udhi to Nana. Then you can go to Khandesh." Ramgir pleaded – "Baba, I have only two rupees with me. The train fare to Jalgaon is one rupee and fourteen annas. To go to Jamner, I do not have money for tonga." Baba assured him – "Do not worry. Everything will be arranged."

Baba's word was a cent per cent guarantee of safe and carefree journey. Everybody knew that one's coming to Shirdi took place only when Baba willed it. Similarly leaving it without his permission was like inviting trouble. Ramgir remembered the experience of a proud British officer! The Britisher had come to seek Baba's grace. He pitched a tent and sent word to Baba that he desired a meeting with him.

Baba paid no heed to him! The Britisher was furious and waited for three days. Ultimately he went to the mosque. He was aghast to see Bhagoji Shinde massaging Baba's hand. He requested him to send away Bhagoji Shinde and sought a private audience with Baba. Baba refused to accede to his request and asked Bhagoji Shinde to give him 'udhi'. The Britisher refused to accept the holy udhi from a leper's hand and got up to leave Shirdi immediately! Baba spoke to Madhava Rao to advise him to postpone his leaving Shirdi by one day. Without heeding to this advice, the Britisher left in a tonga. He met with an accident and was to be in a hospital at Kopergaon for two weeks! Later the Britisher gave up his ego, surrendered himself to Baba!

As a result of such happenings, the devotees listened to Baba and this led to the practice of everyone seeking Baba's permission before leaving Shirdi.

After taking Baba's permission, Ramgir confidently made the train journey and reached Jalgaon around 4 am next morning. He wondered as to how he will make a trip to Jamner. Moreover, the Public Health authorities surrounded him to have plague inoculation! Ramgir was in a fix. Suddenly he heard a voice – "Any Bapugir from Shirdi here?" The Gosavi replied – "Yes, yes, I am here." The caller was a tongawala and he said – "Come, come! Nana Saheb is waiting for you at Jamner." On hearing Nana Saheb's name, the authorities permitted Ramgir to leave without inoculation.

The tongawala looked familiar to Ramgir. A young man with robust physique, a graceful turban tied around his head, a white pant, old fashioned shirt, whiskers, and a well shaped beard – everything made him attractive and outstanding. Ramgir tried to recollect as to where he had met him. His memory failed him! The coachman too did not talk anything.

The tonga started towards Jamner. In the cool breeze and the dim light Ramgir dozed off. Suddenly he woke up when the tonga stopped near a stream. Ramgir was quite hungry and wanted to drink water. The coachman told him that he has brought a packet of food with him. Ramgir hesitated because he appeared like a Muslim. The coachman read Ramgir's mind and told him that he is a Rajput from Gadhwal. He also reminded Ramgir that Sai Baba has been teaching that soul has no caste and food no religion! He told him – "Never say 'No' to food! Eat plenty and then drink water."

Ramgir remembered an anecdote once told by Baba. Once an old widow had come to Shirdi. She decided to fast for three days in connection with 'Holi' festival. In order to change her mind Baba told her that once along with three more persons, he had embarked on a wild goose chase in a forest. All of them were hungry. A tribal met them with food. His friends refused to eat and left the place. Baba took food and soon his Guru appeared before him. The Guru took Baba along with him. He tied both legs of Baba by a rope and left him hanging in a solitary well with his head almost touching the water level. The Guru returned after four hours and what Baba experienced during that time was nothing but bliss. Baba realised that food is supreme God and one should keep the hungry soul satisfied to have Guru's grace! The old widow gave up her fast and she went to Dada Kelkar's place to participate in the holi festival!

Recalling this story, Ramgir took the food offered by the tongawala and offering it mentally to Sai Baba. The journey was resumed and they reached Jamner. The tonga halted near Nana Saheb's residence and the coachman directed Ramgir to go to Nana's place. Ramgir got down with his belongings. The coachman left the place even before he could thank him!

He went to Nana's house. As he reached there, he could hear from inside chantings of 'Durga Sapta Shati' and 'Chandi Homa' going on. Ramgir gently tapped the door. An anxious Nana Saheb came out and was surprised to see Ramgir. When Ramgir thanked him for sending the tonga to pick him up, Nana Saheb Chandorkar expressed surprise as he was not aware of Ramgir's trip and had not arranged any tonga to pick him up. Now Ramgir remembered that tongawala was none other than Sai Baba himself! The familiar voice, the peculiar way in which he called him Bapugir just as Baba did, his familiar face, the style and mannerism – everything Baba's! Only the garments differed. Now both Ramgir and Nana were hundred per cent certain that it was Baba who brought Ramgir! Both folded their hands before Baba's picture and bowed in reverence!

Nana's daughter Maina was having labour pains. Ramgir quickly opened his bag, took out Baba's udhi and the paper on which aarti was written by Madhava Rao and handed over to Nana Saheb and said – "Here is some udhi given by Baba! This is Baba's aarti composed by Madhav Adkar. Baba sent me here for this only."

Baba's udhi was exhausted at Nana's place. But Baba sent it through Ramgir on time. Udhi was given to Maina and they all waved an 'aarti' to Baba. The musical notes produced spiritual vibrations which threw away the calamity. At that time, Maina gave birth to a child! Everybody rejoiced at this event.

There was a surprise visitor! Ganesh Rao had arrived! Nana Saheb was excited and told him as to how Sai Baba had visited Jamner sometime back!

PROPAGATION OF BABA'S FAME

*B*aba's miracle of visiting Jamner as a coachman made Nana Saheb Chandorkar and Ganesh Rao his very ardent devotees. As a result, they came to the conclusion that propagation of Sai Baba's fame would be a proper mission for them to render him an appropriate service. Now looking at this sudden change in their attitude, one wondered with admiration Baba's subtle working of completely converting these two strong critics. For Nana's sake, Baba presented himself as another person but also materialised a full tonga with horses – a miracle that displayed his limitless powers. This may be perhaps the only miracle of its kind in the history of mankind!

Having received a telegram from Ratanji Seth of Nanded, Ganesh Rao had come to Nana Saheb to consult him before going there. He had no plans of performing kirtans at Nanded or any other place unless he was fully prepared for it. But unexpectedly Sethji's telegram had come too soon. Moreover, he had mentioned that he has some urgent work!

Nana Saheb told Ganesh Rao – "In all these things, Sai Baba himself is monitoring. Our life's real work has now begun. To give us success is entirely Baba's business! You can safely go to Nanded and deliver kirtan on this very incident of tongawala. The Ganga of Baba's devotion has begun to flow! Let us channelise it properly! Let us make an effort so that this Loving God is known to all – particularly to those in distress! In fact, I have received a letter from Bhimaji Patil in Junnar. He is almost dead. Having tried everything in medicine and divine remedies he has helplessly written to me. I have asked him to surrender to Lord Sainath, who has incarnated solely for the welfare of human race. This is why we must do our best so that maximum number of persons gets benefit from Sai Baba."

With Nana Chandorkar's valuable advice, Ganesh Rao decided to go ahead with his kirtans. For Nanded programme, he fixed the subject of Baba coming in the form of a coachman.

When Ganesh Rao landed in Nanded there was only one coolie in the railway station. He appeared to be a pious and a virtuous man. From his moustache and beard, Ganesh Rao could make out that he was a Muslim. Though he was prejudiced against Muslims, contact with Sai Baba had changed his attitude to a certain extent. He asked the coolie – "Bade Miya, do you know Ratanji Sethji's bungalow?" He politely answered – "Yes, sir!" and without a word picked up Ganesh Rao's trunk. He did not even ask as to how much he would be paid for his work.

Ratanji was happy to welcome Ganesh Rao. But he appeared happier on seeing the coolie accompanying Ganesh Rao. Ratanji and his wife placed their heads on the feet of the coolie first and then Ganesh Rao. This flattered Ganesh Rao but he kept wondering as to why the coolie was bestowed with that respect.

Ratanji introduced Ganesh Rao to the coolie whom he now called 'Maulavi Baba' – "Baba, this is Dasa Ganu Maharaj! He is an excellent kirtankar! Sai Baba respects him very much!"

This praise pleased Ganesh Rao who joined his hands in response. However his mind was calculating as to how much he should pay the coolie. When Sethji respected him so much it would be below his dignity if he paid him less in their presence. But his problem was solved by Sethji himself. He paid him a rupee coin. In spite of Sethji's protests, Maulavi Baba returned fourteen annas charging only two annas for his labour. He then quickly withdrew! Ganesh Rao was simply dumb founded with such a contented person! He asked Ratanji Seth – "Who is this coolie? Seems very honest!"

Sethji replied – "coolie! Dasa Ganu Maharaj, he is a very great saint! Maulavi Saheb!" "A coolie, a saint?" – It was a day of surprise for Ganesh Rao, because Sethji further said – "Yes, Dasa Ganu Maharaj, he is an accomplished saint! A great man!"

Even after coming in contact with Sai Baba, Ganesh Rao's understanding of divinity was not mature enough to see a saint in an ordinary person. Baba had to perform many miracles to bring home his divinity in Ganesh Rao! Not only this, Ganesh Rao criticised unnecessarily in his kirtans about a few saints whose mark of perfection he did not understand. This was due to his ego which he could not get rid off!

Ratanji further told Ganesh Rao that he went to Sai Baba only at the suggestion of Maulavi Saheb! He was happy that he went to Sai Baba for the boon of a child and Baba has fulfilled it! He said – "Everything is fine! But Maharaj, I could not understand those three rupees fourteen annas! I have never met Sai Baba earlier. How could I have paid him those three rupees fourteen annas? Please make me understand, if you can!"

This exactly was the work Ratanji had mentioned in the telegram. Since the day of their return, Sethji was obsessed with the thought of those three rupees and fourteen annas which had deprived him even of his sleep. He was more than convinced that Sai Baba is a divine incarnation. His wife had conceived soon after their return. Hence he knew that the mention of those three rupees fourteen annas was not without any meaning! He thought Ganesh Rao could throw some light on this. As such he had sent him the telegram. Moreover he was keen on a kirtan at Nanded!

Ganesh Rao was also bewildered! He could not explain the significance of that amount. He prayed to Sai Baba and suddenly an idea dawned on him. He asked Ratanji – "Did you pay this amount to Maulavi Saheb in any form?" "No, never!" - Sethji replied, yet he began to scratch his head. He spoke to Ganesh Rao – "Yes, Maharaj, I remember now! Three months ago, I arranged a dinner for him!"

"Is it? How much did it cost you?" Ratanji and his wife recollected every item. Ganesh Rao worked out the amount spent for the dinner. To their surprise it came out to be exactly three rupees fourteen annas! This solved the mystery of the amount Sai Baba had referred to! Ganesh Rao's eyes were filled with tears as he had thus realised the presence of Sai Baba even in Maulavi Saheb who was miles away from Shirdi. He was made to believe in the truth that even a coolie could also be a divine person of high order!

Next morning, Ganesh Rao's kirtan was arranged in the open yard outside the famous shrine of Guru Govind Singh, which is a pilgrim centre for all communities. Wide publicity about the kirtan was given in the town.

An overwhelming crowd from all communities gathered at the place. Keeping Baba's photograph in the centre, Ganesh Rao gave an excellent musical discourse on Sai Baba explaining as to how this Loving God belonged to all communities. With Sai Baba appearing as a coachman to transport Ramgir from Jalagan to Junnar as the central theme, Dasa Ganu Maharaj narrated the life story of Sai Baba. The audience was thrilled to hear the story and many of them on the spot planned a trip to Shirdi. The fame of Sai Baba thus began to spread through such musical discourses of Dasa Ganu and coming to know about this unknown

God in a mosque, the teeming masses saw a ray of hope in their frustrated lives.

When the kirtan ended, offering of money poured in hundreds of rupees filling the 'aarti' plate. Sethji too paid a very big remuneration to Ganesh Rao which he had least expected!

Ganesh Rao now realised that even though Baba made him resign his police service, he had compensated it with name, fame, and more money!

From here onwards started a chain of Dasa Ganu's kirtans. He chose temples in various towns and cities as venues and covered life of saints and sages with Sai Baba as the central theme. His kirtans on saints made people regard him 'Sant Dasa Ganu'. Many people who never knew about Sai Baba got more information about Sai Baba and Shirdi.

There were many who had dream visions of Sai Baba but were at a loss to know about his whereabouts. They too, when they saw Sai Baba's picture in the kirtans of Dasa Ganu, would be extremely happy and on getting required information would reach Shirdi. An experience of this kind by Lakshmichand, a Rajasthani, is very interesting!

Lakshmichand had a dream vision of Sai Baba at his residence in Santa Cruz, Mumbai, in which he kneeled down to him and was so much in communion that he yearned to meet him personally. Soon he was invited to Manjunath Bijur's place, where Dasa Ganu Maharaj gave a performance. There he saw Sai Baba's picture placed on a high pedestal. Lakshmichand was visibly moved to see the same saint who had blessed him in his dream. Same face, same smile and the same divine pair of lotus feet which had fascinated him in his dream! The subject of kirtan that day was life of Sai Baba! The audience was dumbfounded with Dasa Ganu's style of narration. Dasa Ganu observed that tears were flowing from Lakshmichand's eyes. He interrupted his discourse and called upon Lakshmichand to explain his emotional outburst. Listening to his dream vision the audience was thrilled and many decided to meet the Loving God at Shirdi!

Lakshmichand too craved to go to Shirdi. But he had a problem of meeting the travel expenses. He was a clerk in a private firm called Rallie Brothers and with his meager income he did not have spare money to spend on his trip to Shirdi. That is the reason; Sai Baba gave him a dream vision. However this restless soul wanted to have physical darshan of Baba. As luck would have it, his friend Shankara Rao came to him and requested him to accompany him on a trip to Shirdi. Lakshmichand jumped at the idea, borrowed fifteen rupees from his cousin and in the same night both of them left for Shirdi. At Manmad they changed the train to Kopergaon and in the train heard from fellow passengers many miracles of Sai Baba!

Lakshmichand did not want to meet Sai Baba with empty hands. He learnt that Sai Baba liked guavas very much. In spite of the hectic search, he could not find them at the railway station nor on the way. He felt disappointed. As the tonga moved fast with least possibility of getting guavas for Baba, suddenly he saw an old woman chasing their vehicle with a basket full of guavas! Lakshmichand stopped the vehicle and purchased the fruits. The woman offered the remaining fruits as her offering to Sai Baba and gave the entire basket! In fact, Lakshmichand had an intuition that Sai Baba himself has come in the guise of that old woman to fulfill his desire!

Reaching Shirdi, they prepared themselves for worshipping Sai Baba. Lakshmichand was simply dumbfounded! He was seeing the same 'Mahatma' who had blessed him in his vision. Baba allowed him to worship as he wished. Lakshmichand washed Baba's feet, wiped them, smeared them with sandal wood paste, applied the same to his forehead also, to his neck, then applied turmeric and *kum kum*, fixed rice grains over it, put flowers over his head and placed a garland around his neck. Baba was happy and even though it took a long time and a hindrance to other devotees, he endured Lakshmichand's worship with patience! Then he asked him – "Did you not bring any offering for me?" Lakshmichand was confused and he asked his friend to get some candy. Immediately Baba reminded him – "Why candy? You have brought something very dear to me! Where is it?" Lakshmichand was still more bewildered! He looked puzzled and looked at his friend Shankara Rao. At last Baba reminded him – "Oh dear, did you not bring guavas for me purchased from that old woman?" With this direct reminder, Lakshmichand jumped like a child and offered the fruits. Keeping one, Baba asked Madhava Rao to distribute the rest of the guavas amongst the devotees. Lakshmichand was happy that Baba fulfilled his desire.

Baba allowed Lakshmichand to worship in the manner he liked. In fact, earlier, Baba never allowed anyone to worship him. Later he allowed Mhalsapathy to perform his *pooja* who would apply sandal wood paste to Baba's feet and neck and never on the forehead. Afterwards Nana Chandorkar once brought his four-year-old son Bapu who applied paste to Baba's forehead and worshipped him. Baba happily allowed him to do it. Thereafter he permitted devotees who came from far off places and desirous of worshipping him to perform the pooja'except application of sandal wood paste to his forehead. As such nobody dared touch his forehead.

To this however, there was an exception once! Dr. Pandit visited Shirdi along with Dada Kelkar. He was a follower of another saint, Kaka Puranik alias Raghunath Siddha Yogi of Dhopeswar. Dada Kelkar worshipped Baba by applying sandal paste to Baba's feet as usual. Dr.Pandit took up the plate and drew with his three fingers three vertical

lines right in the centre of Baba's forehead. Devotees were
frightened and expected Baba to flare up! But nothing of the
sort happened! On the contrary, he seemed to be happy and
allowed Dr.Pandit to perform the 'pooja'! This surprised
everyone!

Dada Kelkar asked Baba in the evening – "Baba, you
do not allow anyone to apply *chandan* to your forehead!
If anyone tried we have seen you getting angry. How
come, you permitted Dr.Pandit this morning to draw three
lines on your forehead? Why this discrimination?" Baba
smilingly said – "This doctor is an orthodox devotee of a
'Brahamajnani'! Even then he did not hesitate to worship
me in spite of this Muslim environment. On the contrary, he
visualised me as his Guru while performing pooja and thus
compelled me to accept it in the manner he offered! Now
tell me, how can I hurt him?"

Lakshmichand sat near Baba gazing at him. Suddenly
Baba blurted out – "These chaps come singing devotional
songs. Why enquire others? Come yourself and verify
whether your dream is true or false. Why borrow money to
come to Shirdi? Why am I giving them a vision in a dream?
Do I not go to them in their dream so that they need not come
here all the way? But still they itch to see if their dream was
true! See now, verify, and satisfy!" Lakshmichand realised
that Baba was referring to him only.

That day, someone brought *shira* as grace food.
Lakshmichand liked it very much and desired that it should
be served next day too. Next day someone told him that
shire was not there. Lakshmichand was disappointed and
got a terrible backache for having sat for a long time. But
towards the end of aarti, baskets of shira prasad arrived.
Baba remarked – "My pet sweet is here. Backache also will
vanish" Baba's clairvoyance fascinated him. He went near
Baba and clasped his feet!

As Lakshmichand and other devotees sat in rows for their lunch, everyone was happy at his own experience of Sai Baba's clairvoyance! To this one man was an exception. He was sitting next to Lakshmichand. He was wearing gold threaded turban which he had not removed even while sitting for lunch. He seemed nervous and excited and was looking around with searching eyes. It appeared as if he was not interested in 'prasad' food. When Lakshmichand mentioned about Baba's clairvoyance, he flared up and said – "Then why did he not read my mind?" At that time, a young boy appeared at the door and in a loud tone started singing. On a stick held high in his hand he had a pair of brand new Kolhapuri slippers. He sang – "Hari is his name with a gold threaded turban, he worships not Hari but his slippers, his father called him 'Beta' but he loves 'Feta', that turban so dear he will not remove even while eating." The devotee who challenged Lakshmichand stood up and ran to the boy. He had already become conspicuous with the description in the song capturing the eyes of all in the hall. He told the boy – "They are my slippers! Where did you find them?" The boy answered him – "Baba gave me this pair of slippers and asked me to give it to him whose name is Hari, who has a gold threaded turban on his head and who loves his slippers above everything else!" Since he said that his name is Haribhau and showed him his turban, the boy handed over the slippers to him. He was extremely happy and was about to leave the place without eating the prasad when someone reminded him that food is in his plate. He returned after keeping the slippers in a place so that he could watch on them from where he sat. He told Lakshmichand – "You are right! Baba's clairvoyance is indeed beyond doubt and wonderful! I was restless because I had lost my brand new slippers in Baba's mosque. Now I realise he is God!" Lakshmichand thought to himself – "This man was unhappy because he was attached to his slippers. Otherwise he would have bathed in the bliss of meeting the

Loving God." Lakshmichand realised that his faith in Baba would lead to more devotion and insight into his divinity.

Thus Baba would always have the desires, resolves or vows of devotees fulfilled some way or the other! Once Haribhau Karnik from Dahanu had come to Shirdi for Baba's darshan. He performed pooja and offered dakshina. Baba gave him his blessings and permission to return. Haribhau Karnik came down the steps of the mosque. Suddenly he felt that he should have paid one more rupee to Baba. So he wanted to return to Baba. As there was a heavy rush and Baba had already permitted him to leave, Madhava Rao beckoned him to proceed and not to return. So putting back the rupee in his pocket, Haribhau Karnik left Shirdi. On his way, he visited Nasik and as he entered 'Panchavati' he had the darshan of Narasimha Maharaj, a renowned saint from a distance. Even though he was surrounded by his devotees, Narasimha Maharaj came to Haribhau Karnik and caught by his wrist and said – "Bring me my rupee! You wanted to go without giving it!" Saying so Narasimha Maharaj collected the rupee from Haribhau Karnik. Many may regard this as strange but Haribhau Karnik was happy that Sai Baba himself is taking his dakshina!

Still very strange is the experience of Appa Saheb Kulkarni of Thane. He had obtained a picture of Sai Baba and was worshipping in his shrine. After some days, Appa Saheb Kulkarni had to go to Bhiwandi for some official work. After he left, a fakir resembling Sai Baba visited his house. Appa Saheb Kulkarni's wife was fascinated and asked the fakir as to whether he is 'Sai Baba'. He said – "No, I am only Baba's devotee and on his behalf I have come to inquire your welfare". Out of deep reverence, she bowed down to him and offered dakshina of one rupee. He gave her 'udhi' and left after blessing the family.

. Soon Appa Saheb Kulkarni returned home. His horse was hurt and he had to cancel his week-long trip and return home walking half the distance. He was happy to learn that a fakir resembling Sai Baba visited his residence and felt sorry that he could not have his 'darshan'. Even though he was tired, he did not take food or rest and went in search of that fakir all over the town. He could not trace him. He came home and told his wife – "When Baba comes, you pay only one rupee! If I were at home, I would have paid him at least ten rupees". Appa Saheb Kulkarni had a good desire! How can it go unfulfilled!

After lunch, taking a friend along with him, he again went in search of the fakir. Very soon they saw a fakir who resembled in every detail Sai Baba in the picture at his residence! Emotionally Appa Saheb Kulkarni was so much moved, he forgot about his intention of giving him ten rupees 'dakshina'. He gave him one rupee. The fakir asked – "Give me more." One after another he gave nine one rupee coins. He still wanted more. He brought him home and gave him a ten rupee note. The fakir took the note and returned the nine coins and said – "Take care of these coins. This is Sai Baba's gift to you as a token of nine-fold devotion." Appa Saheb Kulkarni remembered his own intention of giving ten rupees to that fakir and reverentially bowed down to him.

29

TENETS OF FAITH AND SURRENDER

*D*asa Ganu's *kirtan*s quickly spread the cult of Sai devotion among common people like Lakshmichand and countless people started visiting Shirdi. Nana Saheb Chandorkar's personal contact and position brought many of his friends from the official circle – learned people to Sai Baba! As he was in Government service, wherever he went, Nana Chandorkar carried on the mission of propagating Sai Baba's benevolence to humanity. Since his own outstanding experience during his daughter Maina's delivery, he always used to keep Baba's udhi with him. Of course, that was not for himself! It was to give relief to the needy! Since many had the experience of Baba's grace through udhi they would always rush to Nana Chandorkar in an event of emergency!

A friend of Nana Chandorkar had a strange experience. His daughter was staying in a far off place and was affected with plague. He received a telegram from her! He had heard about Baba's udhi and its miracles. He rushed to Nana Chandorkar and requested for Baba's blessings to his daughter. He met Nana outside Thane railway station, as he was proceeding to Kalyan with his wife. Since he did not have udhi with him, he took some mud from the ground and praying to Baba, applied it on his wife's forehead, considering her as his friend's daughter! It indeed worked! The girl in the far off town got relief exactly at the same moment and soon she recovered! No wonder thereafter all members of the family became ardent devotees of Sai Baba!

In this manner, Nana Chandorkar too was responsible for the spread of Sai devotion and for drawing more and more devotees to Shirdi.

One such person had written a pathetic letter to Nana Chandorkar while he was at Jamner. He was Bhimaji Patil of Junnar. He was a benevolent and a virtuous person. Unfortunately he was afflicted with tuberculosis and was counting his last days. Being a moneyed person he had tried all remedies as well as propitiated Gods! With spitting of blood every five minutes, he was reduced to only skin and bone! Frustrated in life, he wrote a long letter to Nana Chandorkar describing his miserable condition and had bid him good bye, as he was facing death! This was the letter that Nana referred to Dasa Ganu when he had come to Jamner. Nana was moved by this letter and wanted to go over to Junnar and personally take Bhimaji Patil to Sai Baba. But it was not convenient, as his son-in-law had passed away at that time and Maina's delivery was also due any moment. Hence he wrote a letter to Bhimaji Patil asking him to surrender to Sai Baba! He had seen where human efforts failed Baba's work began! Hence with that confidence Nana would rush personally to help those in distress.

The letter reached Bhimaji Patil and brought a fresh hope of an extention of his life though he had almost reached his death cell! He now felt certain that the remedy suggested by Nana Chandorkar would prove successful. He prepared to leave for Shirdi. He informed Nana about this.

In the meanwhile, Maina had safely come out of her complicated delivery. Nana was also anxious to visit Shirdi after the tonga incident in which Baba as a coachman brought Ramgir to Jamner. On receiving Bhimaji Patil's letter he immediately left for Shirdi. He knew it was essential for Bhimaji Patil to have an independent room! A patient who spits blood every five minutes is detested by all. Nana found it very difficult to get a suitable place for Bhimaji Patil at Shirdi. Ultimately he spoke to Madhava Rao who was able to get a room from Dada Kelkar in Sathe's wada!

Sathe's wada was built by Dada Kelkar's son-in-law, Rao Bahadur Hari Vinayak Sathe. Sathe had very recently become an ardent devotee of Sai Baba. Since his arrival, Baba had taken out one more coin out of his nine in the pouch, for polishing along with others. Thus Sathe was the sixth coin under Baba's polishing regime. He too was a deputy collector like Nana Chandorkar in the government service. He came in contact with Dada Kelkar while he was posted at Ahmednagar. Sathe was a widower at that time. He was forty-nine and had no issue. Though he was not prepared to marry again, his friends pressurised him. He agreed for a second marriage only if Baba approved. When Dada Kelkar took his daughter to Sai Baba, he readily approved of her marriage with Hari Vinayak Sathe and also predicted a son! In this way both Kelkar and Sathe came in close contact with Baba and both began to visit Shirdi quite often. As Kelkar had no other ties he decided to settle in Shirdi with his wife. Sathe too thought of constructing his own building with a view to use it for himself and accommodate visitors who were now coming in large numbers. In consultation with Baba he selected the land surrounding the neem tree and soon built a spacious building there. Dada Kelkar and his wife shifted there and looked after its management.

Nana Chandorkar was happy that he got a room in this building for Bhimaji Patil in close to Baba's Guru's shrine and now he awaited Bhimaji's arrival!

Next day evening the bullock cart carrying Bhimaji Patil arrived outside Baba's mosque. Since he was unable to sit, he was brought in a lying position. Nana and Madhava Rao rushed ahead to give a helping hand. Bhimaji Patil's condition was far worse than what Nana expected and he wondered as to whether he had rightly advised him to undertake a tedious journey in that condition. Suddenly his mind prompted him – 'It is Baba who has brought him here by prompting you to advice him'. This brought tranquility. Nana prayed to Baba to cure Bhimaji Patil's illness.

Nana and Madhava Rao helped Bhimaji Patil get down from the cart. The moment he stepped down he coughed out blood profusely! Nana was shocked! A stillness gripped the mosque! In fact, everyone doubted as to whether Bhimaji Patil could be carried up to Baba at all! All eyes were transfixed on him and everybody held fast his breath with fear of Bhimaji Patil dying in their very presence! Baba watched all this and felt sorry that Nana in spite of his scholarship and maturity is yet to develop detachment!

Nana and Madhava Rao carried Bhimaji Patil to Baba. There he stood on his legs and tried to kneel down. He lost his balance and fell down! They made him sit near Baba. Everybody was restless. Baba said to Nana – "Nana, how many such thieves you would bring and throw on my feet?" Nana was shocked and was unable to grasp the meaning of Bhimaji Patil being called a 'thief'. He was wondering as to whether Baba was angry that he was brought in there without his consent.

Though Nana kept quiet, Madhava Rao boldly asked him – "Baba, you call this gentleman a 'thief'?" Baba answered him – "Yes Shama, these people who have already reached the door of death deprive me of everything I possess! To save them from death you bring him here. But I have to pay a very high price to bring them back." As he said this, Baba applied udhi to Bhimaji Patil's forehead. Quickly he kept his head on Baba's feet. Baba raised him and said – "So you were dreaming! Tell us what you saw?"

Bhimaji Patil remembered the vision he had just seen as he collapsed while trying to kneel down! He said – "Baba, a dark coloured giant pulled me down and sat on my chest. At that time you came running and chased him out! Baba, I surrender to you! Please save me!"

Baba assured Bhimaji Patil – "Do not worry, dear! Believe me! One who climbs the steps of this Dwarakamai is out of trouble for ever! Sit down here for an hour and have no fear." Nana thought that Bhimaji Patil would not be able to sit for such a long time. He told Baba – "Baba he coughs out blood every five minutes! Will he be able to sit that long?" Baba smiled at him – "Nana, why do you worry for everything? I told you – 'you look to me, I will look to you'!" Baba reminded Nana of this great pronouncement!

Bhimaji Patil on the other hand was calm. He sat leaning against the wall. He had totally forgotten that he was coughing out blood every now and then. He was watching every movement of Baba. Though this Loving God incarnated on this earth to lead people on spirituality, people would come to him with worldly problems. Some pertaining to health, some with money, some with domestic problems and hardly anyone with spiritual inquiry!

Bhimaji Patil who was suffering from tuberculosis was watching Baba's extraordinary remedies prescribed individually in every case. He was highly impressed with Baba's divinity. When the local tailor Bala approached Baba with malaria fever and was shivering, Baba advised him to feed curd rice to a black dog near Lakshmi temple! To one Swami coming from Alandi with earache, Baba applied udhi on his forehead! Dattopant from Harda came rolling with griping pain in abdomen and the duration of illness was fourteen years! Mere application of udhi reduced his pain! Bhimaji Patil realised that now Baba would pull him out of death!

As Dattopant got relieved, another patient was brought before Baba by his two servants and attended by his family doctor too! His name was Gopalrao Buti, a very rich person from Nagpur. His family physician Pillai had tried all remedies to cure Gopalrao Buti's long standing problem of vomiting and diarrhoea, had at last brought him to Baba.

Seeing Gopalrao Buti, Baba shouted – "Mind you, if you come up again!" This was the warning given to the disease! It vanished immediately. Without realising this, his family physician Pillai asked Baba – "He has been vomiting and got diarrhoea. What shall I offer him" Baba casually told him – "Give him walnuts, almonds, pista all mashed up in milk!" Pillai thought that Baba was joking!

Madhava Rao asked the doctor to follow Baba's advice. Gopalrao Buti also had implicit faith in Baba. Though the doctor was reluctant, he followed Baba's instructions! Gopalrao Buti not only recovered from a chronic disease but also he and his doctor became ardent devotees of Baba.

After sending Gopalrao Buti, Baba started polishing one more coin. Madhava Rao could immediately guess that the coin represented Gopalrao Buti. It was Baba's seventh coin!

Baba permitted Bhimaji Patil also to leave. Nana said – "I am taking him to Sathe's wada. I have obtained an independent room for him there."

Baba reacted – "Nana, take him to Bhimabai's house. Let him stay there for a couple of months!" Nana had no guts to contradict! He and Madhava Rao moved ahead to carry Bhimaji Patil. Baba was furious. He said – "Shama, what did I say? Take him – not carry! Make him walk!"

Those who had seen how Bhimaji Patil was brought wondered as to how he could walk to the other end of the village. While entering the mosque, he was carried. His weak legs were unable to support the weight of his own body and he had collapsed! Baba's command to make him walk worried everyone. But Bhimaji was enchanted by Baba's powers. He had forgotten about his illness. He got up, bowed to Baba and started walking slowly!

Just as Bhimaji Patil stepped out of the mosque, a lizard on the ceiling inside chirped conspicuously. A devotee asked Baba – "What does it indicate?" Baba explained in his mystic manner – "Dear fellow, she is chirping happily to express her joy! Her sister is coming from Ahmednagar! Just wait and watch." Everybody thought that Baba was just joking. As they all watched, a devotee riding a horse arrived outside the mosque. Apparently he had travelled a long distance. All eyes turned towards him. Baba now reminded the questioner – "Are you watching? Watch now carefully. The sister of that lizard has arrived from Ahmednagar."

The horseman tied up his horse and emptied the fodder bag in front of the horse. Along with fodder a lizard jumped out, chirped and straightaway moved towards the mosque. It came in and moved over the wall and then on to the ceiling! It went to the first lizard which was already there. Both lizards happily chirped and kissed each other. Dumbfounded with this miracle of Baba the devotees expressed their happiness.

Bhimaji Patil and Nana reached Bhimabai's house. Looking at it they were simply shocked! The ground was recently dug and levelled with mud, with beaters! Naturally the floor was wet! Nana thought that asking a TB patient to sleep on a damp floor is like inviting death! He felt like going back to Baba to seek his permission to shift Bhimaji Patil to Sathe's wada. But Bhimaji Patil was firm in his faith. He told Nana not to worry about the damp ground as he will obey Baba's instructions to stay there for two months. Since Nana was leaving Shirdi next day, Bhimaji Patil invited him to participate in the sathyanarayana pooja which he intended to perform after two months of stay at Shirdi. Nana said in affirmative and left.

That night at Bhimabai's house, Bhimaji Patil had a sound sleep. Cough, spitting of blood every five minutes, pain in the chest – all had vanished! In the early hours, he had a dream. In that dream he saw a teacher of his school days caning him severely. To see oneself being caned in a dream is considered very auspicious. That clears up all our troubles. Whatever it may be, Bhimaji Patil felt very much better next morning and he himself went to the mosque for Baba's darshan.

Two months were over in no time and Bhimaji Patil was cured completely! The Sathyanarayana pooja which Bhimaji Patil performed before leaving Shirdi to his village Narayangaon proved to be a memorable experience! From that function, Bhimaji Patil took a vow that he will observe it on every poornima and it was aptly named 'Sai Sathyanarayana Pooja'.

30

AVOID GREED AND INFATUATION FOR WEALTH

*I*t was 1909! Baba's fame had reached nooks and corners of the country and thousands of devotees hovered around him like the bees around a honey-comb and started coming to Shirdi. The mosque and the pandal outside were not sufficient for the surging crowds. It was inconvenient to all. Even Baba could not sit comfortably and have free space for physical movements. Moreover the mosque needed repairs! Nana Chandorkar had observed this but had no courage to ask Baba for making any changes in the present setup.

Earlier Gopal Rao Gund thought of renovation and extension of the mosque soon after he was blessed with a child. But Baba directed him to undertake repair in Hanuman temple, Shani Deo and later Lakshmi temple. The mosque remained unattended!

Nana Chandorkar was waiting for an opportunity to seek Baba's approval for renovation of the mosque and its extension. Gopalrao Buti was always accompanied by his family physician, Dr.Chidambara Pillai. He developed a guinea worm abscess in his right leg. It was very difficult for him to walk from Sathe's wada and so he sought Baba's approval to stay and lie down in the mosque itself. But there was hardly any space in the mosque to stretch his legs and he was afraid that his legs would touch Baba. However,

Baba told him that even if his legs touched him, he would not mind as he is a slave of his devotees! One day Pillai requested Baba to transfer his suffering to a next birth. Baba smiled at him and said, "Why do you ask for suffering in your next birth! Bear it out for a while! A crow will come and prick you and you will be all right. Just stretch your legs and lie down comfortably."

The very idea of a crow to come and prick him shuddered Dr.Pillai. He looked around to see if a crow was already sitting in the mosque. He could only see a black dog. He was still scared that the dog might eat his leg! So he withdrew his leg! Baba saw that and said – "No, no! The dog will not eat your leg. It has no strength! Come, stretch your leg, and be comfortable."

With Baba's assurance, Pillai stretched his legs. Then Baba spoke to Lakshmi to get him something to eat. She went home and brought three breads with onion. Baba took two pieces of bread and gave them to the dog. Lakshmi was annoyed and protested that if he was feeding the dog, there was no need for him to make her run home and bake the breads. To please her, he took the other piece of bread and ate with the onions!

Seeing Baba eat onions, a visitor in the crowd was shocked! He was a Brahmin Pandit well versed in Vedas and had come to Baba to seek a solution in the Vedanta! He thought in his mind – "How can this saint who eats onions solve my problem?" He wanted to return! Baba read his mind and told Madhava Rao – "Shama, one who can digest onion can eat it! Reading vedas and upanishads will not give you knowledge! You have to practice it! When pandits do not understand it, how can Lakshmi appreciate my feeding this dog?" The learned pandit knew that Baba was referring to his own thoughts. He listened to Baba further. Baba turned to Lakshmi and said – "Lakshmi, am I different from this dog? I felt his hunger because the same divinity within him is also in me. I am one with everyone! Please do not consider anyone inferior or low, nor misbehave with anyone!"

On the pretext of feeding the dog with Lakshmi's breads, Baba enlightened his devotees that he pervades in all beings! This also solved the problem of the Brahmin pandit! One more person, Dada Kelkar also got his lesson!

Dada Kelkar was the father-in-law of Hari Vinayak Sathe and was looking after Sathe's wada. He had come to Baba to seek remedy for his granddaughter who had an eye problem. That morning he had insulted the mother-in-law of Nachane for cutting onions in Sathe's wada, as Dada Kelkar had forbidden use of onions there! Now Baba looked at Dada Kelkar and told him to apply onion juice to his granddaughter's eyes! Dada Kelkar expressed that he does not have onions and may buy one or two! Baba told him to approach Nachane who would oblige him! Dada Kelkar apologised to Nachane and obtained onions from him!

Baba called Dada Kelkar and told him to bring five seers of onion and ten seers of mutton from Korhale next day, as he was planning a feast for devotees! Dada Kelkar was uncomfortable. An orthodox Brahmin to get mutton and onion was unthinkable! Without a word of protest, he collected money from Nana Nimonkar and left the place! His ego was dissolved!

Baba felt a pity for Dada Kelkar! He told Madhava Rao to send somebody else to fetch mutton from Korhale and to advise Dada Kelkar to behave with humility. "Let him follow his discipline of not eating onions but not abuse others. Let him understand that I am in everyone. "

Baba's advice melted the hearts of all! On many occasions Baba has given this fervent call to all his devotees. But how many have practised it?

Dr.Pillai was watching all this. Forgetting his leg pain, he was imbibing Baba's words of wisdom. Baba was aware of his problem!

It was the evening time. Abdulla was lighting up lamps in the mosque! To light the lamp hanging above Baba's seat, Abdulla moved forward carefully making room for himself in the jam-packed crowd sitting around Baba. As he lighted the lamp, unintentionally he placed his foot over the leg of Pillai which he had stretched! Dr.Pillai screamed with pain! Abdulla had placed his foot right over the swollen wound in Pillai's leg, which instantly burst open the abscess. The pus along with worms had come out. Pillai still wailed in pain and to conceal it he started singing! Baba smiled and told Nana Chandorkar – "Listen, Nana! Pillai has begun to sing now!" He stopped singing and asked Baba as to when the crow will come? Baba told him – "Abdulla is the crow! Has he not opened the abscess? You were talking of next birth! Now go and take rest! Your problem is solved!"

Everyone felt relieved that Dr.Pillai has come out of his suffering. Baba looked up at Nana Chandorkar and said – "Nana, now our place is too small to accommodate the crowd!" Nana told his plan of renovation and extension. Baba approved it and asked him to start the work immediately! However Nana had to return next day. He arranged for skilled workers and purchase of bricks, sand, wood and entrusted Nana Nimonkar with the responsibility of supervision.

Next day, after Baba left for Lendi baug, the extension work began. Kondaji, Gobaji, and Tukaram decided to work day and night to complete the task at the earliest. With many ardent devotees sharing the work, it was a smooth issue. But Baba himself created several obstacles! He was only testing the patience and endurance of devotees! Pretending anger he would dislodge and throw away big stones, bricks and pillars! He would abuse and beat the workers! Once he held Tatya by neck, pulled out a pillar and threw his turban into 'dhuni'! Later he asked Madhava Rao to bring a gold-threaded turban! Indeed it was not wrath but worship of the place!

During the renovation work, Baba used to sleep in the chawadi in the nights and spend the day hours with Kushalchand at Rahata or Nana Dengale at Neemgaon. On completion of the work, the devotees planned to reinstall the Loving God in the mosque by bringing him in a procession from Neemgaon to Shirdi. With the usual paraphernalia, a palanquin, Shamakarna horse, beating of musical drums, singing devotional songs and loud cheers of slogans the devotees reached Neemgaon.

As the procession reached Nana Dengale's house, Baba came out and gave darshan to all. Nana Dengale's daughter-in-law waved aarti to Baba. With shouts of slogans, the procession started from Neemgaon to Shirdi. Baba walked in front of the palanquin. Mhalsapathy was dancing like a child to the accompaniment of musical drums. Even though Mhalsapathy was in absolute poverty, Baba did not give him any material wealth but gave him peace of mind and wealth of renunciation!

To receive Baba the entire Shirdi was well decorated with flower garlands, buntings, and flags. Years ago, a similar procession was conducted from Rahata to Shirdi when Baba returned with Jawahar Ali. Now with thousands of people from surrounding villagers, it was a sight to see. Mothers waved 'aarti' to Baba and people broke coconuts. The mosque had a new appearance. Baba went up and sat in his seat. His aarti was done with fervour!

Suddenly Baba shouted – "Throw him out! Throw him out of this masjid! I am a Muslim! He is a Hindu! He says how can a Muslim be a Sadguru? Considers it a sin to bow down to a Muslim! How can he find Shiva in a mosque?

Thinks that God is only in Hindu temples! Send him to Triambakeshwar! Send him to Kashi Visweswar!" As he shouted, Baba ran towards the entrance, picked up a stone, and prevented a young Gujarati boy entering the mosque with Dada Kelkar. His name was Megha!

Megha was a Brahmin boy employed as a cook to Hari Vinayak Sathe when he was posted as a collector at Khaira. Sathe was impressed by this boy who was doing *Divya Nama Smaran* of *Om Namah Shivaya*. Sathe initiated him in *Gayatri* mantra and thought he will be spiritually uplifted if he gets the grace of Sai Baba. At first, Megha refused to go to Sai Baba as he had a hatred against Muslims. On repeated glorification of Sai Baba by Sathe, ultimately he agreed to go to Shirdi. Sathe wrote a note of introduction to his father-in-law Dada Kelkar who was looking after Sathe's wada. Dada Kelkar had now brought Megha to the mosque.

Since he had a prejudice against Muslims and seeing Baba in fury with a stone in hand, Megha knew that Baba's blurting concerned him only. He retraced his steps from the mosque and ran away. Poor Dada Kelkar had to run behind him! After Megha eloped, Baba resumed his seat!

It was a difficult task for Dada Kelkar to convince Megha and bring him back to the mosque. As they returned, a person was getting down from a tonga and inquiring about Sai Baba. Dada Kelkar guided him to the mosque and took Megha with him. Megha chose a place carefully so that he could run for safety, if Baba gets angry again. He was watching Baba!

The visitor who had just entered appeared to be in a hurry. He bypassed the others in the line and went near Baba. He told him that he has everything in life but desired that should grant him *Brahma Jnana*. Baba was very happy and assured him that he will be granted 'Brahma Jnana'.

Baba accosted a village boy sitting in the crowd and told him – "Ganya, go to Nandu Marwadi and tell him I need a loan of five rupees. This man, right here has to go to Mumbai and has no money! He is worried. Tell Nandu that I will return his five rupees as soon as I collect some dakshina!" Indeed that man needed money to go back to Mumbai. He was jobless and had offered all his money to Baba. He felt relieved as Baba will solve his problem!

The boy returned empty-handed as Nandu Marwadi was out of town. Baba sent him to three to four persons. Nowhere he could meet anyone or get the money. Everyone was expecting a divine discourse of granting Brahma Jnana to the visitor. But Baba was wasting time in getting five rupees as loan! Megha too doubted this Muslim fakir's ability to explain Brahma!

The visitor was impatient. He said – "Baba, My tonga is waiting. I have to pay waiting charges. Please give me 'Brahma Jnana' quickly!"

As if suddenly coming out of a forgotten thought, Baba said – "Oh dear! I totally forgot about it! But tell me why was I playing all this drama? You are feeling sorry that you will have to pay two more rupees for delaying that tonga. With that big bundle of currency notes in your pocket your mind is dying for those two rupees!" Listening to this, the visitor quickly made sure that the bundle was still safe in his pocket!

Baba spoke ahead – "Listen dear, what is wrong if the poor coachman gets two rupees more as waiting charges? You are asking for great knowledge of 'Brahma Jnana' – but you cannot get rid of this infatuation for money. How can one have 'Brahma Jnana' like this? To acquire that great knowledge of 'Brahma Jnana' one must strip off these coats of attachments! Attachments cause ego – a desire to possess! This fascination to possess creates infatuation, greed, lust, anger, pride and jealousy in human beings. These are the six enemies – *Ari Shadwargas* which keep man away from Brahma – the God! With this greed for wealth a man does not recognise a man, father forgets his own son, wife knows not her husband, a brother is not a brother, and a friend is not a friend! The only thing a man recognises is money! Let me tell you a story – that of a frog and of a cobra!"

Baba began his story. He was a treasure of such parables. They would always end in preaching spiritual oneness. While narrating such stories Baba would always implicate himself to give a personal touch!

Baba said – "Once I went near the bank of a river along with a friend. We heard a frog croaking in distress. My friend went and saw that a big serpent had caught a frog and told me that he will eat him alive. I told him that it is not possible and I am going to give relief to the frog.

We went near and I spoke to the snake – 'Well Veerabhadrappa, you have come back as a snake in this life due to your enmity in the previous life. This Channabasappa too is reborn as a frog. You have not forgotten your enmity even in this birth!' Listening to my voice, the cobra released the frog and disappeared into a bush. The frog too jumped in the river and was out of sight. Then I narrated their past life to my friend."

Baba told the visitor who had asked for 'Brahma Jnana' this very story of how infatuation for wealth carries on enmity life after life. All devotees gathered in the mosque had a feast of the discourse by Baba.

The story narrated by Baba was a tale of three births. Before two births, Channabasappa who was a frog was now a poor widow. She had mortgaged a piece of land to a rich man for a paltry sum. In that village, people wanted to renovate a Shiva temple and made that rich man the treasurer. He was a miser and did not spend any money for temple renovation and also siphoned off the public collection also. Lord Shiva gave a dream vision to the rich man's wife and asked her to undertake temple work out of her personal funds and in return he would bless her ten times that money! The rich man did not believe in his wife's dream and being selfish, did not want to spend any money. The wife was adamant and offered the jewellery her father had given her. The rich man wanted to cheat his wife as well as Lord Shiva! He valued the jewellery for one thousand rupees and instead of paying her cash, he transferred the mortgaged land of the widow to his wife's name. He had grabbed that land for almost nothing. His wife offered that land to the temple but her dream of paying cash for temple renovation remained unfulfilled! The public had to collect funds again and rebuild Lord Shiva's temple. One day when the widow went to the rich man to clear her debt and get the mortgaged land, she was chased out! She was unhappy and left cursing the rich man!

Soon thereafter, there was a storm which devastated the town finishing up everything. That rich man, his wife, their big house, and the poor widow – all were wiped out due to this natural calamity! What remained were Lord Shiva's temple and its priest, who by heredity and tradition had a claim on the temple property and its income.

The rich man's wife was reborn as the only daughter of the temple priest, perhaps to complete her unfulfilled service to Lord Shiva! The widow was reborn as the only son of that priest, perhaps to re-establish the claim on the land that was presented to the temple! With his desires unfulfilled the rich man took birth in a Brahmin family in a distant place. The priest's daughter was named Gowri while the son was named Channabasappa. The rich man reborn in a distant place was named Veerabhadrappa!

The children grew up. Veerabhadrappa became rich and wealthy! As destiny would have it he reached Gowri's town and became attached to the priest and his family. In course of time he married Gowri. In another body, Sai Baba too lived in that place. Gowri and her family members were devoted to him and used to consult him for solving their problems. Gowri took her husband Veerabhadrappa also to him.

Lord Shiva blessed the family. An offer of a lakh of rupees came for the barren land presented to the temple. Half the amount was received in cash and the balance with interest in installments. As per tradition, half of the temple income should go to the priest and as such Channabasappa put his claim on those installments. In the meanwhile, Veerabhadrappa had grabbed the money received by his wife through her father. He started scheming to do away with the other share too! Thus a fight started between Veerabhadrappa and Channabasappa. The quarrel was referred to Sai Baba and he gave a decision that Veerabhadrappa should return Gowri her share first and the installments of the other half should go to Channabasappa.

This decision was not palatable to Veerabhadrappa. He accused Baba of favouritism. Gowri apologised to Baba on her husband's behalf.

Lord Shiva gave Gowri a dream vision in which he said – "The land is in your name! So half its price goes only to you. The other half belongs to Channabasappa, as the hereditary priest. The interest on it should be spent for temple expenses. For that you consult Baba." The dream was over.

Next day Gowri narrated this dream vision to Baba. He called Veerabhadrappa and Channabasappa and told them about it. Veerabhadrappa was upset and in a fury threatened Channabasappa that he would kill him. Channabasappa urged Baba to save him from the clutches of Veerabhadrappa. Baba assured him that he will protect him!

However, with Veerabhadrappa's threats, Channabasappa was horrified that he collapsed and died! Seeing him dead, Veerabhadrappa too ran away from that place and on the way, he too died! Both had left their bodies leaving behind their desire over the money that land had fetched. As a result Veerabhadrappa was born as a serpent while Channabasappa took birth as an ever timid frog. Even as a snake, Veerabhadrappa had traced his enemy Channabasappa as a frog and wanted to kill him. But Baba, who had promised to save him, appeared near the river bank and the wicked Veerabhadrappa had to give up his prey and run for life!

Here ended Baba's story! Baba spoke to that visitor asking for *Brahma Jnana* – "So, did you see what happens with infatuation for money? You have come here seeking 'Brahma Jnana' while you are carrying a pack of greed in your pocket! Brahma means the understanding of oneness of soul – *Aham Brahmasmi* which means 'I am Brahman myself'! I am the entire universe! This feeling itself is the essence of 'Brahma Jnana'. This poor man is a part of that Brahma. To give him five rupees for his return journey, I have been sending this boy to different persons seeking a loan of five rupees and I could not get it! You have two hundred rupees in your pocket and even after seeing me struggling to get a loan of five rupees, you do not want to help me! You are sitting on a heap of money! Spend some money in charity and have the blessings of those who are deprived of divine grace. With that you will realise 'Brahma Jnana'!" The visitor took out the bundle of notes. It was exactly two hundred rupees! He gave five rupees to the devotee who needed it for his return journey. With Baba's blessings he returned to his place.

Whether the visitor got an inkling of Brahma Jnana or not, Megha who was standing near the entrance was deeply impressed by Baba's clairvoyance and his clear-cut

exposition and guidance on Brahma Jnana. Baba's reference
to Lord Shiva in the parable made him change his opinion
that Baba is a Muslim! Seeing all devotees reverentially
bowing to Baba, Meghan too came forward and bowed
down to Baba! Baba placed his hand of blessings on his
head!

31

ADVENT OF KAKA DIXIT

*M*egha could not sleep well that night! Though he had prostrated before Baba, he was still confused! He was wondering as to whether he has done the right thing. Sathe had requested his father-in-law Dada Kelkar to provide accommodation in Sathe's personal room so that he could attend to his Brahminical rituals like japa, meditation etc., without being disturbed by other inmates in Sathe's wada.

As he went to bed, Megha was absorbed in the thoughts of Baba. In the dim light of a kerosene lamp he was gazing at the full size portrait of Baba hung on the opposite wall. In spite of watching superhuman powers of Baba, his mind was still wavering in accepting him as his Guru. He had half mind to leave Shirdi next morning itself! He thought that the portrait of Sai Baba is making him restless and hence he put off the kerosene lamp and in complete darkness slept off! But Baba had a different plan!

A voice in the room called him – "Megha! Megha!" Megha woke up with a start! The room was filled with a sweet perfume! He could see a brilliant flame approaching his bed! It took the form of Sai Baba! Instantly Megha sat up! He was astonished as to how Baba could enter his room which he had bolted from inside! Baba raised his hand and threw rice from the tips of his fingers! With the halo of light surrounding Baba, Megha could clearly see everything around! As he was still mystified, Baba spoke – "Megha, wake up! Get up soon! Draw a trident!" Saying this Baba gradually disappeared along with the nimbus that surrounded his divine form, leaving the room in total darkness again! Megha quickly got down and ran towards the door to find out where Baba has gone! In the dark he collided against the wall and the framed photograph of Sai Baba fell down with a loud sound and the glass was broken to several pieces! Kelkar who was sleeping in the next room woke up with a start and rushed to Megha's room with a lamp in his hand. The room was still bolted from inside. He began to call aloud – "Megha, Megha, what is the matter? Open the door!" Megha groped for the bolt and finally unlocked the door. He was totally excited and spoke to Kelkar – "Baba came into the room and I ran to the door in dark to find out as to how he entered while the door was bolted from inside. I collided against Baba's portrait and it came down crashing on the ground. I am sorry I have broken it." He was totally frightened!

"Baba entered while the room was closed?" Kelkar was surprised himself. "Yes, Dadaji, he threw rice all over and said –'Megha, wake up and draw a trident'!" With the lantern still in his hand, Dada Kelkar searched the room. Indeed rice was scattered all over the place. Keeping down the lantern, Kelkar prostrated flat on the floor to offer his respect the invisible presence of Sai Baba. The rice and the sweet fragrance that filled the room had emotionally moved him! Kelkar was sure that Baba had visited that room. Both Megha and Kelkar removed the glass pieces and kept the portrait aside.

Kelkar told Megha "Megha, branding Sai Baba as a Muslim you bore a grudge against him. That is why he visited your room. No one truly knows his real religion. He does not like being called a Hindu. He does not want himself to be known as a Muslim. He does not belong to any faith. Being a 'Maha Shivaratri' day tomorrow and as you are a devotee of Lord Shiva, Baba must have asked you to draw a trident. He believes in a faith which teaches that everybody should follow his deity and not criticise others. We will go to him in the morning and ask him as to why he wants you to draw a trident." Dada Kelkar left and Megha too slept into a deep slumber!

Finishing his rituals and worship in the morning Megha accompanied Dada Kelkar to the mosque. Baba was holding a big 'Shiva linga' which a devotee had presented it to him. Seeing Megha, Baba called him "Come on, come on Bholenath!" Convinced with Baba's knowledge of his innermost secrets, Megha went up and sat near Baba. Kelkar too followed. Bala Saheb Mirikar and Madhava Rao Deshpande were also there.

Baba asked Megha – "Well pandit, did you draw the trident?" Dada Kelkar and Megha meaningfully looked at each other. Timidly Megha spoke to Baba – "Baba, I thought it was a mere dream!"

Baba exclaimed – "Dream? My dear young man, did I not throw rice in your room so that you do not consider it a mere dream?" Megha replied – "Yes, Baba! But how could you enter the room while the door was bolted from inside?"

Baba replied – "My movements are not restricted by stone walls, closed doors, or transoceanic distances! I do not move physically! I travel in subtle form! Hence believe me, I am always with you wherever you are! Come, have this Shiva linga! This is for you! Worship it daily!"

Megha was very happy to receive Shiva linga on the day of Maha Shiva Ratri. With tears of gratitude, he kept his head on Baba's feet and mentally vowed that he will not make any distinction between Hindus and Muslims or people of any faith and overcome hatred for anyone on this earth.

Dada Kelkar, however could not keep quiet. He told everything to Baba and said – "Baba, the glass in the photo frame of your picture was broken by Megha as he collided against the wall in darkness. Is it a bad omen?" Baba avoided a direct reply – "A good omen or a bad omen! Why do you worry about it? A body is like a glass! It is bound to break some day! But the spirit in it – the 'Atma' is immortal! Bear it in mind that you have to leave any moment and use every minute of your life in the thought of God and in the service of man! Search opportunities to serve humanity! A day wasted without service to mankind is like a day spent without remembering God!" Then turning to Megha, Baba said – "Megha, send the photo frame to Ahmednagar with Balasaheb Mirikar. He will have a glass fixed to it. Today he will observe Maha Shivaratri here and he is proceeding to Ahmednagar tomorrow!"

Mirikar expressed his willingness to do it. He was on leave and had come to Shirdi for Baba's darshan and was proceeding to his native place Ahmednagar. Baba spoke to him – "Mirikar, you need not come here exclusively to return the photo back to Megha. Shama is coming to Nagar after four days and he will bring it back."

This was a surprise to Madhava Rao as he had no plans to visit Ahmednagar and did not see any reason for it. But he was sure that as Baba has said something might happen which may take him to Ahmednagar in the next four days. However, he made sure to tell Bala Saheb Mirikar to send the photo through someone else, in case he is not able to visit Ahmednagar!

Megha wrapped the photo carefully and handed it over to Mirikar. He placed the Shiva Linga in the place where Baba's portrait adorned. He drew a trident on the wall. He walked all the way to Kopergaon, brought water from river Godavari and some bilva leaves. He then performed 'abhisheka' to Shiva linga and did *archana* with *bilva* leaves. At that time, he desired that he should do the same *abhisheka* and archana to Sai Baba, whom he considered as Shiva in human form! He also desired that he should do daily worship of Baba in the mosque. He decided to seek Baba's permission for all this!

When Bala Saheb Mirikar reached Ahmednagar his father eagerly awaited him. He had received a telegram from their family friend Kaka Dixit, a famous solicitor in Mumbai who was visiting Ahmednagar!

Kaka Dixit's full name was Hari Seetharam Dixit. With an excellent academic record, he had acquitted himself creditably as a leading lawyer earning money and fame. He was a critic of the British Government and had won plenty of political cases. Britishers were scared of him, at the same time adored him for his scholarship. He was connected with Mumbai Municipality and many political and social organisations. He was a member of the Legislative Assembly and was closely associated with Sir Pheroze Shaw Mehta of the Congress party. In 1906, when he was in London for some work he met with an accident causing an injury in his right leg. He developed a permanent partial disablement even though he underwent best treatment possible. Nana Saheb Chandorkar, who was a close friend of Kaka Dixit, suggested that he should visit Sai Baba to have the deformity of his right leg cured! Kaka Dixit readily agreed to go and see Sai Baba not for his physical deformity but at least to seek peace of mind! As the elections to Legislative Assembly were forthcoming, Kaka Dixit as a candidate had to visit Ahmednagar to look after election propaganda work. In this trip he planned a visit to Shirdi also!

Seeing Kaka Dixit's telegram, Bala Saheb Mirikar knew that he would be required to give him a lot of time when he arrived. So he got Baba's photo repaired immediately without losing time. He brought it home and kept it in a central place in their drawing room well covered with a curtain to protect it against dust. May be, Baba deliberately came to stay there because of Kaka Dixit's eagerness to see him.

Baba did not stop there. He had planned to give his would-be devotee Kaka Dixit, to be accompanied by Madhava Rao to Shirdi!

After two days, Madhava Rao received a telegram from his father-in-law in Ahmednagar – 'Your mother-in-law is serious. Start immediately'. Madhava Rao left for Ahmednagar in the night train.

On the previous day Kaka Dixit had arrived in Ahmednagar. Since morning till late in the night both Kaka Dixit and Bala Saheb Mirikar worked hard moving from house to house canvassing for Kaka Dixit's candidature. Both were tired when they came home and went to sleep soon after dinner.

Next morning after finishing their bath, rituals and breakfast, Kaka Dixit sat down leisurely to have a chat with the family members of Bala Saheb Mirikar. The topic of Sai Baba came up all of a sudden! Kaka Dixit was happy that Mirikars too were Sai devotees. He therefore expressed his desire to visit Shirdi for Baba's darshan. Hearing Kaka Dixit's desire, Bala Saheb suddenly remembered Baba's picture! He got up quickly and uncovered the photo of Sai Baba kept in the centre of the hall.

The first darshan of Sai Baba in a sitting posture on a large stone in Dwarakamai thrilled Kaka Dixit. He felt Baba's grace on him! It fascinated Kaka Dixit at its very first sight! A picture of a simple fakir! Grey beard, an imposing look, a kind expression, torn clothes, piece of cloth on his head with a big knot protruding on its left side. Style of sitting with right foot folded over the left one resting on the ground – all these exhibited a rich simplicity of a Loving God! Kaka Dixit had a feeling of achieving something he had missed so far in spite of his having everything in life! The lotus feet of Baba attracted him and he gave them a permanent place in his mind. He shed tears of joy in fulfillment of the emptiness of his life. Kaka Dixit spoke to his hosts – "Bala Saheb , this very moment, I feel, my life is complete! Now I am looking forward to my visit to Shirdi. Who can accompany me now to lead me to Baba's feet?"

An answer to Kaka Dixit's question was being searched. Bala Saheb Mirikar had no time to go to Shirdi again. His father was too old to undertake the journey. There was none in the house who could accompany Kaka Dixit to Shirdi. The quietness was suddenly interrupted by a call from outside – "Bala Saheb! Bala Saheb!" It was the familiar voice of Madhava Rao Deshpande. Mirikar gave a sigh of relief and brought him inside.

He introduced Madhava Rao to Kaka Dixit – "Hari Kaka, here is a proof of Baba's omniscience! He has arranged a company for you to Shirdi! This is Madhava Rao, an intimate devotee of Sai Baba, always remaining in his company. You can call him – votary of that Loving God!" Kaka Dixit sincerely greeted him. Even without seeing Baba, Kaka Dixit was so much enchanted that he had begun to respect Baba's associates as Baba himself. Madhava Rao too bowed in response.

Madhava Rao spoke to Bala Saheb Mirikar – "You remember Baba said that I will be visiting Ahmednagar after four days. Actually I had no reason to come here at all. Yesterday I received a telegram from my father-in-law that my mother-in-law is indisposed and had asked me to come here. So I started by the night train and came here this morning. But she has improved and is better now! I think Baba did all this simply to bring me here!"

"Quite likely! That too for this Dixit Kaka!" Mirikar made Baba's intention of bringing Madhava Rao to Ahmednagar very clear. He further said, "Kaka Dixit came here yesterday only for these elections to Legislative Assembly. He is keen on going to Shirdi for Baba's darshan. I am sure Baba sent you only for his sake!"

Though others may consider it very trivial this very first experience of Baba's divinity was most precious for Kaka Dixit! In fact, the peace of mind derived by devout souls like Kaka Dixit, even through such insignificant instances, is so great that they alone know the joy of it! The very thought that Sai Baba sent Madhava Rao for his sake made him extremely happy! He spoke to Madhava Rao – "Yes, Madhava Rao, indeed I was pining to see Baba since the day Nana Chandorkar told me about him. Really I am happy that I am having your company to go to Shirdi!"

"Why Madhava Rao's? It is Baba's company you both will have!" Mirikar intervened. "Baba's photo is accompanying you!" And true it was! Baba's photo is also equally living, potent, and powerful enough to his devotees!

They reached the railway station in the night. As they entered the compartment four more passengers were proceeding to Shirdi. One of them, Pundalik, a pleader from Nanded was known to Kaka Dixit. They had gone to Rajamahandry in Andhra Pradesh to have 'darshan' of a Datta Avadhuta Sri Vasudevananda Saraswati. When the Swami learnt that Pundalik was proceeding to Shirdi, he had given a coconut and had requested Pundalik to hand it over to Sai Baba. Unfortunately, on the way these four persons unintentionally broke that coconut and ate it along with some eatables. When Pundalik discovered that it was the same coconut given by Sri Vasudevananda Saraswati, he was frightened! Next morning all of them reached Shirdi.

Madhava Rao and Kaka Dixit proceeded to Sathe's wada along with Baba's photo. A surprise awaited there! Megha was lying in the bed with fever and Baba himself was personally attending to him. Megha was unconscious. On seeing Baba, Kaka Dixit went into a trance and became stiff! Madhava Rao was frightened but Baba silenced him saying – "This is my eighth coin! Today all the eight are here! Only one more remains and that will also come soon!

Madhava Rao looked around and found that all the eight –
now including Kaka Dixit – were present! Besides himself
there were Mhalsapathy, Tatya Kote, Nana Chandorkar,
Dasa Ganu, Gopalrao Buti and Sathe. Sathe was called
telegraphically due to Megha's illness. Nana Chandorkar
had arrived the previous evening. And Dasa Ganu had
come the previous night to have a clarification from Baba
as he encountered a difficulty while translating 'Ishavasya
Upanishad' into Marathi. Since Baba had come to sit
near Megha from early hours of the morning they all had
gathered around him in the wada. To this group was added
Kaka Dixit!

Baba applied udhi to Megha. He regained consciousness
but was blurting about Baba's picture! When he saw Baba
himself, he folded his hands and requested him to be with
him always. Baba said – "My dear ones, my body, or my
picture will perish one day or the other. What will remain
forever is my image that you have instilled in your hearts.
That is why I repeatedly tell you to see me in everyone, in
humans and animals! Then you will realise the eternal truth
– the truth that I am Himself, He is yourself, and you are
myself! Once you realise this truth, you need not come to
Shirdi to see me. Believe me, wherever you are, I am always
with you!"

Baba returned to the mosque. Kaka Dixit too was out
of his trance now! On reaching the mosque Baba took out
one more coin from his purse and as he started polishing
it, spoke to Kaka Dixit – "So you have arrived! Since you
desired to visit Shirdi, I sent Shama to Ahmednagar!" Kaka
Dixit's eyes were filled with tears. Baba's words moved
Kaka Dixit emotionally! He totally surrendered himself to
Baba. He came with a temporal distress but the moment he
arrived in Shirdi his lame mind moved towards salvation!

While polishing Kaka Dixit's coin, Baba made him
sit near him. Baba called Pundalik and asked him for the

coconut given by Sri Vasudevananda Saraswati. Pundalik began to tremble and was on the verge of tears. He profusely apologised and offered to get another coconut. Baba told him – "Do not be silly! Nothing can compare with that coconut! And why do you blame yourself? It was my will that Swamiji gave you that coconut, with my will it was broken up and eaten by you all! Remember everything happens according to divine will! Keeping this in mind, offer all your thoughts and actions to God. That way you will not get yourself bound by 'karma' or the so called destiny! Happiness or sorrow is God-given! Accept them equally! Then they will not affect your mind either way! Go home and be happy!" He blessed the group and lovingly gave them a farewell!

It was a feast of philosophy for Kaka Dixit who enjoyed every word of it. Baba turned to Dasa Ganu and enquired about his activities. Dasa Ganu told him that he was writing a commentary on "Ishavasya Upanishad' in Marathi – 'Bhavartha Bodhini'. The work is almost complete but in spite of discussions with a few learned pandits, Dasa Ganu was still not clear on the verse – *'Poornamadah Poornamidam Poornath Poornamudachyute….etc.'*

Baba said – "What is there? Even this Kaka Dixit's maid's daughter will explain!" Dasa Ganu was nonplussed with the way Baba treated his important query as if it was a very trivial matter! He decided to keep quiet at that moment and to discuss with Baba later!

A family from Mumbai had arrived for Baba's darshan. Harishchandra Pitale carried his son in his hands followed by his wife and mother. The child was suffering from epileptic fits. When he heard from Dasa Ganu's kirtan that Baba possessed superhuman powers to cure many intractable diseases, he brought his child with all hopes. But the moment the child was put on Baba's feet his condition worsened. Froth came out of the child's mouth with severe convulsions! The shocked parents started wailing! Applying udhi to the child, Baba said – "Mother, believe me, my fakir takes responsibility for everyone who visits this Dwarakamai. Why do you worry? Get rid of your doubts and sit in front. He will be all right!"

The Pitales kneeled down before Baba and sat before him. Devotees were coming up for darshan one after the other. Kaka Dixit was watching carefully with devotion the proceedings of Sai durbar! Sai Baba was a doctor, a spiritual guide, a psychiatrist and above all an affectionate mother! Different roles for different problems of devotees!

Anantarao Patankar from Pune came up next and placed his head at Baba's feet. He said – "Baba, I have read a number of great books and scriptures. I have studied Vedas, Vedanta, heard discourses, do *divya nama smaran*, meditate but still peace of mind has eluded me! How can I achieve it?"

Baba gave him a patient hearing. The devotee's question concerned a higher level. Kaka Dixit himself was interested in the answer. So he became alert to hear Baba's reply. In fact, ever since he heard that his maid's daughter is going to solve Dasa Ganu's doubt in 'Ishavasya Upanishad' he was watching as to how Baba handled various problems of all his devotees.

Baba answered Patankar's question in his usual mystic manner. "Listen! I will tell you a story! Once a trader came here on a horse's back. He stopped here. The animal excreted nine balls of dung. The trader took a towel and wrapped these nine balls and carefully kept them and he got peace of mind!"

Baba's story meant nothing. Kaka Dixit was perplexed! Patankar could make out nothing! But Dada Kelkar gleamed with joy. Baba said – "Dada Kelkar will now tell the meaning." Dada Kelkar placed his head on Baba's feet and said "Baba, whatever I have understood by your grace, I will tell with your permission. In this story, horse represents God's grace! God cannot be realised by dry learning devoid of devotion. The nine balls represent nine folds of devotion – Listening to His glory, reciting His glory, constant remembrance of God, every service to His lotus feet, worship to Him, and adoration to Him, service to Him with humility, His constant companionship, and total surrender to Him! All these are to be observed with utmost affection! If we readily accept these nine balls of dung of this horse of divine grace and follow the path of devotion by even one of them, we will know the Truth and acquire peace of mind!"

All pandits nodded their heads with joy. Baba spoke to Patankar – "Well dear, did you collect these nine balls?" He replied – "Baba, let this ignorant man have your grace and he will surely collect the nine balls of dung." Baba gave him udhi and blessed him.

It occurred to Sathe as to whether the nine coins polished by Baba represent nine folds of devotion. Reading his mind, Baba said – "Of course! These nine coins will bring the fame of Shirdi to forefront. Their service will be remembered! Now you have built a wada here close to my *gurusthan*. Now everybody takes your name – 'Sathe wada'! Does it not serve all?"

Baba's explanation made Kaka Dixit and Gopalrao Buti also to construct buildings in Shirdi. Baba gave a green signal to Kaka Dixit immediately but asked Gopalrao Buti to wait for some more time!

While everybody enjoyed the bliss of 'nine fold devotion', Pitale's son regained consciousness. His epileptic fits coming up every few minutes earlier had now stopped completely. Overcome with gratitude his mother was now busy in deep meditation over the form of Baba to install him in her heart forever! Baba gave three rupees to Pitale and told him – "Bapu, I have already given you two rupees earlier. Take these three rupees now and worship them. That will bring you good luck." Pitale was hesitant. He thought that Baba has made a mistake as he was coming to Shirdi for the first time. Seeing his dilemma, Pitale's mother prompted him – "Take those three rupees! What Sai Baba said is right. Long back, when you were a child, your father had taken you to Akkalkot Samarth Maharaj. He had given us two rupees to worship. In course of time, we have misplaced those two rupees. Now at least take these three rupees and worship them. Sai Baba and Akkalkot Maharaj are not different!" Pitale was overcome with joy. He obeyed his mother, kneeled down to Baba, and gratefully accepted the gift of three rupees. Kaka Dixit lost himself completely watching the events. Long back he had totally surrendered to Sai Baba.

On the other hand, Sathe was still engrossed in the thought of those nine coins! His inquiring nature would not allow him to rest until he asked Baba – "Who is your ninth coin?" Baba replied - "Oh! That? Thinks too much of himself! Let him come here! I will make him straight!"

Sathe was still restless! As he had already opened up the topic he thought he should be a little clearer on this issue. Hence he further asked – "Out of these nine, whom would you select to be your disciple – the one who would be your heir to carry on your mission divine?" This question alerted Dasa Ganu! This was a thought he was always obsessed with. Baba's mystic powers, Baba's divinity, Baba's appealing philosophy – who would get the heritage of all these? Shall he himself have some? Dasa Ganu wondered. But such things are never transferred by a lineage or heritage! They are gifts of grace of a perfect spiritual Master like Sai Baba!

Baba's reply – "Sathe, Listen! All the eight of you sitting here and the ninth one who will come are all my devotees! You are all my followers! None of you is my disciple! One who will be my disciple comes in rags! I will strip him of all attachments and send him with apparel of divine knowledge!"

One who was unhappy was Dasa Ganu! He felt unhappy as Baba's heritage will be received by an unknown disciple. Dasa Ganu considered Baba as a Muslim and as such, in consultation with him, had already received an initiation from a Brahmin Master, Sri Islampurkar. When Ganga-Yamuna-Saraswati flowed out of Baba's feet, Dasa Ganu just sprinkled over his head and did not partake it as holy tithe'. In fact he felt jealous of the would be disciple, who is supposed to come in rags!

The morning session was over. It was immemorial for Kaka Dixit! On the way to his lodgings, he requested Dasa Ganu to accompany him on his return to Mumbai two days later. He wanted to see for himself as to how his maid's daughter would solve the riddle of Dasa Ganu in translating 'Ishavasya Upanishad' into Marathi.

32

LOVE, DEVOTION AND SERVICE

On the same day in the afternoon, Baba called Kaka Dixit and asked him to return to Mumbai immediately as his presence was essential at his residence as well as office. Kaka Dixit was inclined to stay at Shirdi for two more days. But he had to obey Baba's commands. He sent word to Dasa Ganu and both of them with the approval of Baba left Shirdi for Mumbai.

Next morning they reached Vile Parle in Mumbai. Dasa Ganu was eager to see Kaka Dixit's maid's daughter. The girl had not come to work that day. But Kaka Dixit was shocked to learn about a great mishap that had taken place in his house on the previous day.

On the previous day, around the time when Baba had called Kaka Dixit to the mosque at Shirdi, at Vile Parle in Mumbai, his daughter Vatsali was playing with her toys. A little push brought down a big cupboard with a crash smashing its heavy mirrors into bits. The girl escaped with minor scratches, which otherwise could have been a big tragedy! Baba had already promised Kaka Dixit that he is responsible for the welfare of himself and his family. Accordingly Baba had saved his daughter from untimely death!

Being a Sunday there was no need for him to go to his office. He was discussing Sai Baba with Dasa Ganu Maharaj. He was completely lost in Sai experiences. At that time two of his partners, Narayan Das and Dhanjibhai Shah came to him regarding a case that was posted next day. The partners were upset that even though his presence was essential, Kaka Dixit had neglected his office work! As they sat, an intimate friend, Anna Saheb Dabholkar also came in. With his extraordinary talents, Anna Saheb Dabholkar had risen to the post of a resident magistrate. This had made him very proud of his achievement which created in him an ego and overconfidence in his own ability. Though he had faith in God he firmly believed that a man's destiny and luck are the outcome of his own personal ability and has nothing to do with divine grace. Hence he completely disbelieved in saints, sages, God-men and other spiritual masters! So if anyone opened such a topic he would vehemently ridicule the idea!

Anna Saheb Dabholkar, Kaka Dixit, and Nana Saheb Chandorkar were friends and whenever they met they would discuss Vedas, Upanishads and philosophy. But they had divergent views. Kaka Dixit was immediately drawn towards Sai Baba in the very first meeting. Nana Saheb Chandorkar was prejudiced at first and it took him sometime to become an ardent devotee. Even though aware of his views, Kaka Dixit desired that Anna Saheb Dabholkar too should be benefitted by Sai Baba's darshan. Hence he opened the topic in the presence of his partners. Even Nana Chandorkar had told Anna Saheb Dabholkar about Baba. But with his firm faith in his own ability Anna Saheb Dabholkar refused to see Sai Baba!

Today Kaka Dixit raised the subject of Sai Baba. He described his visit to Shirdi and termed Sai Baba as his Sadguru. Anna Saheb Dabholkar said – "Dixit, excuse me! I thought that with your education and background of visiting several countries, you will be a little more sensible than any of us. With one visit to a fakir in a mosque, you are calling him a Sadguru! It is simply idiotic! How can any

Sadguru protect you? A man should stand on his feet and look after his own progress! For that you do not require a Sadguru! Look at myself! I studied up to fifth class, then passed pleader's course, became a munshi, then a deputy collector and ultimately a resident magistrate too! I read the Vedas; I studied philosophy and all this without a Sadguru! Compared to me you are far more educated and learned! Why do you need a Sadguru at all?"

Listening to Anna Saheb Dabholkar, the two partners of Kaka Dixit were happy! They were sore that Kaka Dixit was busy otherwise and has neglected his solicitor's work. They had come to remind Kaka Dixit about the next day's case. But Dixit's mind was already at the feet of Sai Baba and he had decided that as soon as his work in the court is over, he will rush back to Shirdi without wasting any time!

The partners and Anna Saheb Dabholkar left. Afterwards, Kaka Dixit and Dasa Ganu had a dialogue about Anna Saheb Dabholkar. They felt that Dabholkar will soon go to Shirdi and Baba will correct him!

Kaka Dixit was awake till midnight preparing for the next day's case. But Dasa Ganu was exhausted and slept off well. He did not get up early also. All of a sudden, Dasa Ganu heard a sweet rustic voice of a girl singing a melodious song. That simple song described a beautiful orange saree the girl had seen someone else wearing. The song was in Marathi. It meant:-

"She wore a saree which captured my heart
Its colour was marigold – indeed it was golden art
She moved with glamour with her border in green
Its colour and beauty surpassed even a dream
No it was not marigold; she has bathed in pure gold
Her saree was a charm which captured my heart"

Instantly Dasa Ganu was out of sleep! Quickly he got up and looked out of the window to see who enjoyed a beautiful saree which someone else wore! Dixit's maid's daughter, a girl of about twelve years was engaged in scrubbing vessels and was singing this song. Though clad in rags herself she shared the joy of someone else's saree! To experience that joy she did not care to have that saree herself! Though she did not have that she was equally happy without it!

Dasa Ganu realised that Baba has begun to solve his riddle in Ishavasya Upanishad – 'In this universe which God has created, we cannot perceive him in reality, yet we can experience his existence through everything of his creation!' The verse *'Poornamadah Poornamidam'* in short means 'The universe is complete even without Him'. Dasa Ganu was enlightened on the first part of the stanza. Joyfully he went to meet Kaka Dixit. He was extremely busy with his legal papers and hardly listened to Dasa Ganu.

Moreswar Pradhan had come to see Dasa Ganu. Dasa Ganu requested him to bring an orange saree to be presented to that girl. When Pradhan brought the saree the girl had left after completing her job. Dasa Ganu handed it over to her mother.

The court case of Kaka Dixit was memorable that day. He defended the case in an excellent manner. He won name, fame and plenty of money. All newspapers praised the legal acumen of Kaka Dixit.

On the other hand Dixit's mind was again engrossed in the thoughts of Sai Baba the moment he was out of the court room. He craved to go to Shirdi!

Dasa Ganu now awaited the complete solution to his riddle in Ishavasya Upanishad! The next day dawned. The girl of that maid servant came with her mother. She was wearing the new saree she had received. Today she was so much fascinated with her new saree that her mother did not want her to work. Being free she was simply looking at her new saree and playing with her little friends. She was happy at the unexpected gift!

Dasa Ganu was watching and studying her behaviour. The other part of the first line of the verse was now getting clear to him now. *Poornath Poornamudachyuthe* which meant that if we can experience the very presence of God, that too makes the Universe complete! The girl could experience the joy of existence of that saree even without wearing it! She was equally happy when she got it and actually wore!

The girl went home and returned in the afternoon in her old rags! And yet she looked quite contented and cheerful! As she scrubbed the utensils she sang the same song – the song of that orange saree!

Dasa Ganu's riddle was now completely solved! *Poornasya Poornamadaya Poornamevavasishyate*– once we have experienced the existence of God we still can enjoy the same bliss even without Him, knowing very well the Universe is complete by itself! Here the state of joy is the same as that of the girl! Without wearing that saree she was happy, she was equally happy after getting it herself, thereafter she was still happy without it again though she was in her usual rags! A joyful bliss in all states!

Dasa Ganu was extremely happy that his riddle was solved! He began to ponder and came to the conclusion – " Sorrow and happiness, then sorrow again – is all a divine plan!" It is God's will! Hence we should accept sorrow and happiness equally with complete surrender to God! They are God-given! They are the outcome of our own feeling! 'Sorrow is not mine – neither the happiness is mine!' With this attitude if we give up the ego of everything being our own, then we can forever feel the presence of divinity in everything around us!

When Kaka Dixit came home, Dasa Ganu explained to him as to how his riddle was solved by his maid's daughter! Kaka Dixit's wife was happy that her husband came home with a trunk full of one rupee silver coins! But Dixit wanted to gift away the entire money to Sai Baba!

In the same night Kaka Dixit left for Shirdi with the trunk full of one rupee coins and Dasa Ganu Maharaj went to Pandharpur.

Kaka Dixit reached Shirdi and offered the entire money to Sai Baba. Baba distributed it to all those present in the mosque – poor villagers, needy devotees, fakirs, others dependent on his dakshina money.

As the treasure in the trunk was coming to its end a poor farmer came with his two sheeps and a half-dead goat. He sought thirty-two rupees for the two sheep and nothing for the goat. Baba paid him fifty-two rupees adding twenty for the goat. The farmer was pleased and started to go. Baba made him sit in the mosque. He obtained two seers of gram and fed the sheeps. The goat did not even touch as it had no strength to masticate the grams.

Baba returned the sheep and gave ten seers of grams as bonus. He asked the farmer to feed them properly and whenever his financial position didn't allow him to feed his sheeps, he could come to Baba. The farmer left the place. Madhava Rao grumbled – "Baba what kind of bargain is this? You paid sixteen rupees for a sheep worth not even three! You returned the sheep too and retained this dying goat! We have lost money and sheep!"

Baba explained – "Shama, bargaining is only in the materialistic world. How would you know the divine practicality of such a bargain! Do you know they were brothers in the past birth! They loved each other! They would come to me always together – the elder one was a lazy chap! He did nothing to earn. The younger one was active and earned a lot. This made the elder brother envy his prosperity. Both started fighting over the money. And one day that ended in their killing each other with axes. The result was that they are born again – but as two sheeps! That is why I repeatedly tell – 'Do not have this infatuation for money! It makes you suffer life after life! Seeing them today

I took pity on them and so after feeding sent them away! You regretted that I lost money and sheeps both! But what is this money Shama? Man does not love man. He loves his money. Just now I gave money to so many! Tell me how many of them love me really?"

Many in the crowd said – "Baba, we love you, we love you. Do test us."

Kaka Dixit was quiet. He was wondering as to what a wealth of information Baba offers through such anecdotes!

Baba caressed the goat and spoke to Bade Baba, "Bade miya, what can we do with this?" He asked Baba himself – "What can we do? It is not worth even slaughtering! Let it go." Bade Baba was regarded as a very important person in Sai Darbar. This fakir had come from Nanded and permanently settled in the mosque as he was getting a share from the 'dakshina' money!

Sai Baba retorted – "Why allow it to go? I have paid full twenty rupees for it. I will feed all with its mutton today. Shama, bring a large knife and chop it into bits. Let us cook mutton today!" Madhava Rao left and did not return! He respected Baba's word but he was a Brahmin and how can he slay a goat? Madhava Rao did not want to return till it was all over.

Baba now wanted to test Tatya. He asked him – "Tatya, I feel like eating mutton today. This Shama will not listen to me. Since childhood you are in my company. Get a chopper and cut this goat. Be quick! Go!" Tatya returned with a butcher's knife. He escaped excusing himself to go to toilet.

Bade Baba was a Muslim! Baba asked him to cut the goat! Bade Baba disliked being asked to do any work. That is why he preferred staying with Baba. He would get easy money! Moreover he had a dominant attitude and told Baba – "Look, is there anyone left to eat your mutton? They all have fled away. And who will eat the meat of this weakling?"

Baba noticed that except Kaka Dixit no one else had stayed back. They all had left fearing that they too may be asked to slaughter the animal. They stood far away and were eagerly watching as to who would obey Baba! Kaka Dixit did not leave his place and was minutely observing the drama!

Baba spoke to Bade Baba – "What does it matter if all of them have left? After all you are with me to enjoy the feast! We will finish up the entire vessel of mutton between ourselves! Come, take this knife, and finish this goat! I will cook it in no time!"

Bade Baba tried to escape – "Baba I am full! I do not feel like eating. However I will wash my hands and come back to chop him!" It was an utter lie as Bade Baba was quite hungry. He also left the mosque for washing his hands and did not return at all!

Now Kaka Dixit remained alone! No one else was in sight! Baba knew this man was hundred per cent devout! In spite of his several visits abroad, his exposure to materialistic world, Kaka Dixit had a firm belief in his Sadguru! Though he was not initiated by any Guru, in the first sight itself, he accepted Sai Baba as his spiritual master! Turning to Kaka Dixit, Baba said – "Will you cut this goat for me? After all you are a Brahmin! How can you do this work of a butcher?" Kaka Dixit replied – "Baba, you are my spiritual Master! My Sadguru! Order anything, any difficult job! It is my duty to obey you!"

Kaka Dixit took the knife from Baba and led the goat to the centre of the hall. A frightful silence filled the atmosphere! Looking at the pitiable expression in the eyes of the goat, Kaka Dixit's heart heaved with compassion. He gazed at the animal. At that moment there arrived with Gopalrao Buti, Dewan Bahadur Dada Saheb Khaparde, a famous Lawyer and political activist and member of the legislative council of central provinces from Amroati. He was considered an intimate of Lokmanya Bala Gangadhar Tilak in politics. He had come to Shirdi with his wife and only son Balwant. As they entered the mosque, he was terrified at what he saw! His close friend Kaka Dixit who had made the front page news on the previous day for winning a case against British Government is here with a butcher's knife about to slaughter an innocent goat right in the presence of a great saint! He could not believe his own eyes and stood transfixed looking at that horrible sight! Dada Saheb Khaparde heard Baba's voice – "Why have you stopped? Cut the animal!"

Baba knew the emotional conflict going on in Kaka Dixit's mind. Still he wanted to test him. Kaka Dixit raised his hand with a force to strike down the knife on the goat's neck, when suddenly Baba intervened, shouting aloud – "Stop that, stop Kaka! Take back your hand! You fool, if you Brahmins cut a goat what will the butchers do?"

Kaka Dixit stopped his hand in time and saved that innocent animal! Baba further said to Kaka Dixit – "Well done! You have put others to shame. You have obeyed Guru to the word! Keep down that knife and bring here that Brahmin friend of yours! See there he stands with a large turban, thick moustache, a long coat – that Patel from Berar! He has come to see you!"

Kaka Dixit looked there and saw Dada Saheb Khaparde, all in smiles. He was amused with his own description in Baba's words. But he was more interested in Baba's clairvoyance! Baba had correctly said that he was from Berar, that he is a friend of Kaka Dixit. This convinced him that he had not erred in coming to Sai Baba. Only that he had come at a time which made him misunderstand Sai Baba and Kaka Dixit!

Dixit brought Dada Saheb Khaparde to Baba. Baba made him sit near him. The mosque was crowded again. Baba sent away the goat with Bade Baba to the animal rest house where it died soon after reaching there. Baba knew its destiny beforehand but to test his devotees he had started a play!

The crowd had hardly settled when Kondaji, his brothers, and a few villagers came running to Baba. As they panted for breath, Kondaji said – "A great calamity is threatening our village, Baba! At five or six places, we have found plague infested rats! What is to be done now?"

The news terrorised the crowd and they stood up in fear! Dada Saheb Khaparde was frightened and had second thoughts! To avoid one danger he has jumped into the other! Indeed he was in a dangerous situation! He had run to Sai Baba to avoid the risk of his own arrest by the British Government who wanted to involve him in a sedition case against Lokmanya Tilak. He wondered as to where else he could go now since there was an outbreak of plague in Shirdi. All seemed worried and the devotees coming from outside began to plan their departure.

Baba got up. He was furious. He began to shout aloud – "Sit down! Sit down! Why should you be scared when I am here? Sit down all of you! Look here! Look at me carefully?"Saying so he raised his gown and held it up. Two plague buboes were peeping out of his arm pit.

33

KHAPARDE'S EXPERIENCE

*I*t was the first experience for Dada Saheb Khaparde to see before his own eyes as to how a Sadguru takes upon himself a calamity that befalls on his devotees! This thrilling experience prompted him to note down in his diary his experiences of Sai Baba and whatever he experienced in Shirdi. He knew that his stay at Shirdi would be prolonged and for Khaparde, maintaining a diary proved to be a great source of information for posterity!

That night Khaparde's son Balwant had high temperature and by morning two buboes appeared in the armpit indicating that he is afflicted with plague. The family decided to seek permission from Baba to leave Shirdi. Even though it was only five in the morning they went to the mosque.

Even small details of Baba's life are interesting. Khaparde observed Baba's routine and has recorded it in his diary.

According to his daily routine, Baba would sit near 'dhuni' and kindle the fire with fresh billets. Then he would ask Bhagoji Shinde to massage his right hand with oil. This hand was burnt when he put his hand long back to save a child from fire! Even though it had healed up, Baba gave an opportunity of service to Bhagoji. After the massage is complete, Bhagoji would fill up the pipe, light it and hand it over to Baba. Baba would have a couple of puffs and give it back to Bhagoji. He would smoke and return it to Baba. This touching scene of co-existence would go on for some time. By then, Abdulla would heat water for Baba's mouth wash. Baba would use warm water for his wash. After washing the mouth he would sprinkle hot water on his face, nose, ears, eyes, even tongue and hands and would clean them thoroughly and tenderly. And later wipe them with a clean cloth. He would never hurry through all this procedure. Naturally it would take some time and the day would be dawn by the time it finished. After this he would leave for begging in the village.

Dada Saheb Khaparde and his wife were so much engrossed in watching all this early hour routine of Baba that only when he came down with his bowl and called them aloud they came to their senses – "You are a wonderful man, Khaparde! You came to tell me about your son and you both kept quiet." Dada Saheb Khaparde did not reply as he was wise enough to know that Baba knew everything. It was not necessary to tell him at all. Khaparde, who was known for his oratorical skills in the Legislature and in the courts, maintained stoic silence in the presence of Sai Baba out of reverence to him. Baba spoke to Khaparde's wife – "Mother, the sky is overcast! It will rain, crop will ripen, sky will be clear and the earth will glitter with glee!"

With these words Baba left for his begging round. He did not ask them anything more, neither gave udhi nor did he suggest any remedy. He left with a mere glance of grace at the boy. Khaparde knew that his work is done and along with his family returned to Sathe's wada!

Learning that Khaparde's son had an attack of plague, his friends in the wada – Gopalrao Buti, Dada Kelkar, Kaka Dixit and others rushed to their room. Dr.Pillai examined the boy and to his surprise found no fever or plague buboes. They had disappeared. Though Dada Saheb Khaparde kept quiet, his wife revealed everything. Everyone had a fresh experience of Baba's omnipotence. By then they heard the 'aarti' song – "Jaya Jagadeesha Hare, Sai Shambo Mahadeva!' from Megha's room and this added to their devotional mood. They all went to Megha's room. Waving an 'aarti' before Baba's big picture on the wall, Megha was singing the prayer completely lost in emotional ecstasy! The image appeared to be fully naive and gleamed with an unusual luster! Megha also worshipped the Shiva linga given to him by Baba. Megha started this worship two days earlier and many devotees attended it for the effect it had on them. Khaparde was fascinated by Megha's prayer and with his own experience, decided not to leave Shirdi until Baba permitted. After Megha's prayer, the group left for the mosque.

As a daily routine Baba would go begging. Then later on feed the dogs, crows, and birds with the charity food he got, eat some if he felt like and then would sit down for first 'darshan' session of the morning. He would narrate anecdotes with morals which may include indirect answers to devotees coming with problems. Baba would also distribute udhi to those who would be leaving! After this Baba would go to Lendi baug. On return from there the second session would begin. In this session devotees were offered opportunities to worship Baba by themselves. In between Baba would give short discourses. With noon 'aarti' the second session would be over. Baba will participate in a collective lunch and after this he would once again go to Lendi baug. The third session would begin around five in the evening and would go on till night. After 'aarti' again and 'palanquin procession' in the night devotees would disperse bidding 'adieu' to Baba.

After having his wonderful experience in respect of his own son, Dada Saheb Khaparde decided to participate in every aspect of this programme in Shirdi in order to have maximum benefit of Baba's association.

After attending Megha's prayer, when the group reached they witnessed a strange sight! Nanavalli, a very queer natured devotee had come to the mosque along with many children who were all dressed like monkeys. They were jumping and dancing in the mosque like monkeys.

Actually Nanavalli was a Brahmin devotee and was staying in Shirdi for quite some time. He would render all types of 'seva' to devotees. He would refer to Baba as 'Kaka' in the same familiar tone like Tatya referring to Baba as 'Mama'. Of course he had whims of insanity when he would be a nuisance to devotees. He was good at heart and Baba loved him!

Today Nanavalli was dressed like Hanuman. He asked Baba to vacate his seat. When Baba willingly left his seat and sat at a little distance, Nanavalli occupied Baba's seat and made children dance around him for some time. Baba watched all this gimmicks for some time. Devotees like Kaka Dixit, Dada Kelkar, and Gopalrao Buti watched it undisturbed considering it all as Baba's play. At last Nanavalli stopped his antics, kneeled before Baba, and left the mosque with his group. Everyone admired Baba's tolerance!

As everything was normal again, Khaparde and others went up and sat near Baba. Just then a village woman came running up with her child held in her arms. The child was already dead and she wailed hysterically requesting Baba to bring the child back to life. Her sorrow brought tears in all. Baba kept mum! Kaka Dixit pleaded with Baba to relieve the sorrow of that mother. Baba told him that the child's soul has already entered another body and by interfering in the divine plan, he will be doing injustice as the child will have to leave that body to re-enter this body again – making his new mother unhappy! The wailing mother accepted Baba's verdict and said – "Baba, if my boy is going to be happy in his new birth, let him remain there! Be anywhere, my boy, be happy!" With sobs, she blessed her son!

A sadhu was in the crowd. He had seen that Baba did not bring back to life that dead child. He stepped ahead and requested Baba to save his ailing mother his native place from death. He carried with him a letter conveying his mother's illness. This sadhu from South India, had come to Shirdi two days earlier and his name was Vijayananda. He was on his way to Mansarovar in Himalayas. He met Swami Somadev at Shirdi who explained the difficulties in reaching Mansarovar. Vijayananda was in two minds as to whether to proceed to Mansarovar or not and in the meanwhile had received a letter informing that his mother is on the verge of death! When Vijayananda approached Baba for permission, he was furious and asked him as to why he took 'sanyas' when he is attached to his mother. Baba asked him to go to Lendi baug and do three weekly 'parayan' of Bhagawatha. In a mystic way, he told him that many thieves are waiting to attack him!

Vijayananda did parayan for two weeks. He started the third parayan and uneasiness gripped him. As he walked towards the wada, he collapsed and fell down. Bade Baba rushed to help him but he was already dead!

Vijayananda's death created different reactions and reflections. Dada Saheb Khaparde looked at a practical point. While Baba did not save the child and Vijayananda from death, he saved his son from the jaws of death! He looked forward to Baba's help in rescuing from the wrath of British Government. Kaka Dixit felt that Baba has given Vijayananda 'Mukti' in Shirdi instead of sending him to Himalayas or back to his mother! Dixit looked forward to Baba's help in his coming out of worldly attachments. Buti was always a worried man and was getting guidance from an astrologer, Nana Dengale on a day to day basis! On Vijayananda's death, Buti consulted Nana Dengale about danger to his own life. Nana Dengale predicted a danger awaiting him next day! This frightened Buti and though in Shirdi, he decided not to leave his room even for Baba's darshan that day.

Next day as all other devotees, except Gopalrao Buti, were sitting around Baba, a couple from Bandra, Mumbai, Raghunatha Rao Tendulkar and his wife Savithribai came for Baba's darshan. Tendulkar had published a book 'Bhajanawali' describing many of Baba's miracles and it had helped in spreading Baba's name in Maharashtra. Tendulkar's wife pleaded that her husband is due for retirement and a pension of seventy five rupees may not be adequate. Baba assured a pension of one hundred ten rupees and blessed them. She also represented that her son due to appear for his final medical examination is diffident as an astrologer has predicted his failure!

Baba said – "What nonsense! These astrologers tell you about the favour of stars, not of God! How do they know what He has on mind! Go and tell your son that my fakir asks him to study as usual and go for the examination! He will pass this year itself!"

Baba's word was a cent per cent guarantee – Tendulkar knew! Hence he did not say anything further. Moreover both his problems were solved! Baba himself said – "Listen Bapu, I will tell you one more fun of these astrologers! Do you see this Nana Dengale sitting here? He has come to Shirdi to tell everybody's forecast. He had told that Buti that there is a great danger to his life today. Therefore that mad chap has locked himself in his room in Sathe wada. I will tell you one thing, this Sai will not interfere with anyone's death, but he will certainly save one from an untimely death! Come on Dengale, call that Buti. Ask him to face the danger. He simply cannot avoid by locking himself in a secluded place! Tell him that he is going to live long, build a big wada in Shirdi – a place that attracts visitors!"

Nana Dengale ran to Sathe wada and told Gopalrao Buti about Baba's assurance. However Buti did not leave the room till evening. When he went to attend nature's call, he saw a big cobra there. He screamed and his servant came and killed the cobra. The danger was averted. However Buti relied more and more on Nana Dengale as his forecast came true!

As Baba referred to the topic of constructing a wada, Kaka Dixit enquired about his plan. Baba told him to start construction in right earnest. He can settle down in Shirdi after fulfilling all family responsibilities!

Dada Saheb Khaparde also wanted to get back. He knew that if he returned with Baba's blessings he need not worry about any danger from the Britishers. His prolonged stay in Shirdi would affect his legal practice. So he decided to seek Baba's permission through his wife.

Mrs. Khaparde soon came with a tray of food covered with a cloth as an offering for Baba after the noon prayer. On seeing her, Baba yelled with pain – "O mother, I am dying, I am dying." He started rubbing his right shoulder and leg as if someone had beaten him up. Mrs.Khaparde kept the tray aside and started massaging Baba's leg with care. After some time, Baba said – "Mother, I went to eat curds and had thrashing on my shoulder and leg." Baba had not even moved from the mosque. How then could he have gone to eat curds? He pointed at a Brahmin in the crowd and said – "Well brother, are you happy? You have beaten me on my shoulder and leg for no fault of mine!" That Brahmin was frightened! He spoke nervously – "How will I ever beat you Baba? It is unthinkable." Baba raised his gown and showed fresh swollen marks on the shoulder and right leg.

Baba spoke to that Brahmin – "Listen, did I not come to you sometime back? To eat your curds?" The Brahmin virtually wept – "Oh God, it was you, Baba, in the form of a cat?" He recollected the entire episode. He was suffering from Asthma and Baba had advised him not to eat curds. But he was fond of curds. So he prepared curds every day. But a cat used to come and eat the curds. To prevent this, he kept the vessel in a hanging sling. Even then the cat ate away the curds. He laid a trap and when the cat came today, he trashed it on its shoulder and right leg! Baba did not want his devotee to eat curds and ruin his health. But he missed Sai Baba in the cat!

Seeing this great 'Leela' Mrs.Khaparde recollected what happened a while ago. On her way, she came across a pig. She offered a chapatti to it mentally considering it as a form of Sai Baba. Baba referred to this and told Mrs.Khaparde – "Mother always remember me! I am in every living being – whether animal or human? Just as you love me here, love everybody else everywhere." He asked her to come closer. In her ears he said – "Mother, whatever you may be doing anytime, remember to recite the name of Prabhu Ram! Let 'Rajaram, Rajaram' be on your lips! Sure he will look after you!"

Mrs.Khaparde was extremely happy. She felt she had achieved everything in life! Keeping her head on Baba's feet she prostrated before him to have his blessings. Baba muttered – 'Allah Malik'! Immediately Baba pulled the tray brought by Mrs.Khaparde. He relished the entire food brought by her.

Madhava Rao protested that Baba has favoured Mrs. Khaparde. Generally he will taste bits of everyone's offering after 'aarti'. Today he had eaten the entire food brought by Mrs.Khaparde and may not eat after aarti.

Baba told Madhava Rao – "Shama, you will never know the sweet taste of this mother's food! Do you know, once she was a cow belonging to a Bania – very fat cow, full of milk! Everybody was pleased with her sweet milk! Later she came as a human, born in a Mal family. When grown up she was married. The food she cooked for her husband he cherished so much that he would forget even his job before it. Later she was born as a Kshatriya. And here she is now a Brahmin lady married to Khaparde! Shama, everybody cooks food, but she puts her heart in it! She pours love in it! And with affection she serves it to all – even to her servants, the beggars, and the poor coming at her door, the dogs, crows, and sparrows – all getting it with love! Why should it not be tasteful? I met her after a long time and that is why I ate so much more from her plate alone! Tell me, was it wrong?"

Madhava Rao had no answer to this question.

Seeing Baba in a jolly mood, Dada Saheb Khaparde beckoned his wife to seek permission to leave. When she opened the topic Baba simply evaded an answer – "We will see tomorrow!" That is what he said.

For the next nine months Khaparde got the same reply to his query to go back to Amroati. Khaparde knew well that leaving Shirdi without Baba's permission would be inviting trouble and falling in the trap of Britishers! Still there was a plan to put him behind bars but the great Loving God of Shirdi was protecting him. Hence he decided to stay in Shirdi till Baba permitted him to leave! He maintained his diary which is a rich source of information on Sai-history. He also undertook scholarly exposition of *Panchadashi* and *Paramamrith* to other friends. This kept him busy.

He came in closer contact with Gopalrao Buti, Dr.Pillai and Nana Dengale.

Just as Baba kept Dada Saheb Khaparde against his will, he had sent back Kaka Dixit to Mumbai to set right his domestic and office problems. Dixit faced a dilemma when he reached Mumbai. He had given away the entire trunk full of silver coins to Sai Baba and so his wife was hostile. His business partners were not happy with socio-political activities and sought dissolution of the firm! Dixit had to start afresh in his profession. Dixit's wife had a fear that he may become a 'sanyasi' and stay permanently at Shirdi! Dabholkar too was surprised to see Sai Baba's hold on Kaka Dixit and promised Mrs. Dixit that he would get him released from Sai Baba!

34

BUTI AND HEMAD PANT

*A*s 1909 was about to end, Khapardes returned to Amroati. Soon in January Makarsankranti arrived! Megha was waiting for this day. He was convinced that Sai Baba is Lord Shiva himself. He wanted to give a bath to Sai Baba with the water from river Godavari.

Baba showered his grace on Megha. He changed his mental set up and enabled him to be engaged in rituals to attain 'Moksha'. He not only permitted his daily worship but asked Megha to worship all village deities. This endeared him to Baba so much so that both began to feel restless without seeing each other! Megha did not stay in the mosque but his spirit hovered around Baba. *Om Namah Shivaya* always used to be on his lips.

In fact, Megha had not even obtained Baba's approval to bathe him with Godavari waters on Makarsankranti' day, as he knew Baba would never say 'no' to him in view of his intense love and devotion. Moreover he had decided to carry out his plan after the noon 'aarti' and all devotees would have taken a lunch break and Baba would be free for a *mangal snan*.

One more reason for Megha's confidence! On the previous day, an astrologer from Nasik, Mulay Shastri had predicted that Megha's heart's desire would be fulfilled on Makarsankranti day! Mulay Shastri read Megha's palm and told him about his previous birth, the way he came to Shirdi and purpose behind it, Baba's wrath and grace, his dream of Baba, and how Baba's gift of a Shiva linga simply baffled him. Being convinced of his accuracy in reading his past, Megha was certain that his desire of bathing Baba on that day was a certainty. He was almost in an ecstasy!

Megha got up early on the Sankranti day. Even though it was extremely cold, he walked to Godavari river near Kopergaon, took bath, and with wet clothes carried two pitchers full of water to Shirdi. He kept them in the wada and decided to visit Baba at noon for aarti.

Being Makarsankranti day the mosque was overcrowded with visitors. Baba himself started peeling banana skins and distributed them among devotees. Mulay Shastri who had accompanied Buti was deeply impressed by Baba's divine luster and had a transfixed gaze. As he was an orthodox Brahmin, he refused banana prasad and sought to examine Baba's palms. Baba ignored him completely! Where is the need for Baba to show his palm to any astrologer! Mulay Shastri was disappointed and returned to wada.

Baba started for Lendi baug! With him were Mhalsapathy, Tatya Kote and others. While starting, Baba asked them to get some ochre, as he intended to wear saffron clothes that day! On the way he saw Megha in wet clothes carrying water. When he expressed his intention, Baba laughed at him saying, "Why does a fakir need this?" He asked Megha to get back to wada and change clothes, as he had come out of an illness very recently!

Baba returned to the mosque after some time. In Sathe's wada Bapu Saheb Jog was getting ready with his preparation for the 'aarti'. As he started for the mosque he asked Mulay Shastri if he would accompany him. In the morning, Shastri had a second bath as he considered the mosque as a polluted place and if he goes again, he has to take a third bath! So he told Jog that he will come in the evening. So Jog left.

Baba observed that Mulay Shastri was not in the crowd. So he asked Gopalrao Buti to go and bring Mulay Shastri and also to bring dakshina.

A multi-millionaire like Gopalrao Buti went running to Sathe's wada with Baba's orders. He gave Baba's message to Mulay Shastri. Now Shastri was in a dilemma! - 'A multi-millionaire runs to me with Baba's message! A great saint like Sai Baba asks for 'dakshina' from me! How can I refuse?' Mulay Shastri did not know what to do! How can he leave his meditation on his Guru incomplete? Besides why should he pay dakshina to Baba as he was an 'Agnihotri' Brahmin maintaining perpetual fire? He can accept dakshina and not give it! Even with this storm of thoughts brewing in his mind, Mulay Shastri got up, tucked some dakshina money in the border of his *dhoti*, took some flowers, and left with Gopalrao Buti to the mosque.

The noon aarti had begun. Since Mulay Shastri considered the mosque impure, he stood outside. Gopalrao Buti went in and stood near Baba. He told him that Mulay Shastri was there standing outside. Baba just smiled! As the aarti was sung, Mulay Shastri lost himself completely with the vision he saw before himself! In the place of Sai Baba he perceived his own Guru Gholap Maharaj, in his saffron clothes, happily enjoying the aarti song. Mulay Shastri was amazed with what he saw! His Guru who had left his body years back had occupied Sai Baba's seat! The vision started changing to Sai Baba, then Gholap Maharaj and so on! Mulay Shastri could not believe his own eyes. He wiped them again and again. He made himself sure that he saw both Sai Baba and Gholap Maharaj! His ego ended in realisation! He realised that his own Guru Gholap Maharaj, Sai Baba and all other saints are but one! While others sang Baba's aarti, Mulay Shastri recited the prayer of his Master! He forgot his conviction that the mosque is impure and walked in to approach Baba. With Gholap Maharaj's prayer, he offered flowers on Baba's feet and holding them tight he placed his head on them!

Buti and others looked at him with wonder. Mulay Shastri offered his 'dakshina'and bowed again. Baba blessed him! Mulay Shastri felt that he had achieved whatever he had missed in spite of his great scholarship.

As soon as the crowd dispersed after the noon 'aarti', Megha arrived at the mosque. Quickly he made arrangements for Baba's bath and called him. Baba declined a bath, persuaded Megha in many ways. But Megha did not give up. Ultimately he yielded. He put one condition – "Megha, I already had my bath in the morning. Sprinkle a little water on my head for your satisfaction and achieve all that merit you will get by bathing Lord Shiva!"

Megha agreed. He was thrilled at bathing Sai Baba! He took the pitchers and in that excitement forgot the promise made to Baba. Chanting *Har Har Gange* he poured water on Baba's head. Immediately he realised his mistake and pulled a towel to wipe Baba's wet body. He was surprised that Baba's body was dry except for a few drops on the head. Not a drop of water on the floor or on his clothes! Megha was dumbfounded!

Makarsankranti was over and Maha Shivratri came! A full one year had passed since Kaka Dixit and Megha had come to Baba's fold. Both of them had progressed in the spiritual path!

Kaka Dixit visited Shirdi now and then. He was virtually mad after Baba. His friends and colleagues made fun of him. He was constructing his own building at Shirdi. Dixit's wife was more disturbed about Kaka Dixit not concentrating in his profession. Annasaheb Dabholkar too planned a trip to Shirdi and had given a definite assurance to Dixit's wife that he will get her husband relieved from the clutches of that fakir in Shirdi.

During this period the glory of Baba had dazzled the world! Dabholkar too had heard many stories about him through number of reliable people. This had set him rethinking about his own opinion. Even Nana Saheb Chandorkar had told him so much about Sai Baba. So, being a judge himself, he decided to study all details personally before forming his own opinion and coming to any conclusion. He knew that Kaka Dixit's infatuation for Sai Baba was increasing day by day. He had seen that irrespective of what others thought, Dixit visited Shirdi quite often. Under the circumstances, as promised to Dixit's wife, Dabholkar felt he must meet the fakir in Shirdi to assess his own opinion and decide the matter once for all! For that he planned to visit Shirdi after Holi festival.

But on the night prior to Holi festival, Baba appeared in Dabholkar's dream and told him that he was going to visit them next day for lunch! Dabholkar had seen Baba's picture at Kaka Dixit's house. So he could guess it was Sai Baba who appeared in the dream. He woke up with a start. Nana Chandorkar had also told him that Baba visited people in dreams too. Those made him believe that he would certainly pay him a visit next day and have lunch with them. He was glad! He thought that would save his trip to Shirdi as he could thrash out the matter with Sai Baba personally at his own place. And if it is proved that he is a real saint he would be a follower like Dixit!

Next morning Dabholkar asked his wife to prepare a little extra food for Sai Baba who was expected for lunch. She was immensely happy! She had heard a lot about this great saint. Since her husband was prejudiced against him, she could not visit Shirdi as many of her relatives did. Naturally she was very happy now that Baba was visiting them himself. Dabholkar invited many of his relatives for lunch on account of Holi festival. Dabholkar's wife prepared special sweets for Sai Baba!

The guests arrived! Wooden seats were arranged on the floor. Between two rows a special seat was placed for Sai Baba. Rangoli was drawn and leaves were placed. Food was served. The guests occupied their seats having waited long for Sai Baba. It was noon and everybody was hungry. Dabholkar was restless and was moving in and out eagerly waiting for Sai Baba. He had simply informed the guests that Sai Baba was coming. He did not tell them it was a dream vision. Now he was wondering that a rational minded person like him has fallen flat for a dream vision! At last he bolted the door and sat for lunch. There was a knock on the door and a call 'Anna Saheb, Anna Saheb' was heard. Everyone thought that Sai Baba had come!

When the door was opened, an old friend Ali Mohamed Peerbhoy and his friend were at the door. They had a small packet in their hands. They profusely apologised when they saw many guests about to partake food. Ali Mohamed Peerbhoy handed over the packet and said – "Sorry Anna Saheb, we did not know you were taking food. We have brought this packet for you. Take this. I will tell you the background later." They left.

When the packet was uncovered, Dabholkar saw a portrait of Sai Baba! He reverentially placed it on the special seat meant for Sai Baba. He told his guests about his dream vision on the previous night. They all had food!

Much later Dabholkar was told by Ali Mohamed Peerbhoy that his spiritual Mentor had commanded him to remove all pictures and images of saints from his house as it was against their religion. He had thrown all of them in the sea at Bandra. However this portrait was left out by mistake. He had an intuition that Dabholkar would love to keep it and so brought it to him!

This incident convinced Dabholkar that Sai Baba is a super power and his hostile attitude softened! But still he did not accept him as a Sadguru. Dabholkar still believed on the strength of his special powers Sai Baba was getting importance and had allured Dixit to himself! Hence he decided to visit Shirdi for his fact finding mission during summer vacation.

In the meanwhile, his friend's son became seriously ill in Lonavala. To save him his friend got his Guru sit next to the ailing boy and arranged special prayers. Even then that boy died. Dabholkar lost faith in Guru-cult and found no reason to go to Sai Baba or give him importance as a Guru!

But once again, Nana Chandorkar met him and earnestly explained the concept of Guru and extracted a promise that Dabholkar would visit Sai Baba at least once. He advised – "Dabholkar, our Guru is not necessarily our protector in all our calamities. Deaths, calamities, richness, poverty – all are outcome of our deeds in our past life! It is a divine plan! When a person is under the care of a Sadguru, he gets his guidance, his actions become balanced and he is able to face the calamities boldly! In fact, your wavering mind needs a Sadguru! Incarnations like Sai Baba do not take birth often. We are indeed fortunate that he is among us. Do not think that you are going to him on your own. He has given you a dream vision, has graced your house in the form of a portrait, which means he has already taken you into his fold! Go to Shirdi, see for yourself and then form your opinion. You are dispensing justice to others – why not to your own mind? To your conscience? Then only you will have a right to talk on Sai Baba!"

This appealing counsel of Nana Chandorkar in a friendly manner moved Dabholkar! He decided to visit Shirdi.

Thinking of catching the Mail train for Manmad at Dadar, Dabholkar purchased a local railway ticket from Bandra to Dadar. Suddenly he met a Muslim passenger who told him that Manmad Mail will not stop at Dadar and advised him to proceed to Bori-Bandar. This spared him from unnecessary ordeal. Suppose he had missed the train, his wavering mind would have cancelled the trip to Shirdi. But how can Sai Baba allow it? He wanted Dabholkar to be in his fold. He had to pen the great epic of Sai Baba's life – 'Sai Satcharita'. He may be egoistic! He may not be easily believing! But he was a great writer! Baba therefore preserved a coin – the ninth one, the last one in the garland of nine-fold devotion for Dabholkar

Dabholkar could reach Shirdi next morning. Since Kaka Dixit and Nana Chandorkar were already there, he was comfortably placed in the wada. As he was getting organised, somebody came running to say 'Baba is coming, Baba is coming'! There was a lot of commotion! People left everything and rushed out! Some were sipping tea, some in meditation, some in rituals, some turning rosary – they all madly ran for Baba's darshan. Dabholkar wondered as to why they are making so much of fuss about Baba. They already had morning darshan and Baba was not going away anywhere! Clearly Dabholkar had not understood the sentiments of devotees who so much loved Baba. He was learned; he knew court-room manners but could not comprehend the relationship between a Sadguru and his followers! To Dabholkar this commotion was sheer nonsense!

Nana Chandorkar also came running and tried to hurry up Dabholkar. He was sipping his tea. But he respected his friend's word and went along with him. Baba was on his way to Lendi baug. Nana, Dixit and others put their heads on his feet irrespective of dirt and dust on the road. Dabholkar found it difficult to put it as Baba stood on a dusty ground. He was afraid that his clothes might get soiled. But they were already soiled during journey. Dabholkar thought if he alone does not touch his feet, it may look odd and hence he also put his head on Baba's feet. Nana stepped ahead and introduced him – "This is Anna Saheb Dabholkar! Resident

Magistrate at Bandra in Mumbai!" Baba did not even bother to look at him!

This was Baba's way of treating an egoistic person! One was to express his wrath and the other to totally ignore! Dabholkar felt humiliated!

Baba left for Lendi baug. The devotees went to their respective rooms. Tatya Saheb Noolkar spoke to Dabholkar – "It was good that you had your first darshan on road! Baba will come back only after two hours! So you can finish your bath and everything else now."

Dabholkar was sore that Baba had not spoken to him. He told Nana Chandorkar – "I am surprised at the way you educated people behave? What is all this? First darshan, morning darshan, darshan on road? All this excitement when Baba comes – this running about to have darshan leaving everything else?" Nana Chandorkar did not want to argue. But Balasaheb Bhate who sat there did not like Dabholkar's attitude. He could not keep quiet and said – "Well sir, what is wrong with us educated people? You did not like us to bow down to Baba on the road! Then why did you touch his feet on a dusty road? Were you not afraid that your clothes will get dirty?"

Dabholkar's outspokenness made Balasaheb Bhate also hard-hitting! Dabholkar softened and said – "Right Bhate! Tell me why this running when Baba comes along." Bhate retorted – "Because Baba is our Sadguru – our God! We come all this distance to place our heads on his feet. To get an opportunity to place it again and again we simply run like mad men! And even after keeping it a number of times we are not contented!"

Dabholkar asked plainly – "But I do not understand why you need a Guru?" Bhate replied – "No doubt man can stand on his own legs, but he steps into the world with a future full of misfortune! To come out of it he needs a

Guru!" Dabholkar dismissed this theory – "It is all trash! If a man perseveres he can conquer the worst of his difficulties!" Dabholkar was emphatic. He had come up in life through in his own efforts.

Balasaheb Bhate would not agree. He said – "Dabholkar, it is true perseverance takes you out of your difficulties! But when? When divine help is there? That help comes from a Guru, direct or indirect! If you do not get it even the greatest of talents go waste for want of opportunities. That is why man needs a Guru to push him up. Even Kabir has said – 'Who else offers you his succour other than your Guru?'"

Though nobody supported Dabholkar, many came forward on behalf of Bhate. They had come to Shirdi and surrendered to Baba and he would put them back on their tracks! He would lead them to God! With such experience behind them they naturally believed in the concept of 'Guru'.

The discussion was very warm. Dabholkar was quite disturbed. Nana Chandorkar pacified Dabholkar and took him to the mosque. Looking around and seeing the crowd of intellectuals Dabholkar was simply surprised! He found that madness of running after Sai Baba was not restricted to Nana, Dixit, Bhate but many learned and highly educated people known to him personally, were amongst those who were fascinated by this fakir! He wondered as to whether he was a making a mistake himself. In fact, he too had a personal experience of Sai Baba. It could not be a sheer coincidence that Baba came to him on the 'Holi' day as a portrait after that dream! So Dabholkar decided to give up his ego and study Baba in an impartial manner! Even as he was thinking like this, Baba was facing him! He had just returned from Lendi baug and had come straight to Dabholkar. Dabholkar had seen Baba in a disturbed mind in the morning. Now he could see Baba in a balanced outlook. Unaware he folded his hands and kneeling down placed his head on Baba's feet. Now with sincere reverence! Baba placed his hand on his head in blessing and said to Nana – "Nana, what was this 'Hemad Pant' blurting in the wada? He says a Guru is not required and yet places his head on my feet! Look at his hypocrisy! At Bandra he serves me food and here he abuses me openly!"

Dabholkar hung his head in shame! 'So Baba knows everything of my arguments in the wada' – Baba's clairvoyance instantly sowed the seed of devotion in the mind of Dabholkar which melted his ego which had engulfed his personality. He could now enjoy the bliss of keeping his head on the feet of a Sadguru! He realised that greatness lies in leading a life of humility rather than dominating others with an air of ego! Thus Baba brought in a transformation in Dabholkar who now looked at him with adoration! Nana, Dixit, Bhate and others wondered as to whether he was the same Dabholkar who argued on the concept of Guru just a while ago!

Dabholkar also wondered as to why Baba called him 'Hemad Pant'! He realised that Baba called him so for his role in the morning's discussion! Hemad or Hemadri was a learned Minister in the court of King Mahadev in Yadav dynasty of Devagiri (the present Daulatabad) in the 13th century. He had written a number of books in Sanskrit and was an authority on religion and politics. Dabholkar wondered as to why Sai Baba compared him to that great person while he was nowhere near the capacity of Hemad Pant! As he was thus engrossed in these thoughts, something he saw astounded him! Baba who is worshipped by rich, poor, learned, and great people was now sitting to grind wheat! Since Baba did not need wheat flour, devotees thought that he will distribute the flour later!

Baba had taken out half a sack of wheat for grinding. Nobody dared to go forward as Baba might get angry. However Lakshmi and three other women rushed forward and offered to grind wheat! Taking charge of the quern the four of them sat on the four sides and started the wheels moving and singing a folk song glorifying Sai Baba! Baba was moved by the love and affection of these women! He enjoyed their songs. Dabholkar heard these songs and deep in his heart composed a few lines on the life of Sai Baba!

After the grinding was over, the women thought that Baba will gift the flour to them. They divided it among themselves and waited for Baba's nod. But Baba had a different plan. He asked them to pour the flour along the entire boundary of Shirdi village! The women were taken aback. They realised that it was Baba's remedy to prevent the entry of Cholera epidemic into Shirdi which had created a havoc in the neighbouring villages! They obeyed him and drew a line around the border of their village which was more powerful than the famous *Lakshman Rekha* in Ramayana to protect Mother Sita! It was a fact that the epidemic did not enter Shirdi!

From now onwards started Dabholkar's close observation and study of Baba's life and outline of his great classic *Sai Satcharita* began to take shape. It needed sincerity of purpose and devotion which was now unknowingly planted into him by Baba.

Dabholkar asked through Madhava Rao Deshpande, permission from Baba to write down his life story. Baba said – "I am a beggar! I move from door to door seeking charity. Whatever I get I eat and pass the day. I have no life beyond this! People will laugh if you write all this!" Dabholkar told him – "Baba, do not say like this! You are indeed a diamond – a jewel! It must be properly set in a socket! You just give me your blessings! All difficulties will be crossed and I will write your biography."

Baba gave him udhi, placed his hand on his head, blessed him and said – "Indeed you want to write yourself?"

Dabholkar had his doubts – "Yes Baba, I will do it! But why.....why?"

Baba said – "Do not worry! Go ahead! I will have it done!" Dabholkar instantly realised that 'I' feeling should not used before Baba. He placed his head on his feet and prayed within that he should come out of that obsession of egoism! Baba read his thoughts and said – "Those devotees who surrender their ego will get every help from my fakir! Carry on! Your work is done! Make notes on all my stories, thoughts, and talks! Preserve those. Observe and study. You will write like that Hemadri Pant – and they will remember you just as myself!"

Dabholkar could not start write this epic during Baba's life time. But his notes helped him and before his own demise he completed this masterpiece of Baba's life! It is a living memorial dedicated to Sai Baba!

35

MAN IN RAGS

*D*abholkar who promised Dixit's wife that he will get Dixit released from the clutches of the fakir at Shirdi, himself became a great devotee of Baba. The garland of Baba's nine coins was now complete with the addition of Dabholkar! All these nine devotees have played an important role in Baba's life. Baba used to polish their devotion every now and then which kept them ever shining. They were all graded silver! Baba was waiting for a gold coin. In fact, Baba did not have a golden coin! However he waited for a person comparable to gold. He was elsewhere! He was a person in rags!

Dabholkar came to Shirdi in 1910, went away with the blessings of Baba to write his biography, and came again and again rich with devotion! In the same year Dixit completed his wada and kept it open for all irrespective of caste, community, and religion. He also started a mess for the poor and needy. He made arrangements to feed animals. He made Bade Baba stay in his wada much against the wishes of many orthodox Brahmins. Dixit saw a divine element in all and practised Baba's advice sincerely! Even then, Baba wanted him to continue his legal practice and look after his family, though Dixit's mind craved for renunciation and stay at Shirdi!

In Sathe wada, Dada Kelkar, the father-in-law of H.V.Sathe had imposed lot of restrictions, as he observed strict religious discipline!

Baba wanted to groom a person to be his disciple who would carry on his mission. He wanted to mould a spiritual guide. Possibly he could have transferred his powers to one of his followers. He did not do this. In fact, he enabled Kashinath Krishnaji Joshi to materialise udhi from nothing but this was only to enable him to help the needy! For a disciple, a Guru bestows on him everything of himself, his power, strength of spiritual achievement and the divine grace! Unfortunately Baba did not nominate his disciple!

A devotee may not necessarily become a saint's disciple. The eligibility to become a disciple is not his devotion or his personal service. It needed the Guru's grace, because only a true and fully graced disciple can carry ahead his Guru's mission! For that a Guru bestows on him everything including his achievement and knowledge of the Supreme! Sai Baba did not establish an ashram or a Mutt! His mission was to transform atheists into theists and humans by winning their hearts with display of his divine powers and thus get their obeisance and devotion! To continue his mission he wanted his disciple as an accomplished Sadguru! He wanted to strip him off his desires, attachments, lust, and ego putting him on a sack cloth of renunciation!

The name of this disciple-designate was Kashinath Govind Upasani! He was the second of five sons born into a Brahmin family in the village of Satana in Nasik district. He was born on 5th May 1870 and his parents were Govinda Shastri and Rukmini. A great saint Uddhav Maharaj of Mulher gave a dream vision to Rukmini that he will be taking birth as her son!

Upasani did not have any formal education. Right from childhood he had a religious temperament of observing rituals, fasts, meditation, etc. He had an outlook that he and his body are different! Upasani's family life was short-lived. He had three marriages and the first two wives died and the third one was in his native place. He learnt Ayurveda at

Sangli and for some time practised at Amroati and earned good money. Sai Baba's devotee Dada Saheb Khaparde was his patient. He also published an Ayurvedic magazine *Bhishaj Rathna*. Whatever money he earned as a Physician, he invested it in land in Gwalior but incurred heavy loss as the tenants cheated him!

He was penniless and virtually in rags. In his itinerant life, he heard a singing voice which he could not explain. He had a vision in which a Hindu and Muslim stood on either side and quickly removed his complete skin. Though his skin appeared dull and dirty his inner body gleamed with divine luster! He went to Khedgaon and met Narayan Maharaj. The Hindu in the dream vision was none other than Narayan Maharaj. Narayan Maharaj virtually ignored him and advised him to meet Sai Baba at Shirdi!

He practised different yogic postures and due to a wrong posture developed breathing trouble. He had to pant for breath every now and then. A yogic teacher by the name Kulkarni Maharaj in Rahuri diagnosed his problem as awakening of 'Kundalini' in a wrong yogic posture and suggested him to meet Sai Baba at Shirdi for a remedy. Also a Muslim fakir told him 'it is a spasmodic affliction' and advised him to use only hot water as a remedy for his breathlessness! The Muslim fakir also told him that he will be close behind his thoughts always. This Muslim fakir appeared at two places to save him from virtual collapse! As Upasani felt Sai Baba to be a Muslim, he did not want to seek his help. However he followed the suggestion of using only hot water by the Muslim fakir, as it gave him instant relief!

Once at Omkareshwar temple at the confluence of Narmada, Upasani lost consciousness and his breathing stopped completely! He had to heave his belly and chest to get back his breathing! Since Kulkarni Maharaj repeatedly advised him to meet Sai Baba to seek a remedy Upasani finally met Baba in June 1911.

Upasani finally reached Shirdi and was hesitant to enter the mosque. He decided to rest outside and panted for breath. Dasa Ganu who was walking towards the mosque took pity on him and led him into the mosque. Upasani was surprised to see the Muslim who stripped his skin in the dream vision was Sai Baba himself. The Muslim fakir who advised him to take only hot water also bore resemblance to Sai Baba!

When Upasani arrived, Baba was making fun of Anna Saheb Dhabolkar that he had gone to the market to get grams in his sleeve packet to eat alone! Dhabolkar protested that he always shared food with others and was not accustomed to eating alone. Baba told him that he was never alone, as He was always with him! 'Offer to me before you enjoy' was Baba's advice!

The bellowing noise of Upasani's breathing turned all eyes towards him. But Upasani had fixed his gaze on Sai Baba. Baba exclaimed – "He is here! He has come! The man in rags! Call him, Shama, call him here!"

'The man in rags' – all devotees exclaimed with one voice! A wave of jealousy passed through Dasa Ganu! Many others were also disturbed that this man in rags is to inherit Baba's powers. They had served and worshipped Baba with profound devotion. Of course, Dixit, Sathe, Buti, Mhalsapathy, Tata, Nana Chandorkar remained undisturbed!

Baba's eyes were fixed on Upasani! His respiration had now become normal! His disease almost disappeared! He still wondered whether he should go near Baba! His orthodox mind did not permit him to go into a Muslim shrine! But looking at the large Brahmin society and his old patient Khaparde, Upasani came near Baba but did not kneel down! When Madhava Rao reminded him to bow down, Baba said – "He need not kneel before me! He will get everything of me!" This shocked many.

Baba narrated a story- "Shama, I was having a stroll. On my way I came across a woman who was pregnant! She had a big belly, balanced on two thin legs and panting for breath! She was going to drink cold water! I told her – 'Mother, do not drink cold water. Drink it warm! Or else you will die!' She did not heed! How can I simply watch? I hit on her hands and spilled the water! Listen Shama, she had so many children in her tummy! Will they not die with her? One must not think of oneself! He must think of others who depend on him! She went to the village and had hot water. She felt greatly relieved! It is a mere spasmodic affliction caused by breath! To have God's grace these fools practice 'pranayama'! The breath goes and gets stuck up! Do you know Shama; we are closely related in life after life for many births? How then can I allow her to die? One went up and the other came down! I gave a hand of support and saved the other!"

While all others thought that Baba was just gabbling, only Upasani realised that it was all about him. Even the last reference to two birds was exactly the same by a sadhu in Haridwar to his brother. The fact that Baba was after him through many past births made Upasani move with gratitude! He remembered Kulkarni Maharaj's words that Sai Baba would further guide him in yoga. However what happened soon after revolted his mind!

Since one year Amir Shakkar of Bandra had brought with him Siddique Phalake, a Haji to have Baba's grace. This Haji had visited Mecca and Medina and craved for Baba's grace. Somehow Baba did not permit him to enter the mosque! However Phalake did not leave Shirdi without Baba's blessings and waited with tolerance. Today, Madhava Rao represented his case to Baba again, making Phalake stand outside the mosque.

Initially Baba said that Allah has not permitted Phalake's entry into the mosque. When Madhava Rao persisted, Baba put a condition as to whether Phalake will walk the way beyond the Barvi well. Phalake did not understand the deep meaning in Baba's question. He knew one thing that the way Baba referred is to go through thorny bushes, snake pits, and other dangerous spots. So he submitted to Madhava Rao with a little ego that if Baba wants, he is prepared to reach and return from the other end of the world too! Baba ignored this and asked for forty thousand rupees. Still with ego, Phalake submitted that he can even offer forty lakhs!

Once again ignoring him, Baba said – "Shama, tell him, I am going to slaughter a goat in the mosque today! Ask him what he wants? Flesh from loins, liver, brain, legs – what he desires?" Baba would not generally use such language among the gathering as it would be nauseating for Brahmin devotees! But today he was testing Upasani as he was brought up under strict orthodox culture. That is why he talked of slaughter and varieties of meat! Indeed his trick worked! Upasani's mind revolted! He felt like leaving Shirdi immediately! He wondered what sort of guidance Baba can give! Baba wanted Upasani to be above all such feelings and this was just a beginning of Upasani's journey of spiritual understanding!

Phalake was wise and knew he was being tested. Whether they liked it or not all other devotees had implicit faith in Baba. As such they watched the fun. Ultimately Phalake submitted – "Baba, I am not particular about flesh etc.! If you favour I will be happy with whatever crumbs of bread you throw in your bin outside!" Baba started abusing and broke the bin into pieces! He broke all the earthen pots! Phalake was bewildered! For Upasani it was a new experience! Baba went out of the mosque, purchased a basket full of mangoes from a fruit-seller. He brought that basket and kept it in front of Phalake. He took out a few ripened fruits and pressed it even to make it soft and holding it before Phalake he said – "Eat, eat this mango! Why should you eat crumbs of bread in Sai Durbar? If you have to eat anything – eat mango! Eat sweets! Eat whatever you desire."

As he thus spoke, Baba pulled out a number of currency notes from his pocket and pushed them to Phalake's hands. They were fifty-five rupees! Holding him by his hand he dragged him into the mosque and made him sit near himself. This is exactly what Phalake wanted! He had waited for one year for this grace. Then onwards there was a change in him and Phalake became an ardent devotee of Sai Baba!

While Phalake was thus extremely happy in Baba's company which he could secure after waiting for one year with patience, Upasani thought of leaving Shirdi immediately. So he told Baba – "Baba, I have come from a long distance. I had your darshan. Please permit me to go. I have a long journey." Baba said – "Long journey? Dear, this is the end of your journey." Upasani himself was shocked! He would not mind his breathing problem but he detested the idea of staying in a Muslim environment! So he said – "I am not keeping well. Moreover my people are waiting for me at home!" Baba said – "You are here to improve your health! As for your people, I will attend to them. Go and stay in the wada!"

Upasani persisted in his plea to leave Shirdi. Baba said – "All right! Go if you like! Come back after eight days! I will see what I should do."

Upasani did not waste a minute more. Picking his stick and collecting his sack cloth he made for the exit. But he soon realized that some tremendous force was pulling him back. With his firm decision to go home he could not go beyond the banks of Godavari in Kopergaon. The hypnotic spell of his Master in Shirdi had transfixed his disciple-designate like the gaze of a mother tortoise shielding her young ones from a distance. Upasani was now under Sai Baba's protection. To come out of that magnetic spell he visited the Datta temple on the banks of the river. There a priest requested Upasani to take a group of visitors to Shirdi. Upasani gave several excuses that he was not well and did not have money to make a trip to Shirdi. The visitors promised to take care of him and ultimately Upasani took them to Shirdi.

On seeing him, Baba smilingly said – "Well pandit, you have come back again? Now tell me when did you leave from here?" Upasani realised that he was back exactly after eight days as Baba had predicted! He felt certain that he was under Baba's spell and power! So giving up the thought of returning home he decided to obey Baba and leave his destiny in his hands!

Without a word he moved to Sathe's wada for his stay in Shirdi – not knowing for how many days!

36

UPASANI'S INTERNSHIP

*A*t last Baba had his own man, the man in rags in Shirdi. Baba had countless devotees and thousands of followers! They came and many more were to come! They did not come on their own accord but as was desired by Him! And true it was! Those who wished to visit Shirdi necessarily needed his grace! Nana Saheb Chandorkar and Dasa Ganu came as disbelievers and antagonists but turned to propagate Baba's mission! Baba pulled Dabholkar to present to the world *Sai Satcharita!* He pulled Kaka Dixit for his spiritual progress! But still he wanted someone who would not directly project his mere image, but lead the masses to 'Bhatia Margi' after Baba casts off his mortal coil! In short he wanted to mould an able Sadguru!

Upasani never wanted Baba's discipleship. Whether he liked it or not Baba wanted to grace him with it. For that he did not take recourse to usual methods of initiation like personal service, close company, verbal instructions, etc. He showered his grace on Upasani like a mother tortoise feeding her youngsters with her mere glance from a distance!

And thus began Baba's great experiment of moulding a disciple! One day Upasani was sitting in the mosque with other devotees. Baba asked him for one-rupee dakshina. Upasani went to the wada and brought a dirty one rupee coin. Baba commented on its dirtiness. Then Upasani brought one more rupee which was bright and shining. Baba retained both the rupees!

Upasani had carefully retained twelve rupees with him towards his expenses. But now Baba had taken away two rupees! In the meanwhile another devotee gave away whatever he had and Baba remarked that he will give ten fold the money he receives as dakshina. This made Upasani also to give away everything he had! Baba told him – "You have done a right thing! I will give you all I have"

Many people in the gathering felt jealous of Upasani getting everything of Sai Baba. Baba declared that he will give everything to Upasani on a golden plaque! This created heartburn among devotees and so unknowingly Upasani developed enemies! Actually he had not come to Shirdi for Baba's discipleship! He wanted to get his breathing problem corrected by Baba through Yoga and then go back to his native place and stay with his family!

Baba said – "Shama, I have to complete his account. Let him go and sit in Khandoba temple for four years. He will get everything." When asked as to what he is supposed to do there, he curtly replied – "Do nothing." This implied that Upasani will reach a perfect sainthood after four years. This open announcement created devotees as well as enemies for Upasani.

In order to avoid the harassment by the devotees in the wada, Upasani shifted to Khandoba temple. Inside the small space of the shrine he spread his sack cloth in a corner and would lie down for the entire day. He did not encourage any visitors. This gave him enough solitude to brood over his miserable plight for which he blamed himself! But it was Baba's plan.

He planned *Divya Nama Smaran* – nonstop recitation of divine name by turning beads of rosary. One day Baba came suddenly. He snatched the rosary, broke it into bits, and threw them away. He told him that he should sit idle and do nothing. Khandoba will grace him after four years!

A number of people tried to harass Upasani so that he leaves Shirdi once for all. They spread rumours that he is a spy, a police informer, a British agent to keep an eye on Baba's devotees and many such things. But they could do nothing as Sai Baba was close behind Upasani!

Though Baba asked him to sit idle in Khandoba temple, he found it boring and started attending classes in *Panchadashi* and *Paramamrith* by Dada Saheb Khaparde.

Having given all money to Baba, Upasani became penniless. Initially he was given free food by Balabhav. Later he took one piece of bread and few grains. This created bleeding in motions. Megha took pity on him and arranged for his meals with Dada Kelkar. After some days, Upasani started taking from him only uncooked grain or begged charity in the village and prepared food at the temple. Though he still led a solitary life in Khandoba temple as per Baba's instructions he regularly attended the noon aarti in the mosque. The day he first cooked food in the temple he carried some to the mosque as an offering for Baba. While cooking he saw a black dog sitting outside and looking at him expectantly. Moved with pity, Upasani decided to feed him after offering the food to Baba! Upasani was bewildered when Baba told him that he was already there in the form of a black dog.

Next day Upasani cooked food and looked for a black dog. Of course it was not there! He saw a dirty beggar covering himself with a rug staring intently at food. Upasani did not like it! Covering it with a leaf he took the food to the mosque. Baba revealed to him that he was already there in the form of a beggar! Baba brought home the truth to Upasani that he is present in all beings! From then onwards, Upasani visualised Sai Baba in all!

Upasani also had hallucinations. His dead grandfather appeared before him and uttered the word 'Ahmednagar' again and again in a peculiar style. Upasani thought that his grandfather is instructing him to leave Shirdi and go to Ahmednagar. Then he split the word emphasising accent on each of its components and divided it as *Aham-Madan-Gar* which in Sanskrit, 'Aham' means ego, 'Madan' means lust and 'Gar' means poison. Actually Sai Baba had appeared in the form of his grandfather to point out that ego and lust are obstacles to spiritual progress!

Besides this, while sitting idle in Khandoba temple he perceived a number of mystic visions before his eyes. Sun rays entering his head and emerging out still brighter from the other side, dazzling and revolving circles moving before his eyes, in those rays a black person *kali purusha* and a fair complexioned person *sath purusha* competing with each other to push him into a valley of sins or merits, finding himself among many women himself being devoid of gender sense, sometimes feeling himself as a woman, vision of Sai Baba, formation of universe by atoms and molecules, fast moving universe himself being an independent entity and other bewildering hallucinations! Khandoba mandir was also infested with snakes and other reptiles moving freely over Upasani! Upasani used to get frightened and run to Baba! Baba would reassure him with affectionate words of consolation!

To avoid visitors in the day time, Upasani used to help agriculturists! It was surprising that with no food for days together; he was active in the field.

While Upasani's mind was thus getting revolutionised and prepared for the future he received a letter informing him about his third wife's death. This put an end to the last thread of attachment that held his mind bound to his home! Sai Baba had decided to drag him out of all worldly ties of temptations and its process was under way! Later he found food also repulsive – nauseous as excreta and had to stop taking it. Though spiritually advanced, his body became weak and fragile! He also developed insanity, abusing visitors to Khandoba temple and throwing stones at them. Adding fuel to fire, Nanavalli and his group of mischievous children would harass Upasani! Thus humiliation, suffering, starvation, death of dear wife and all calamities of degradation one after the other increased the faculty of forbearance in him and his gender consciousness totally disappeared!

Upasani developed clairvoyance! He was in a position to know the mind and movements of Sai Baba from his own place! He could read the past, present and future of anyone! Cobra and other poisonous reptiles moved around without harming him. He had lost his consciousness!

Once an astrologer from Narsobawadi visited Shirdi. Sai Baba did not permit him to examine him. Somehow after two days of waiting, the astrologer could meet Upasani. He could see an accomplished saint in him!

Megha always had a soft corner for Upasani. One day he took coffee to feed him. But on seeing Megha, Upasani started crying. Megha did not get an explanation. He went and told Madhava Rao about this. Madhava Rao felt some calamity for Upasani. When he went and told Baba that Upasani started crying on seeing Megha, Baba too shed tears. It was not possible to ask Baba anything. By the time Madhava Rao went home, he learnt that Megha had diarrhoea and vomiting and soon his end came! However, one thing everybody realised that Upasani could see Megha's death!

When Megha's body reached the cremation ground, Baba reached there! He was very sad! He offered flowers and shed tears as the body was cremated!

Guru Poornima arrived. Baba told his devotees to worship Upasani first and later come to the mosque. The period of four years Baba had prescribed was still not fully over. But his experiments to make him a perfect saint came to their conclusion. Without speaking, without looking at him, without keeping him in his constant company, Sai Baba had prepared his disciple! On the day of Guru Poornima (1915) he had a sudden whim of offering Upasani the position of a full fledged spiritual Master! So he commanded some of his devotees to worship Upasani first before they performed his own 'pooja'! Those who had realised Upasani's high state of spiritual achievement rushed to him. In spite of his protests they worshipped him as they would do to Baba! It was all new for the man in rags. He did not want this honour at all! He was furious! But obeyed Baba's orders!

It was three years ten months that Upasani had come to Shirdi! Only two months were left for Baba's mandatory four year internship for Upasani! He now had tremendous respect for Baba! He honestly believed that he was like dust under his Guru's feet! He could not bear the idea of being worshipped as 'Guru'. So to stop this worship forthwith the only remedy was to leave Shirdi – he thought. He knew Baba would not permit it. So he decided to leave without asking him. He secretly left Shirdi with the co-operation of Dr.Pillai and his brother! Clothes on his body were already torn or stolen by village urchins. The only thing that was left was his piece of sack cloth. Before leaving Shirdi he prostrated thrice on the sacred land in front of Khandoba mandir where Sai Baba had kept his lotus feet long ago! Though he came in rags, now he left with a treasure of spiritual wealth!

Sai Baba felt sorry that his disciple did not complete the four years of internship to become his disciple! So he declared that 'there is no heir or disciple to him and he will continue to look after the welfare of his devotees. When he casts off his mortal coil, the bones in his tomb will be ever vigilant and take care of his devotees!'

Upasani came and left! The wheel of time moved fast! The mission of the Loving God was almost over. Thousands came and benefitted. Saints like Rama Maruti, Gadge Maharaj visited Lord Sainath. Lokmanya Tilak too visited. Kaka Dixit retired from his profession, renouncing his family life, he wore saffron clothes to live like a 'mendicant'. His mission of life was to serve Sai Baba. His presence in Shirdi was very helpful! Shirdi was full of life! But Baba himself was now sinking due to his ageing body!

And as if an indication of Sai Baba's departure from this world, an attendant dropped a brick, which was tenderly preserved by Baba, while cleaning the mosque. On seeing the brick broken into bits, Baba exclaimed – "It is over! It is finished! My luck is smashed!"

It was brick given to Baba by his Guru. It was now broken. It was Baba's practice to talk in first person while it referred to his devotees. By saying 'My luck is smashed' he meant the good luck of his devotees was smashed. It was a clear announcement of his shedding the mortal coil! But as usual it went unnoticed! No one took it seriously!

On the auspicious day of Dasara another suggestive incident took place. Ramachandra Patil had a vision in the early hours. He was ill and bed-ridden for many days. Sai Baba assured him that his death is waived and Tatya is going to die his place on the next Vijayadashami day. He specifically asked him not to inform him as he may die of fear. "

Ramachandra Patil was sore that Tatya is going to die next Vijayadashami. He confided in his friend Bala Shimpi. Both went to the mosque to seek a remedy from Baba. But what they saw in the mosque astounded them.

Baba was in terrific rage! He was abusing Hindus and Muslims alike! He threw everything in the dhuni! Nana Chandorkar, Kaka Dixit, Dhabolkar, Sathe and others had assembled for Dasara festival. Baba was blurting – "Damned you all! So many years have passed! Still you ponder whether I am a Hindu or a Muslim! Can you not see I stay in a mosque, read Koran, recite Namaz, yet burn a dhuni, celebrate Rama Navami and Ramzan with equal zeal. Still you want to know Who am I? What is there to guess? Hindus doubt I am a Muslim? Muslims doubt I am a Hindu? See with your own eyes – see who I am?" One by one he removed all his clothes and put them into dhuni! The flames threw a golden hue on Baba's naked body!

Bhagoji Shinde moved into action and speedily pulled out a 'suspender', put it around Baba's body, dressed him with a lungi, put over a gown and he himself kneeled and put his head on Baba's feet! Baba was calm again! The devotees moved in a line to have his darshan on the Vijayadashami day!

This divine vision in 1917 left a deep imprint on the devotees.

37

CROSSING OF BORDER

*S*trangely enough, after he had the dream vision, Ramachandra Patil recovered very fast and was back to normalcy again. He was afraid that his beloved friend Tatya was leaving for his heavenly abode by next Vijayadashmi. Both Ramachandra Patil and Bala Shimpi looked after Tatya's welfare and advised him to entrust his affairs to his eldest son! Tatya also fell sick and the shadow of death was hovering over him!

The year 1918 began. On the first day of the new year both Madhava Rao and Gopalrao Buti had a similar dream vision in the early hours. Both of them were sleeping in the Dixit wada. Baba appeared in Buti's dream and said – "Buti, you wanted to build a wada in Shirdi? I had permitted Sathe and Kaka. Only you were left out! Now you can immediately start work!" Buti's dream was over. Buti was a multi-millionaire! Constructing a building at Shirdi was nothing to him! But he used to be sad that Baba had not permitted him so far. Now he was happy that Baba wanted him to construct a building soon. Looking aside he found Madhava Rao in tears!

Madhava Rao was a sentimental person. Baba's remembrance or vision would bring tears in his eyes. Once when he went for Gaya, Baba told him that he will reach there ahead of him! When Madhava Rao reached Gaya he found Baba's picture on the wall of the priest's house! Madhava Rao was emotionally moved and shed tears realising the significance of Baba's assurance! Seeing him shed tears, Buti asked him the reason.

Madhava Rao embraced Buti and told him – "You are lucky! Baba came in my dream and asked me to hasten you to build a wada. He has asked you to include a shrine. Baba will inaugurate it on the Vijayadashami day!"

Buti was simply surprised! Both had the same dream! By now Kaka Dixit was also awake! He heard the dream and reverentially bowed in the direction of the mosque. Then they sat together to plan a building including a shrine. They decided to have Baba's sanction when he sat for darshan.

All three of them went to Baba's darshan. Baba was meaningfully looking at them. Madhava Rao lovingly told him – "Baba, you are God no doubt! Please allow us to enjoy sound sleep at least." Baba smiled and told – "What nonsense! Shama, why should I disturb your sleep. I am always in the mosque watching the play of the Lord!"

Madhava Rao said – "Oh, we wish you did that! You take sides! You help some – you hate some!" Baba answered – "No Shama, it is not like that! I am only a witness to divine plan! They all come taking birth again carrying with them the award of their earlier acts – getting bad or good luck – and leave the world again to visit and suffer again and again!" Shama submitted – "May be you are right. But today we are concerned with our dreams – a common dream that myself and Buti had! You want Buti to build a wada"

Baba told Buti to start the work immediately and complete before Vijayadashami. He wanted one hall for a temple inside! He said the shrine be dedicated to any deity. He said – "Everyone of us is a fraction of divine identity! We will sit there, chitchat, sing songs and enjoy life! The idol is only to decorate the shrine!" Kaka Dixit then explained Baba the plan.

And on the same day the construction of Buti's wada began starting with digging for foundation! Buti had ample money! And this project had Baba's blessings! So delay was out of question.

Buti's wada began to take shape. Devotees coming from outside also helped in the construction work. Baba who was past eighty would visit the site almost every day and personally watch the progress.. He himself would suggest placing of windows, doors and such details.

Kaka Dixit suggested to Buti to have the shrine dedicated to Lord Muralidhar. There was no shrine for Krishna in the village and everyone liked the idea. A well known sculptor at Jaipur was given the work of carving out an idol of Muralidhar!

The festival of navaratri began. Buti's wada was almost complete. Baba was satisfied with the work. Devotees poured from different parts on hearing the news that Baba is inaugurating a new temple on the Vijayadashami day. A few close associates like Ramachandra Patil, Bala Shimpi were sad that Tatya Patil would die on that day. But in the heart of hearts they had a hope that Baba would give an extention to his life!

It was the Durga Pooja day. Four nomadics entered Shirdi with a wild tiger chained and tied in a bullock cart. The tiger was sick and the nomadics sought Baba's permission to bring the animal inside the mosque. They told him that the tiger was sick and they requested him to cure its illness.

Baba told them to unchain the tiger. Everyone was scared! Even the nomadics were diffident and dared not free the animal. But with implicit faith in Baba, they unchained it and led him inside. The tiger looked at Baba. The devotees ran in fright. Baba was unmoved, calm and looked steadfast at the animal! It was a tense moment. The tiger struck its tail three times on the floor and then suddenly collapsed down dead! The tiger offered its salutation to Baba by striking the tail!

The nomadics were sorry that the tiger was dead! They were also happy that after a prolonged illness it had its end in the presence of Sai Baba. Baba blessed them saying – "Allah has taken away the tiger but has arranged an alternate source of livelihood for you" The tiger was buried a little away from the mosque!

Placing his hands on Buti's shoulder, Baba went to see Buti's wada. Madhava Rao, Kaka Dixit and others followed. Bhagoji held an umbrella over Baba's head to cover him against bright sunshine.

Baba was happy with the wada and the temple in it. He said – "Shama, this is beautiful! I feel like coming to stay here myself!" Buti was happy and told him – "Then why not shift here immediately, Baba."

Baba said – "Oh, no! I just blurt like that! I have passed my life in that mosque! You have all come to see me there! You turned my masjid into a mandir! You have made this fakir as your Madhav! That is your greatness! I got everything there in. But have the same feeling for the entire mankind. See Madhav in every man! That would be the right reward of my mission. That would be my true worship!"

Buti felt highly elevated that the money spent on the wada was worth it! The mandir was immensely liked by Baba!

Baba came out of the temple and said to Madhava Rao – "Shama, all these people have come from outside and given me boundless love! But you all in this village have actually brought me up – from my tender age to what I am today! Indeed I cannot repay this debt of Shirdi village! When I came here, I was a boy of sixteen years and I have spent over sixty years with you all in your loving company!

A beggar like me you accepted as God! When I used to go out for my begging rounds I would meet you all. Now, Shama it is difficult for me to walk! Still I feel like seeing all once again!" Baba was immensely emotional that day! Hence Madhava Rao said – "Let us go round the village, Baba, slowly, slowly."

Baba took his support and moved towards the village. Others also followed. On his way Baba would stop before all the village temples, fold his hands before deities to express his reverence and then proceed again. He always respected the Hindu Gods! He would personally offer flowers from Lendi baug, inquire whether regular worship is done and offer financial help and would look after renovation of old temples. He would advice his Hindu devotees to offer worship at these temples. The only thing he hated most was when these people worshipped stone idols but ill treated humans!

His age-old feet moved slowly. When he reached the cemetery, he remembered Megha. He sat there for a few minutes. He halted near Kondaji's house and inquired about the three carpenter brothers. Going ahead he met the children of Appa Jogale, Kashiram tailor and recollected the fragrance of their departed parents' love for him. In all houses, Baba saw his pictures being reverentially worshipped!

He arrived at Vaman Potter's house. He was no more and his children and grandchildren welcomed Baba. Baba blessed the children and recollected as to how Vaman supplied one hundred eight earthen lamps for him to light lamps on a 'Deepawali' night!

Madhava Rao remembered all those miracles of Baba! All his obligations! All his acts of nobility! He began to wonder why Baba was so much emotional today!

Baba moved ahead. He came across Appa Kulkarni's house. When his widow bowed down to him, he recollected

Appa's efforts in making Nana Saheb Chnadorkar and Dasa Ganu come to Shirdi! He went to Kulkarni's house and saw him deeply meditating on Sai Baba! He looked at his wife's picture and recollected her devotion.

Baba walked ahead! The news that Baba is going round the village reached Lakshmi Bai Shinde. She quickly baked one crisp bread, applied ghee to it and keeping it ready with chutney and jaggery in a plate, she awaited Baba's arrival. Baba blessed her and ate the bread she gave.

Next was Tatya's house. Baba remembered his mother Bayja ma. He recollected as to how she used to tread the jungle path to feed him those days. He saw Tatya who was bedridden. He cheered him up! He applied udhi on his forehead and assured him that he will take care of his welfare! He declared that Tatya was not going to die! Someone else will take his place. He did not disclose as to who that someone else was! On hearing about Tatya, somebody brought sweets. Baba distributed sweets to all those present! While others were jubilant and out of anxiety, deep in his heart Madhava Rao wondered as to whether this 'someone' who has to take the place of Tatya is Sai Baba himself!

Baba went round the houses of other devotees in Shirdi. Ultimately he reached the mosque. He fell sick with fever. Even then he kept sitting resting against a cushion. He gave darshan to thousands of devotees. He had asked Vaje to recite Ramayan for the the last three days. Vaje was tired and seeing his condition, Baba asked him to wind up.

Madhava Rao asked Jog to finish aarti early. Baba took rest. His condition caused concern to Madhava Rao, Dixit, Nana Chandorkar and others. Buti was restless! He was upset because he could see no future for his wada if Baba suddenly left this world! Baba read his mind and told Madhava Rao – "Shama, look, this Buti is very nervous! He is worried what will happen to his wada! Put my body in that! Build a tomb over it! The bones in my tomb will respond to the call of all my devotees."

'Indeed, Baba, what will happen to us devotees after you have left?" Kaka Dixit asked.

"Kaka, you are a wise man! A learned person – with implicit faith in myself! Do I have to tell you all this? Listen my body will die – but not this shrine – this place! It will be ever awake with my unseen presence! For that remember me always and call me in your difficulties! I am always with you. The udhi from my 'dhuni' will always give you protection! I always look after your welfare." This assurance by Baba gave confidence to all devotees. Their minds were getting prepared for Baba's last journey!

It was 15th October 1918. Vijayadashami dawned!

There was hope and despair inside mosque alternately! That was the state of mind of Madhava Rao, Nana Chandorkar, Kaka Dixit and others who were constantly attending on Baba! One moment Baba showed hopes, another his condition became hopeless! Baba's condition had gone from bad to worse.

That day the noon aarti was short! The lunch hour was already over – yet no one thought of having lunch! Though serious Baba was conscious! He was aware that his time for 'Mahasamadhi' had come! He wanted to avoid the utter confusion caused by wailing, weeping and crying of devotees! But they were not prepared to leave him alone. Baba told them to go for food. Nana Chandorkar, Buti, Madhava Rao, Kaka Dixit, Sathe, Mhalsapathy, Dabholkar were all near him. It was hard for them to disobey! They all left for lunch. Those who remained behind with Baba were Lakshmi Bai Shinde, a villager Bayaji Kote and a couple of others.

Baba sat up in his bed. He took out from beneath his pillow the purse of his nine coins – the coins of his nine devotees! With his polishing now they were gleaming with extraordinary shine. Holding them on his right palm and looking at them intently he told Lakshmi – "Lakshmi, now you have to preserve this precious wealth of mine! These coins represent the nine fold devotion of my nine intimate devotees. Keep them with you. They will set an example of an ideal devotion! You too have served me selflessly giving boundless love! But I gave you nothing in return! Accept these coins as my gift! My fakir will look after your welfare!" He placed the coins in her hand, first five and then four! Lakshmi's eyes were filled with tears! It was a unique achievement in her life! She was simply enchanted!

It was 2.30 pm on 15th October 1918. Vijayadashami too ended and the eleventh day of the lunar month 'Ekadashi' was about to begin. Baba chose this auspicious moment of transition from *Dashamai* to *Ekadashi* for his *Seemollangan* – crossing the border of this world to merge with the Supreme! Soon after gifting nine coins of devotion to Lakshmi, Baba rested his head on Bayaji Kote's shoulder and in a split second left his human body! Baba was gone! Gone forever! Gone into infinity merging with the Spirit Eternal!

Bayaji Kote and Lakshmi cried aloud "B....A....B....A". Their wailing cries carried the news to the entire village. The devotees, visitors, villagers all rushed to the mosque. Looking at his calm, lifeless body lying in an eternal slumber they were almost in a breaking point! Though their hearts wept, their tears wanting to come out were frozen between the eyelids with emotional frigidity! The gushing out sorrow was bundied before it burst!

The emotionally disturbed devotees came to their senses! They realised they had to think of what is to be done next! The Hindus and Muslims talked of disposing the body according to their own faiths. Heated arguments took place! None of them would budge from their stand!

Kaka Dixit had to intervene! In clear words he pointed out Baba's last desire that his body be buried in Buti's wada and a Samadhi be built over it! It was then decided to place it in the Temple meant for Muralidhar in the wada and build a shrine over it. For Muslims it was a tomb and for Hindus a Samadhi. That was a satisfactory solution for both communities!

Baba's body was kept for darshan for two days for devotees coming from outside. Telegrams were sent everywhere. In thousands they rushed to Shirdi! Baba's body remained fresh, smiling and shining till the end!

On the same night when Baba left his body he appeared in Dasa Ganu's dream at Pandharpur. He told him – "Ganu, I have given up my body! Come there and adorn me with Bakul flowers!" Dasa Ganu rushed to Shirdi.

Madhava Rao's uncle Lakshmana Kaka too had a dream – "Lakshman, that Bapu Jog thinks I am dead! It is not so! I shall be ever living for you all! He will not do aratii! At least you do it." Early morning Lakshmana Kaka went to the mosque and made the preparations for the morning prayer. Ignoring all protests, he performed 'arati' as usual!

Dasa Ganu reached Shirdi and looking at Baba's lifeless body he was very much moved! The emotional vibrations caused in his heart shaped into words which flowed out of his lips singing Baba's glory! He began to decorate the body with flowers of poetic compositions! Other devotees too cheerfully joined him in offering flowers!

Time to place Baba in the samadhi pit arrived! Dasa Ganu began to offer the last rites with repetition of 'Om Namah Shivaya'. With every name thousands joined to recite the pranava – 'Om' the mystic syllable of the Divine! It was joined by *Il-e-Ila-hee* of the Muslim devotees! The body was placed with utmost care along with Bilva , Tulsi, flowers and finally covered with earth!

Sai Baba's physical body is gone but his divinity stays on! He is still responding to his devotees with the assurance 'If you look to me – I look to you'. He is immortal.

38

APOSTLES OF LOVING GOD

*S*ai Baba attained Mahasamadhi in 1918 and Shirdi thereafter generally faded out of public memory. People visiting Shirdi were very few and by 1936, hardly ten people visited on any day. Close devotees of Sai Baba thought that his power was over as in the case of any contemporary saint. Sai Baba's samadhi was being worshipped like a Muslim Darga!

Prior to 1940, all over India, hardly anyone knew about Sai Baba or heard of the place 'Shirdi'. But today we find temples of Sai Baba in nooks and corners of the country. Associations of Sai devotees, Satsangs, Samaj are in plenty. Many have given Baba's name to their children. Many shops, institutions, industries bear Sai Baba's name. Shirdi is now on the international map and lakhs of people visit Shirdi to seek Baba's blessings.

Sai Baba's invisible but unmistakably perceptible presence in Shirdi pulled Sri Narasimha Swamiji in 1936 to take him all over the globe in the next two decades. Sri Narasimha Swamiji is the heart of Sai movement. He is the embodiment of Sai grace and through his Herculean efforts affected a silent revolution by which he made Sai Baba known all over India initially and now the world over. A revolution in which innumerable low and sinful people turned over a new life of piety by taking up worship of Sai Baba. He gave direction and life to Sai movement which had become static by 1936.

Sri Narasimha Swamiji's pioneering efforts of Sai prachar from village to village, city to city and making individual house visits to take Sai Baba out of Shirdi in the remote corner of Maharashtra to all over the country and even abroad. For this purpose, every Sai devotee should be ever grateful for the strenuous efforts of Sri Narasimha Swamiji from 1936 till he attained 'Mahasamadhi' in 1956. When we offer obeisance to Sai Maharaj, our foremost 'Pranams' should be to Sri Narasimha Swamiji.

Who is Sri Narasimha Swamiji? How did he live? How did he realise Sai Baba? What are his efforts to distribute the treasure of 'Sai Baba's grace' to one and all? An attempt is made here in all humility to tell the fascinating story of this messenger of Sai Baba.

Sri Narasimha Swamiji took birth in a beautiful village of Bhavani in Tamil Nadu, on the banks of the confluence of three rivers – Kaveri, Bhavani, and Guptagamini, on 21st August 1874. At a tender age he mastered the scriptures and later acquired a degree in Law. He became a prominent lawyer in Salem city and acquitted creditably as the president of Salem municipality for two decades and as a member of the State Legislature. He took part in the freedom struggle and was a follower of Annie Besant's home rule movement. A tragedy in which two of his children were killed made him renounce his home in 1925 to perform severe austerities and realise God. For eleven long years he travelled all over the country, stayed with great saints like Jagadguru Shankaracharya, Sri Chandrasekhara Bharathi Mahswamigal of Sringeri, Ramana Bhagawan of Tiruvannamalai, Siddharooda Swamiji of Hubli, Narayan Maharaj of Khedgaon, Meher Baba and Upasani Maharaj. In fact, Sri Narasimha Swamiji is mainly responsible for introducing Ramana Bhagawan to the world through his book -*Self-Realisation – Biography of Ramana* published in 1929. Subsequently through another book '*Sage of Sakori* published in 1936, he introduced Shri Upasani Maharaj. When Sri Narasimha Swamiji arrived at Sai Baba's Samadhi on 29th August 1936, he found his liberating truth. He felt Sai Baba engulfing his body and transforming him into a new personality. A great surge of compassion and devotion flooded his mind and he felt at peace with him. Thus an ardent devotee of Sai Baba who could spread his message in the length and breadth of the country was thus reborn.

Sai Baba's *Ashtothara* recited by millions of his devotees has been composed by Sri Narasimha Swamiji in which he has poured out his devotion. He guided the Samsthan authorities to adhere to a set pattern of worship, which is followed even today. With the help of Dasa Ganu Maharaj, he rationalised the singing of different aartis. He also composed 'Sai Sahasranama' for elaborate worship of Sainath Maharaj. He also introduced chanting of Vishnu Sahasranama in the daily routine of worship.

Sri Narasimha Swamiji learnt Marathi and interviewed the contemporaries of Sai Baba and brought out a book 'Devotees Experiences'. He undertook a whirlwind trip of Maharashtra during 1936-39 along with Dasa Ganu and Awasthi Maharaj to carry the message of Sai Baba. Sai Baba prompted Sri Papaiah Chetty of Nellore to gift a sum of Rs.11, 455/- to Sri Narasimha Swamiji at the Samadhi Mandir in Shirdi which Swamiji refused. But Sai Baba made him accept it for establishing 'All India Sai Samaj' at Madras in 1939 which became a nucleus for Sai prachar. He brought out booklets, pamphlets and made extensive lecture tours all over the country to carry the message of Sai Baba. In fact, he took 'Sai Baba out of Maharashtra and placed him all over India.' He wrote extensively on Sai Baba in newspapers.

Sri Narasimha Swamiji's divine personality attracted people of all faiths to join Sai path that rapidly grew to hundreds of thousands. During Sri Narasimha Swamiji's very life time, devotees worshipped him as 'Sadguru'.

During 1936-56, Sri Narasimha Swamiji travelled alone and at times with a few volunteers – from the icy peaks of the Himalayas, through valleys and deep jungles to Kanyakumari, from Guwahati to Lahore and thus the whole of India. He had covered more than 11,500 villages, sanctified more than 1,50,000 homes, written about 2,00,000 letters, built 450 satsangs called Upasamajams and initiated over 50 temples and given countless discourses.

He never worried whether twenty people attended his lectures or two thousand! His Sai prachar work always started on time and in a systematic manner. Caring little for his personal comforts, he has comforted thousands by directing them to Sai Baba. All those who are fortunate to come into his divine presence breathe a divine peace and experience a touch of Lord Sainath because of his constant rapport with him.

Sri Narasimha Swamiji took Mahasamadhi on 19th October 1956 and the mantle of carrying Sai movement fell on his worthy successor Sri Radhakrishna Swamiji, who was associated with him since 1943.

Sri Radhakrishna Swamiji was born in a beautiful village Poyyamani near Tiruchi city in Tamil Nadu on 15th April 1906. He had a great spiritual inclination right from childhood. As a young lad of seven he had 'darshan' of Goddess Kanchi Kamakshi. Since his elder brother was employed in Pune, he had the privilege of visiting holy places in Maharashtra. When he was in deep meditation for 48 days in one of the caves in Lonavla near Pune, he was blessed by Lord Dattatreya. His eldest brother Sri Rajagopala Iyer initiated him into the spiritual realm. He was associated with great saints like Jagadguru Shankaracharya Sri Chandrasekharendra Saraswati Mahaswamigal of Kanchi Kamakoti Mutt, Bhagawan Ramana, Mahan Seshadri Swamigal, Sri Narayan Maharaj of Khedgaon, and others. When Sri Narasimha Swamiji came to Ooty in the Nilgiris, he was deeply impressed by him as his God-sent Guru and in 1943 renounced home to perform severe austerities and redeem countless souls.

Sri Radhakrishna Swamiji's devotion to his Guru, Sri Narasimha Swamiji was characterised by a supreme spirit of dedication and self-effacing service. He was in a dilemma – 'Who is Sai Baba? Why did Sri Narasimha Swamiji pulled me to Madras?' When he broached this subject, Sri Narasimha Swamiji advised him to read the tenth chapter of the Gita. Then he saw the entire sky filled with various forms of Gods and Goddesses. He prayed to Baba – "I do not want all these. I want to know your real form, who you are and that alone. Please show that to me." All the forms in the sky vanished and only those of Rama and Maruti remained. It became clear to him that Sai Baba and Rama are one.

Once he had a vision of Radhakrishna. He was fasting and also had fever. He saw a bright light in the sky. Gradually he perceived it as Radha, who appeared to be an eighteen year old girl. After a while, Krishna came in the same way and stood in front. Radha and Krishna were hugging together as we see in the traditional pictures. Radha held Swamiji's hand and showed Krishna – 'This is Krishna'. Then the vision disappeared. Actually Swamiji had prayed to Radha to show him Krishna and this had proved effective.

He was sent to Bangalore in 1953 for Sai prachar work. He established Sri Sai Spiritual Centre and became a life sculptor of thousands in Karnataka with the only goal of human upliftment. He initiated devotees into chanting Vishnu Sahasranama and 'Om Namo Narayanaya'. He impressed upon devotees to take up three G's – Gowpuja, Gayatri, and Gita. He transformed many agnostics into Sai Baba centred lives.

Sri Radhakrishna Swamiji was closely associated with hundreds and thousands of devotees from all walks of life irrespective of caste, creed, or religion. He was a spiritual giant following the humble way. A mantle of simplicity and humility covered his extraordinary stature. He went about his work in the affirmation of the divine. Only to a few discerning souls was it given to see the man behind the mask.

What he took in by contemplation, he poured out in love and action in a variety of fields of human service – spiritual and intellectual, cultural and philanthropic. In fact, his life in Bangalore for twenty-nine years was a saga of self effacing austerity of a new type through which abundant good flowed to humanity. Through lectures, conversations and instructions, he scattered what he had gathered.

Sri Radhakrishna Swamiji was truly an 'Apostle of love'. His universality is depicted in the divine incantation, which he wrote at Dark, which epitomises his innermost feelings and concern. Here it is:-

May the wicked turn
May the good attain peace.
May the peaceful be freed from all bondage and
May the liberated redeem others.
May everybody be happy.
May everybody be free from disease.
May everybody have good luck.
May none fall on evil days.
May everybody surmount difficulties.
May everybody have good fortune.
May everybody realize his ambitions.
May everybody rejoice everywhere.

Sri Radhakrishna Swamiji lived a full and active life. He was constantly travelling and propagating Sai Baba's teachings. He was in tune with Sai Baba all the twenty-four hours and his actions were in response to the Master's command.

Sri Radhakrishna Swamiji attained 'Mahasamadhi' on 14th January 1980 and he is ever present in the hearts of his countless devotees in spirit and his guiding hand and loving eyes hover every home of his devotees reminding us of Sai Baba's assurance – 'Why fear when I am here'.

In fact, you can see the portraits of Sri Narasimha Swamiji and Sri Radhakrishna Swamiji adorning the central hall of the Samadhi Mandir in Shirdi along with the greats like Mhalsapathy, Shama, Dixit, etc.

Though physically no more, we are experiencing the ever living presence of Sai Baba, Sri Narasimha Swamiji, and Sri Radhakrishna Swamiji. They are close behind our thoughts and in the true spirit of *Apantharathma* they appear in different forms and continue to bless the devotees.

'When I am gone, only love can take my place' – is the common factor running in these three perfect Masters.

To a generation of humanity which was starved of love, had not known what love is, these three perfect Masters, with the soothing balm of love have opened a new world of peace and harmony, as we knew only suffering and pain, hatred, violence, jealousy and envy. Those of us, who are worshipping Sai Baba, have become better men. We have understood what it is to love and to be loved. We have found a meaning and purpose in life that life is to be lived nobly, courageously, with faith in Sai Baba and loving all creations of God. We have learnt what all the religious books and teaching could not convey to us. These three perfect Masters have shown us to make this world a real heaven.

Let us lead a life of simplicity as shown by Sai Baba.

Sri Narasimha Swamiji is our model to develop an attitude of renunciation.

Instead of chanting – 'I want this – I want that' all the twenty four hours, let us take up 'Divya Nama Smaran' – recitation of Vishnu Sahasranama and epiphenic chanting of 'Om Namo Narayanaya' as part of our life, as guided by Sri Radhakrishna Swamiji.

Then we will attain spiritual maturity and develop a detached attachment.

Our worshipful pranams to the Trinity - Sai Baba, Sri Narasimha Swamiji, and Sri Radhakrishna Swamiji.

"You will never be able to understand thoroughly how great Sai Baba was.

He was the very personification of perfection.

If you know him as I know him you would call him the Master of Creation"

Avatar Meher Baba

***

*"The lives of men like Sai Baba are the very proof
of the truth*

that the Master blesses the seed which he sows in us

*and time does the rest in accordance with the pupil's
worthiness of His grace.*

Not all the seeds fall on stony ground

Some give a rich harvest.

Therein lies hope for the future of erring mankind

Mouni Sadhu

Eleven Solemn Promises As Pledged by Baba for Material Success, Prosperity & Happiness

1. Whoever comes to my abode, their suffering will come to an end once and for all.

2. The helpless will experience plenty of joy, happiness and fulfilment as soon as they climb the steps of the Dwarakamai.

3. I am ever vigilant to help and guide all those who come to me, who surrender to me and seek refuge in me.

4. There shall be no dearth of any kind in the houses of my devotees. I shall fulfil all their wishes.

5. If you look to me, I shall look to you and take care of all your needs.

6. If you seek my advice and help, it shall be given to you at once.

7. If you cast your burdens onto me, I shall surely take them on and relieve you of them.

8. I shall be ever active and vigorous even after casting away my body.

9. I shall respond and act in human form and continue to work for my devotees from my tomb.

10. My mortal remains will speak, execute and discharge all the needs of my devotees.

11. My tomb shall bless, speak and fulfil the innumerable needs of my devotees.

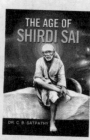

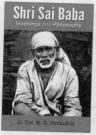

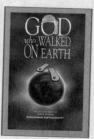

SHIRDI SAI BABA

Baba's Vaani: His Sayings and Teachings
Compiled by Vinny Chitluri
ISBN 978 81 207 3589 1
₹ 200

Baba's Gurukul SHIRDI
Vinny Chitluri
ISBN-978-81-207-4770-8
₹ 200

Baba's Anurag Love for His Devotees
Compiled by Vinny Chitluri
ISBN 978 81 207 5447 8
₹ 125

Baba's Rinanubandh Leelas during His Sojoum in Shir
Compiled by Vinny Chitluri
ISBN 978 81 207 3403 6
₹ 200

The Gospel of Shri Shirdi Sai Baba: A Holy Spiritual Path
Dr Durai Arulneyam
ISBN 978 81 207 3997 0
₹ 150

Sai Baba's 261 Leelas
Balkrishna Panday
ISBN 978 81 207 2727 4
₹ 125

Spotlight on the Sai Story
Chakor Ajgaonker
ISBN 978 81 207 4399 1
₹ 125

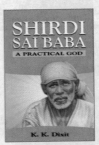

Shirdi Sai Baba A Practical God
K. K. Dixit
ISBN 978 81 207 5918 3
₹ 75

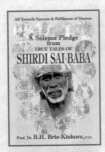

A Solemn Pledge from True Tales of Shirdi Sai Baba
Dr B H Briz-Kishore
ISBN 978 81 207 2240 8
₹ 95

I am always with you
Lorraine Walshe-Ryan
ISBN 978 81 207 3192 9
₹ 150

Shirdi Sai Baba
Vikas Kapoor
ISBN 987 81 207 59701
₹ 30

Unravelling the Enigma: Shirdi Sai Baba in the light of Sufism
Marianne Warren
ISBN 978 81 207 2147 0
₹ 400

**Shirdi Sai Baba
The Divine Healer**
Raj Chopra
ISBN 978 81 207 4766 1
₹ 100

**Shirdi Sai Baba and
other Perfect Masters**
C B Satpathy
ISBN 978 2384 15081 207 9
₹ 150

The Miracles of Sai Baba
ISBN 978 81 207 5433 1 (HB)
₹ 250

Sai Hari Katha
Dasganu Maharaj Translated by
Dr. Rabinder Nath Kakarya
ISBN 978 81 207 3324 4
₹ 100

Shri Sai Baba- The Saviour
Dr. Rabinder Nath Kakarya
ISBN 978 81 207 4701 2
₹ 100

**The Thousand Names of
Shirdi Sai Baba**
Sri B.V. Narasimha Swami Ji
Hindi translation by
Dr. Rabinder Nath Kakarya
ISBN 978 81 207 3738 9
₹ 75

Sri Sai Baba
Swami Sai Sharan Anand
Translated by V.B Kher
ISBN 978 81 207 1950 7
₹ 200

**Sai Baba: His Divine
Glimpses**
V B Kher
ISBN 978 81 207 2291 0
₹ 95

**Shri Shirdi Sai Baba: His
Life and Miracles**
ISBN 978 81 207 2877 6
₹ 25

**108 Names of
Shirdi Sai Baba**
ISBN 978 81 207 3074 8
₹ 50

Shirdi Sai Baba Aratis
(English)   ₹ 10

**Shirdi Sai Speaks...
Sab Ka Malik Ek
Quotes for the Day**
ISBN 81 207 3101 200978 1
₹ 200

STERLING

Divine Gurus

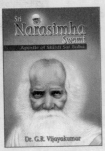

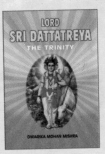

Hazrat Babajan:
A Pathan Sufi of Poona
Kevin R. D. Shepherd
ISBN 978 81 207 8698 1
₹ 200

Sri Narasimha Swami
Apostle of Shirdi Sai Baba
Dr. G.R. Vijayakumar
ISBN 978 81 207 4432 5
₹ 90

Lord Sri Dattatreya
The Trinity
Dwarika Mohan Mishra
ISBN 978 81 207 5417 1
₹ 200

Sri Swami Samarth
Maharaj of Akkalkot
N.S. Karandikar
ISBN 978 81 207 3445 6
₹ 200

Guru Charitra
Shree Swami Samarth
ISBN 978 81 207 3348 0
₹ 200

Shirdi Sai Baba Box

Shri Sai Satcharitra

Vibhuti

Dateless
Calendar

Shri Sai Baba
978 81 207 6920 5
Box size: 23.5 x 16.5 cm
₹900

Sai Baba Mandiramdhil
Arataya & Mantrochar - Mp3

Sai Baba Photo Frame

श्री शिरडी साई बाबा

शिरडी अंतः से अनंत
डॉ. रबिन्द्रनाथ ककरिया
978 81 207 8191 7
₹ 750

श्री साई सच्चरित्र
श्री शिरडी साई बाबा की अद्भुत
जीवनी तथा उनके अमूल्य उपदेश
गोविंद रघुनाथ दाभोलकर (हेमाडपंत)
978 81 207 2501 0 ₹ 250 (PB)
978 81 207 2500 3 ₹ 300 (HB)

साई सुमिरन
अंजु टंडन
978 81 207 8706 3
₹ 90

बाबा की वाणी-उनके वचन तथा उपदेश
बेला शर्मा
978 81 207 4745 6
₹ 100

बाबा का अनुराग
विनी चितलुरी
978 81 207 6699 0
₹ 100

बाबा का ऋणानुबंध
विनी चितलुरी
978 81 207 5998 5
₹ 125

बाबा का गुरूकुल-शिरडी
विनी चितलुरी
978 81 207 6698 3
₹ 125

साई की आत्मकथा
विकास कपूर
978 81 207 7719 4
₹ 200

साई संवाद
उर्मिल सत्य भूषण
978 81 207 7777 4
₹ 200

बाबा-आध्यात्मिक विचार
चन्द्र भानुसतपथी
978 81 207 4627 5
₹ 150

साई शरण में
चन्द्रभानु सतपथी
978 81 207 2802 8
₹ 150

स्टर्लिंग

श्री शिरडी साई बाबा एवं अन्य सद्गुरु
चन्द्रभानु सतपथी
978 81 207 4401 1
₹ 90

पृथ्वी पर अवतरित भगवान शिरडी के साई बाबा
रंगास्वामी पार्थसारथी
978 81 207 2101 2
₹ 150

साई - सबका मालिक
कल्पना भाकुनी
978 81 207 3320 6
₹ 125

साई बाबा एक अवतार
बेला शर्मा
978 81 207 6706 5
₹ 100

साई सत् चरित का प्रकाश
बेल शर्मा
978 81 207 7804 7
₹ 200

श्री साई बाबा के परम भक्त
डॉ. रबिन्द्रनाथ ककरिया
978 81 207 2779 3
₹ 75

श्री साई बाबा के उपदेश व तत्त्वज्ञान
लेफ्टिनेन्ट कर्नल
एम. बी. निंबालकर
978 81 207 5971 8   ₹ 100

साई भक्तानुभव
डॉ. रबिन्द्रनाथ ककरिया
978 81 207 3052 6
₹ 90

श्री साई बाबा के अनन्य भक्त
डॉ. रबिन्द्र नाथ ककरिया
978 81 207 2705 2
₹ 75

साई का संदेश
डॉ. रबिन्द्र नाथ ककरिया
978 81 207 2879 0
₹ 125

शिरडी संपूर्ण दर्शन
डॉ. रबिन्द्रनाथ ककरिया
978 81 207 2312 2
₹ 50

मुक्ति दाता - श्री साई बाबा
डॉ. रबिन्द्रनाथ ककरिया
978 81 207 2778 6
₹ 65

श्री नरसिम्हा स्वामी
शिरडी साई बाबा के दिव्य प्रचारक
डॉ. रबिन्द्र नाथ ककरिया
978 81 207 4437 0   ₹ 75

साई दत्तावधूता
राजेन्द्र भण्डारी
978 81 207 4400 4
₹ 75

साई हरि कथा
दासगणु महाराज
978 81 207 3323 7
₹ 65

शिरडी साई बाबा - की सत्य कथाओं से प्राप्त - एक पावन प्रतिज्ञा
प्रो. डॉ. बी.एच. ब्रिज-किशोर
978 81 207 2346 7   ₹ 80

शिरडी साई बाबा की दिव्य लीलाएँ
डॉ. रबिन्द्र नाथ ककरिया
978 81 207 6376 0   ₹ 150

श्री साई चालीसा
ISBN 978 81 207 4773 9
₹ 50

शिरडी सांई बाबा
विकास कपूर
978 81 207 5969 5
₹ 30

Shirdi Sai Baba Aratis
(Hindi)   ₹10

शिरडी साई के दिव्य वचन-सब का मालिक एक
प्रतिदिन का विचार
978 81 207 3533 0
₹ 180

Oriya Language Books

ଶ୍ରୀ ସାଇ ସଚରିତ୍ର (Oriya)
ଶ୍ରୀ ଗୋବିନ୍ଦଯାନ ରଘୁନାଥ ଦାଭୋଲକର
(ହେମାଦପନ୍ତ)
978 81 207 6332 4   ₹ 300

ଶ୍ରୀ ଶିରିଡ଼ି ସାଇବାବା କଥାମୃତ
ପ୍ରଫେସର ଡ. ବି. ଏଚ୍. ବ୍ରିଜକିଶୋର (Oriya)
978 81 207 7774 3
₹ 80

ଶିରୁଡ଼ି ସାଇ ବାବାଙ୍କ
ଜୀବନ ଲୀଳା (Oriya)
ଅମୂଳ ଶାସ୍ତ୍ରୀୟ ରାଓ
ଅନୁବାଦ – କିଶୋର ଚନ୍ଦ୍ର ପଟ୍ଟନାୟକ
978 81 207 7417 9   ₹ 100

Other Indian Languages

ଶିରିଡ଼ିସାଇବାବା (Telugu)
ପ୍ରୋ. ଡା଼. ବି.ଏଚ. ବ୍ରିଜ–କିଶୋର
978 81 207 2294 1
₹ 80

(Kannada)
ପ୍ରୋ. ଡା଼. ବି.ଏଚ. ବ୍ରିଜ–କିଶୋର
978 81 207 2873 8
₹ 80

(Tamil)
உண்மைக்கதைகளிலிருந்து
பெருமிதமான வாக்குமூரி
 ப்ரோ. டா. பி.எச். ப்ரிஜ்–கிஷோர்
978 81 207 2876 9
₹ 80

Shirdi Sai Baba Aratis
(Kannada)   ₹10

Shirdi Sai Baba Aratis
(Tamil)   ₹10

Shirdi Sai Baba Aratis
(Telugu)   ₹10

शिरडी साई बाबा (भोजपुरी)
विकास कपूर
978 81 207 7558 9
₹ 30

शिर्डी साईबाबांची दिव्य वचने (Ma
सबका मालिक एक
दैनंदिन विचार
978 81 207 7518 3   ₹ 180

STERLING PUBLISHERS PVT. LTD.
A-59, Okhla Industrial Area, Phase-II, New Delhi-110020,
For Online order & detailed Catalogue visit our website:
www.sterlingpublishers.com, E-mail : mail@sterlingpublishers.com, Tel. 91-11-26386165, 263